Handbook of Physical Fitness Activities

Handbook of Physical

Fitness Activities

DONALD R. CASADY, Ph.D.
Course Chairman, Physical Education Skills
State University of Iowa, Iowa City

DONALD F. MAPES, Ph.D.
Assistant Professor of Physical Education
Temple University, Philadelphia

LOUIS E. ALLEY, Ph.D.
Professor and Head, Physical Education for Men
State University of Iowa, Iowa City

THE MACMILLAN COMPANY, NEW YORK • COLLIER-MACMILLAN LIMITED, LONDON

Fifth Printing, 1971

Library of Congress catalog card number: 65-11603

THE MACMILLAN COMPANY
866 THIRD AVENUE, NEW YORK, NEW YORK 10022
COLLIER-MACMILLAN CANADA, LTD., TORONTO, ONTARIO

PRINTED IN THE UNITED STATES OF AMERICA

preface

This book is designed to serve as a basic textbook for physical fitness courses and as a source of authentic information for any person interested in improving or maintaining his level of fitness. Together with the *Handbook for Instructors,* this book provides instructors with the information needed to conduct physical fitness classes.

Information has been provided that will enable the reader to understand *why* he should be concerned about his level of fitness as well as *how* he can improve this level. Because an understanding of the effects of exercise on the human organism is requisite to intelligent efforts to improve one's physical fitness, information concerning the manner in which the body adapts to the demands of regular, vigorous exercise—and how it degenerates if such demands are not made—is provided. Also included are physical fitness tests which will enable the reader to evaluate his present level of physical fitness and to measure his improvement from week to week.

The book is an outgrowth of an M.A. thesis by Donald F. Mapes which was completed at the State University of Iowa under the direction of Louis E. Alley and Donald R. Casady. Two hundred universities were contacted to learn whether they offered courses designed specifically to improve physical fitness and, if so, the content of these courses. From the responses obtained and from a careful survey of pertinent literature, a comprehensive list of activities to develop physical fitness was assembled. Criteria for the selection of activities for fitness programs were developed, and each activity on the comprehensive list was rated in terms of these criteria. Those activities that satisfactorily met the criteria were utilized to develop a physical fitness program for students at the State University of Iowa. Over a period of six years, this program was presented, evaluated, and annually revised. The information and the activities that appear in this book represent the cumulative results of these efforts.

D. R. C.
D. F. M.
L. E. A.

contents

21. ACTIVITIES FOR CIRCUIT TRAINING 168

PART 4 *The Evaluation of Physical Fitness*

part 1

Information Basic to an Understanding of Physical Fitness

1. physical fitness—a national problem

The dangerously low level of physical fitness of the youth of America was officially recognized as a problem of national concern when, in June 1956, President Dwight D. Eisenhower established the President's Council on Youth Fitness. This action resulted from the discovery by Dr. Hans Kraus, of the Institute of Physical Medicine and Rehabilitation of New York University's Bellevue Medical Center, that the physical fitness of American youth was far below that of their European counterparts.

Utilizing six simple tests of muscular strength and flexibility—originally designed by Dr. Kraus and Dr. Sonja Weber for use with patients suffering from low back pain—Dr. Kraus and Ruth P. Hirschland tested 4,264 American children, 6 to 19 years of age, and 2,870 children of corresponding ages in Austria, Italy, and Switzerland. Almost 58 per cent of the American children failed one or more of the tests, and the incidence of failure for these children was 80 per cent. Only about 9 per cent of the European children failed one or more of the tests, and their incidence of failure was only 9 per cent.

Because the Kraus-Weber tests were designed to measure only a minimum level of physical fitness, many physical educators felt that the tests were unsatisfactory for assessing the physical fitness of American children, particularly for comparing American children with children in other countries. To accurately evaluate the physical fitness of American youth, during the year 1957–1958 the American Association of Health, Physical Education and Recreation (a department of the National Education Association) sponsored the administration of a carefully selected battery of physical fitness tests to a nationwide sample of over eight thousand American boys and girls, 10 to 17 years of age. From the scores obtained, national norms were developed.

Utilizing this improved battery of tests and the norms for American children, various researchers proceeded to compare the physical fitness of American children with that of children of other lands. The tests were administered to British children (from England, Scotland, Wales, and Cyprus), to Chinese children, and to Japanese children. In each

3

instance the level of physical fitness of American children was markedly lower than that of the children from the other countries.

President John F. Kennedy recognized the urgent need for improving the physical fitness of American youth. In an article, "The Soft American," that appeared in the December 26, 1960 issue of *Sports Illustrated,* President Kennedy (then president-elect) wrote,

> But the harsh fact of the matter is that there is also an increasingly large number of young Americans who are neglecting their bodies—whose physical fitness is not what it should be—who are getting soft. And such softness on the part of individual citizens can help to strip and destroy the vitality of a nation.
>
> For the physical vigor of our citizens is one of America's most precious resources. If we waste and neglect this resource, if we allow it to dwindle and grow soft then we will destroy much of our ability to meet the great and vital challenges which confront our people. We will be unable to realize our full potential as a nation.

Upon assuming office, President Kennedy continued to focus national attention upon this serious problem.

Why are American youth not as physically fit as their peers in other lands? Why do the youth of a nation in which housing, medical care, nutritious food, public sanitation, and public recreation facilities are second to none fail to "measure up" in physical fitness? Although a definite cause-and-effect relationship is difficult to establish, the impact of the fruits of technology on everyday living must be considered a factor that contributes materially to the lack of fitness of American youth.

Technological advances have enabled industry in the United States to produce in ever-increasing numbers such mechanical contrivances as automatic washers and dryers, vacuum cleaners, automatic dishwashers, automatic gas furnaces, and power-driven tools, which have greatly reduced the amount of human energy required to operate the average American home. In most households the chores formerly reserved for children have all but disappeared, while the time and means for reading, watching television, listening to records, and similar sedentary pastimes have greatly increased. Elevators, escalators, endless-belt sidewalks, school buses, and automobiles have markedly reduced the amount of walking formerly required to get about.

One by one these mechanical contrivances have become an integral part of American life. Collec-

tively, they have reduced significantly for both children and adults the amounts of physical activity required in daily living. Because physical fitness can be developed and maintained *only* by engaging regularly in vigorous physical activity, the widespread use of these energy-saving devices in the United States is currently reflected in the lowered level of physical fitness exhibited by American youth.

In the future the amount of physical exertion required of youth and adults from day to day will continue to diminish. From the research programs sponsored by industry will come new and improved devices that are designed to further reduce the physical labor required to maintain the average home. Expanded programs of automation in industry will continue to lessen both the manual labor and the working hours required for the production of goods. If successfully harnessed for industrial use, the energy of the atom will provide a source of power that will revolutionize the working and leisure habits of men and women throughout the world.

That American children and adults will continue to make full use of all energy-saving devices available to them is certain. To fail to use an available mechanical device that will reduce the physical labor and the time required to complete a given task is contrary to human nature. Consequently, the physical fitness of American youth and adults will likely sink to lower levels than at present unless some means other than daily work are utilized to provide the vigorous exercise required for adequate physical fitness.

The primary purpose of this book is to provide for high school and college students a comprehensive source of vigorous activities and methods suitable for developing and maintaining physical fitness. Because physical fitness is a transient quality that can be maintained only through regular exercise, activities suited to the exercise needs of the adult population as a whole are included, as well as activities suitable for high school and college students. Those activities that require little or no special equipment and that can be adapted for use in the home or office are emphasized.

Although the natural exuberance of youth may serve to keep many persons active through their early adult years, an understanding of the permanent need for physical fitness is required to motivate most persons to engage in vigorous activity after the vitality of youth diminishes or vanishes completely. To provide a means by which this understanding may be acquired, the effects of exercise on the human organism and the manner in which the body degenerates when it is not exercised sufficiently are discussed in Chapter 3.

To enable the reader to determine his present status and to measure subsequent improvement or deterioration in physical fitness, appropriate batteries of physical-fitness tests, together with norms for each test and for each test battery, are presented in Chapter 22.

2. what is physical fitness?

When a person is said to be "physically fit" or "in condition," what is indicated about that person? What is the meaning of the term *physical fitness?* Does *physical fitness* mean the same thing to all people?

During the past years medical doctors, physiologists, physical educators, and others have advanced various definitions for the term *physical fitness* and have discussed various types of fitness. *Total fitness, youth fitness, organic efficiency, organic fitness, motor fitness, physical efficiency, physical vitality, physical condition, anatomical fitness, physiologic fitness,* and *muscular fitness* are terms that have been used to refer to a general condition of the body of which physical fitness is a component, to refer to physical fitness itself, or to refer to some facet of physical fitness. However, the meanings given to these terms and to the term *physical fitness* vary considerably. When defining physical fitness, the viewpoint assumed by physical educators has often differed from that assumed by physiologists and medical doctors, and within all three groups definitions of physical fitness have been advanced for a variety of purposes and reasons. The manner in which various authorities disagree on the meaning of physical fitness is illustrated by the following definitions.

DEFINITIONS OF PHYSICAL FITNESS GIVEN BY MEDICAL DOCTORS

The Subcommittee of the Baruch Committee on Physical Medicine has reported that "physical fitness describes the functional capacity of the individual for a task. It has no real meaning unless the task or job for which fitness is to be judged is specified."[1] A functional description of physical fitness, advanced by Bruno Balke, a medical doctor, is that "physical fitness depends on the individual's *biodynamic potential* which is composed of his functional and of his metabolic potential. The best test of physical fitness would be man's ability to survive

[1] Robert C. Darling, Ludwig W. Eichna, Clark W. Heath, and Harold G. Wolff, "Physical Fitness—Report of the Subcommittee of the Baruch Committee on Physical Medicine," *Journal of the American Medical Association,* March 13, 1948, p. 764.

under extraordinary biological demands."[2] Another medical doctor who is a prominent researcher, Edward Bortz, states that "physical fitness implies that the body systems are capable of carrying on their activities satisfactorily."[3] K. Lange Anderson, a medical doctor employed at the Institute of Work Physiology in Oslo, Norway, has defined physical fitness as "the ability for respiration and circulation to recover from a standard work load."[4]

DEFINITIONS OF PHYSICAL FITNESS GIVEN BY PHYSIOLOGISTS

In writing about physical fitness and performance, three authors whose professional careers are devoted to physiological research state that "physical fitness can be defined as a quantitative expression of the physical condition of an individual. It could also be defined as the fitness to perform a specific task requiring muscular effort in which speed and endurance are the main criteria."[5] Peter Karpovich, who conducts research on the physiology of exercise, has written that "physical fitness means that a person possessing it meets certain physical requirements."[6] He also states that "physical fitness measures merely the ability to pass physical fitness tests."[7]

DEFINITIONS OF PHYSICAL FITNESS GIVEN BY PHYSICAL EDUCATORS

The members of a national conference of physical educators wrote that "physical fitness, as used herein, refers to the capacity for physical performance and survival, founded on basic health."[8] Other

physical educators state that "physical fitness can be described as the total functional capacity of an individual to perform a given task. The ultimate test of physical fitness is the ability of the individual to carry a desired task to successful completion without undue fatigue."[9]

Other brief definitions of physical fitness offered by physical educators are: "the nature and degree of adjustment in activities requiring muscular effort,"[10] "physical fitness is a capacity for sustained physical activity,"[11] "the capacity of an individual to perform a given task,"[12] and "the type of fitness that is produced primarily by physical training."[13] According to two women physical educators, "physical fitness means: the body is an efficient instrument of the self for meeting life situations."[14] In a book on physical conditioning written during World War II the following statement appears: "The term physical fitness has become a common expression used to identify the movement which aims to bring back the virility and robustness which typified the men who built this great Nation of ours. These sturdy pioneers possessed a type of fitness characterized by the efficient functioning of all body parts as shown by their ability to adapt themselves to the environmental demands of their time."[15]

DESCRIPTIONS OF THE PHYSICALLY FIT PERSON

Other definitions of physical fitness have been limited to descriptions of the characteristics of the physically fit person. Two women physical educators have described the physically fit person as follows: "The fit person is one who is free of limiting and debilitating ailments, who has the stamina

[2] Bruno Balke, "The Effect of Physical Exercise on the Metabolic Potential, a Crucial Measure of Physical Fitness," in *Exercise and Fitness* (Chicago: The Athletic Institute, 1960), p. 74.

[3] Edward L. Bortz, "Exercise, Fitness and Aging," in *Exercise and Fitness* (Chicago: The Athletic Institute, 1960), p. 7.

[4] K. Lange Anderson, "Respiratory Recovery from Exercise of Short Duration," in *Health and Fitness in the Modern World* (Chicago: The Athletic Institute, 1961), p. 115.

[5] C. Frank Consolazio, Robert E. Johnson, and Louis J. Pecora, *Physiological Measurements of Metabolic Functions in Man* (New York: McGraw-Hill, 1963), p. 340.

[6] Peter V. Karpovich, *Physiology of Muscular Activity*, 5th ed. (Philadelphia: W. B. Saunders, 1959), p. 262.

[7] Peter V. Karpovich, *ibid.*

[8] The Athletic Institute, *Report of the National Conference on Interpretation of Physical Education*, Kellogg Center for Continuing Education, East Lansing, Michigan, December 9–16, 1961, p. 10.

[9] Clifford Lee Brownell and E. Patricia Hagman, *Physical Education—Foundations and Principles* (New York: McGraw-Hill, 1951), p. 353.

[10] Leonard A. Larson, "Defining Physical Fitness—With Procedures for its Measurement," *The Journal of Health and Physical Education*, January 1942, p. 18.

[11] Carl E. Willgoose, *Evaluation and Physical Education* (New York: McGraw-Hill, 1961), p. 105.

[12] Donald K. Mathews, *Measurement in Physical Education*, 2nd ed. (Philadelphia: W. B. Saunders, 1963), p. 3.

[13] Charles Harold McCloy and Norma Dorothy Young, *Tests and Measurements in Health and Physical Education*, 3rd ed. (New York: Appleton-Century-Crofts, 1954), p. 127.

[14] Rosalind Cassidy and Hilda Clute Kozman, *Physical Fitness for Girls* (New York: A. S. Barnes, 1943), p. 31.

[15] George T. Stafford and Ray O. Duncan, *Physical Conditioning Exercises for Sports and Healthful Living* (New York: Ronald Press, 1942), p. 1.

and skill to do the day's work, and who has sufficient reserve of energy not only to meet emergencies but to provide a zest for leisure time living."[16] Two other physical educators have stated that "persons who function physically at a high level of efficiency are said to be in 'good condition' or 'physically fit'."[17] Two physiologists have written that "a person is considered to be fit for a particular task or activity when he can accomplish it with a reasonable degree of efficiency, without undue fatigue and with rapid recovery from the effects of the exertion."[18] David Bruce Dill, a physiologist, has described physical fitness by stating that "in strenuous physical exercise, the degree of fatigue experienced depends on the state of physical fitness."[19] The author of a textbook on evaluating physical education writes:

In performance the physically fit person has the following characteristics:

1. Strength enough to be ready for tasks encountered in everyday routine and in emergencies.
2. Stamina (endurance) to continue necessary tasks without undue fatigue, and energy enough to participate in recreational activities after a day's work.
3. Cardiorespiratory endurance for sustained effort in activities involving motion of the entire body.
4. Agility to be able to make a wide range of movements easily.
5. Speed to be able to move rapidly when personal safety demands it.
6. Control to coordinate body movements skillfully.[20]

Physical fitness is "composed of qualities best represented by strength, power, speed, skill and endurance for the task, plus proper enthusiasm (mental equilibrium, morale, and mind-set) as shown in that feeling of responsibility for continued effort necessary for the completion of the task"[21] according to the authors of a book on physical conditioning.

[16] M. Gladys Scott and Esther French, *Measurement and Evaluation in Physical Education* (Dubuque, Iowa: Wm. C. Brown, 1959), p. 277.

[17] Charles Harold McCloy and Norma Dorothy Young, *Tests and Measurements in Health and Physical Education*, 3rd. ed. (New York: Appleton-Century-Crofts, 1954), p. 127.

[18] Lawrence E. Morehouse and Augustus T. Miller, *Physiology of Exercise*, 3rd ed. (St. Louis: C. V. Mosby, 1959), p. 310.

[19] David Bruce Dill, "Fatigue and Physical Fitness," in Warren R. Johnson (ed.) *Science and Medicine of Exercise and Sports* (New York: Harper and Brothers, 1960), p. 397.

[20] Carl E. Willgoose, *Evaluation and Physical Education* (New York: McGraw-Hill, 1961), p. 16.

[21] George T. Stafford and Ray O. Duncan, *Physical Conditioning Exercise for Sports and Healthful Living* (New York: Ronald Press, 1942), p. 2.

COMPONENTS OF PHYSICAL FITNESS

Physical fitness is sometimes defined by listing the components that comprise physical fitness. Even here disagreement exists, although most authorities include a majority of the following components as being facets of physical fitness:

1. Good health.
2. Strength.
3. Agility.
4. Muscular endurance.
5. Speed.
6. Balance.
7. Flexibility.
8. Coordination.
9. Cardiorespiratory endurance.
10. Proper body weight.
11. General motor achievement.
12. Neuromuscular skill.

THE AUTHORS' DEFINITION OF PHYSICAL FITNESS

From the variety of definitions of physical fitness cited previously, one must conclude that *physical fitness* is a nebulous term. In this volume, physical fitness is arbitrarily defined as "the ability of the body to accommodate efficiently and effectively a variety of vigorous physical tasks."

When discussing physical fitness, the most obvious question is, "physical fitness for what?" The need for, and the capacity to develop, a high degree of physical fitness varies from person to person, depending upon his daily level of physical activity, the possible emergencies that he may encounter, his physical needs, and his hereditary background. In this volume are presented activities which are designed to enhance the primary components of physical fitness. These components are:

1. Strength.
2. Muscular endurance.
3. Circulorespiratory endurance.
4. Flexibility.
5. Neuromuscular skill.
6. Agility.

By understanding and practicing the physical conditioning techniques described in this book, the reader will be able to develop each of these components and, hence, will realize his potential capacity for physical fitness.

3. physiologic adaptations to exercise

How does the body adapt to the demands made by vigorous exercise? More specifically, what changes take place in the muscles, the circulatory system, and the respiratory system? These and similar questions concerning the physiologic adaptations that the body makes in response to exercise are answered in this chapter. These changes within the body do not occur independently of one another. Exercise affects the whole organism simultaneously. Specific effects on one part of the body in turn affect other parts of the body. The human organism reacts to exercise as an intricate, complicated, integrated whole.

When a person exercises vigorously, the exercise affects his body immediately. Certain changes take place in order for his body to accommodate the exercise. These changes are termed the *immediate effects* of exercise. If a person engages in vigorous exercise regularly, day by day, week by week, other, more gradual, changes occur as his body adjusts to the continued demands of exercise. These gradual changes are termed the *chronic effects* of exercise.

IMMEDIATE EFFECTS OF EXERCISE

What are the immediate effects of vigorous exercise upon the body One of these is an automatic increase in the rate and the depth of breathing. This increased respiratory rate is a normal response motivated by the need of the body to increase its oxygen supply while eliminating the increased concentration of carbon dioxide within the blood.

Vigorous exercise also causes an immediate increase in the rate at which the heart beats. This increased rate of heartbeat results in an increase in the flow of blood to the muscles. The capillaries in the muscles dilate—that is, increase in diameter —allowing an increased amount of blood to flow through them. The blood supplies the muscles with the oxygen and the nutritional material necessary for increased energy expenditure. At the same time, the amount of waste material removed from the muscles is increased. The increased supply of energy to the muscles, coupled with the increased removal of waste material, allows the muscles to

9

work for long periods of time without being unduly fatigued.

In addition to the increased circulation of blood which results from an accelerated heartbeat, the circulation is supplemented by what is called the *peripheral heart action of the muscles.* As a person exercises, the muscles alternately contract and relax. The contraction of the muscle tissue compresses the capillaries that lie within it, forcing the blood that is in the capillaries forward into the veins. When next the muscle relaxes, fresh blood enters the capillaries. Moreover, the major veins in the body lie between the muscles. During exercise, therefore, the veins also are squeezed each time the muscles contract. When the muscles relax, the pressure on the veins is released. Thus, the alternate contraction and relaxation of the muscles produces a sort of milking action which forces the blood through the veins toward the heart. One-way valves in the veins allow the blood to pass through toward the heart, but prevent the blood from flowing backward away from the heart. This peripheral heart action of the muscles can take place only when one is engaged in physical activity.

Another immediate effect of exercise upon the muscles is the production of heat. The temperature of the muscles is increased as a result of exercise. This increase in temperature causes the viscosity of the muscle to decrease. The viscosity of a muscle is determined by the resistance of the molecules of the muscle to internal rearrangement. Just as motor oil flows faster when warm than when cold, the muscles, because of decreased viscosity, may be contracted and relaxed faster when one is sufficiently "warmed up" than when one's muscles are "cold." Consequently, it is believed that one should "warm up" before engaging in strenuous physical activity. The increased temperature of the muscles allows them to be contracted or stretched vigorously with little danger of injury. The muscles, when properly "warmed up," are less subject to tearing than when they are "cold."

CHRONIC EFFECTS OF EXERCISE

The immediate effects of exercise are temporary effects. These changes take place during physical activity regardless of the regularity with which one has exercised previously. Shortly after the exercise is discontinued, these immediate changes reverse and the body processes revert to their normal resting state. For example, the heartbeat slows to its original rate, and the rate and depth of breathing soon return to normal. The question now arises, "What gradual changes occur in the body when one engages in a regular, vigorous exercise program extending over a long period of time?" What chronic effects result from regular exercise?

Chronic Effects on Muscular System

Regular, vigorous exercise causes the muscle fibers to increase in size. The exercise stimulates the growth of the muscle fibers, causing them to thicken. The connective tissue which binds the muscle fibers together increases in amount and in tensile strength. This increase in the size of the muscle is called *hypertrophy.* Hypertrophy is accompanied by increased strength which, in turn, is accompanied by improved muscular endurance.

The repeated use of the muscles increases the efficiency with which the motor units within a given muscle are used. A motor unit is a group of muscle fibers which are stimulated by their own independent nerve supply. Each motor unit responds to stimulation by the "all-or-nothing law." When stimulated, the unit either responds completely with a full contraction of its muscle fibers or it makes no response at all. The entire muscle is made up of many motor units which work in relays. As a muscle increases in strength, the number of motor units which need to be contracted to exert a given force is reduced. Consequently, the number of motor units that can rest during the exercise is increased. As the exercise is repeated, the resting motor units may be brought into play, allowing the motor units that have become fatigued to rest. This arrangement results in a considerable increase in the endurance of the muscle.

Chronic Effects on Cardiovascular System

Vigorous activity results in an immediate increase in the heart rate and in the dilation of the capillaries within the working muscle. If one engages regularly over an extended period of time in vigorous exercise, other changes (adaptations) that enable the body to tolerate increased work loads gradually occur in the cardiovascular system.

The cardiovascular system is comprised of the heart, the arteries, the veins, and the capillaries. The function of the cardiovascular system is to supply blood to the tissues of the body. The blood furnishes the tissues with the food materials and oxygen necessary for the production of energy and removes from the tissues the waste products which result from energy-making processes. The heart constantly pumps the blood through the arteries, through the capillaries, through the veins, and back again to the heart.

Chronic effects on the heart. The heart is a muscular organ and, as such, may be developed by exercise. Although the heart cannot be directly exercised, it may be indirectly exercised by exercising the other muscles of the body. One of the immediate effects of exercise is a temporary increase in the heart rate. Participation in a regular exercise program will, in time, cause certain adaptive changes to take place within the heart. Speed-type exercises, such as running or swimming, cause the heart to increase in strength. As it becomes stronger, the amount of blood pumped during each stroke (stroke volume) is also increased. Because the stroke volume is increased, the heart, to supply a given amount of blood, need not beat as rapidly as before. A lowered heart rate allows the heart additional time to rest between beats. Other things being equal, the greater the time for rest between heartbeats, the longer the heart will be able to operate under a given working load without undue fatigue.

Chronic effects on blood pressure. As the heart adapts to the demands imposed by the conditioning program, other adjustments are made in the circulatory system. When a poorly conditioned person exercises vigorously, his pulse rate becomes very rapid; but his blood pressure remains relatively low. As his body becomes well conditioned, his pulse rate during exercise does not rise as sharply as before, and his blood pressure during exercise increases. This increase in blood pressure forces the blood through the circulatory system at a faster rate than before and increases the amount of blood that is returned to the heart. Just as a water pump can pump only the water available to it, so the heart can pump out into the arteries only the blood that comes to it through the veins.

Chronic effects on the capillaries. Another chronic effect of exercise on the cardiovascular system is the formation of new capillaries within the muscle fibers. The additional capillaries increase the supply of blood to the muscle, which, in turn, increases the supply of oxygen and nutritional material to the muscle and increases the rate at which waste products are eliminated from the muscle. Regular, vigorous exercise can cause an increase of up to 50 per cent in the number of capillaries within a muscle. In addition, latent capillaries, which ordinarily lie dormant in a poorly conditioned muscle, open up and function in a conditioned muscle. This further facilitates the flow of blood within the muscles.

The increase in the number of functioning capillaries, the increased blood pressure in the arteries and the veins, and the increased stroke volume all result in an increased supply of blood to the active muscles.

Changes in blood composition. Regular, vigorous exercise causes a change in the composition of the blood as well as an increase in the supply of blood delivered to the muscle. This change in blood composition increases its oxygen-carrying capacity. The number of red corpuscles in the blood increases as a result of regular, vigorous exercise. The red corpuscles contain hemoglobin, which unites with oxygen and carries the oxygen to the muscles. The number of red corpuscles in the blood may be doubled as a result of participation in a vigorous exercise program. An increased supply of oxygen to the muscles results from this change. The additional oxygen supply vastly improves the endurance of the conditioned individual.

Chronic Effects on Respiratory System

The efficiency with which the respiratory system operates is increased as a result of participation in regular, vigorous exercise. When well conditioned, one can perform a given exercise with a slower breathing rate than when he is poorly conditioned. The tidal air capacity of the lungs, which is the capacity of the lungs to take in and expel air, is increased as a result of participation in a regular, strenuous exercise program. Accompanying this change in tidal air capacity is an increase in the flexibility of the chest wall. The muscles used in respiration also benefit from participation in a long-term conditioning program. They become stronger and thus contribute to the increase in the effectiveness of the respiratory system.

Resistance to Fatigue

The changes that take place in the body as a result of regular, vigorous exercise increase the ability of the body to withstand fatigue. Fatigue is a result of an accumulation of waste products within the muscles, coupled with a lack of sufficient oxygen in the muscles. The changes which result from regular exercise improve the ability of the body to delay the onset of the factors which produce fatigue. It is important that more-than-ordinary resistance to fatigue be developed, because chronic fatigue lowers the general resistance of the body to pathogenic organisms. Chronic fatigue ap-

pears especially to predispose a person to respiratory infections such as the common cold.

Chronic Effects of Exercise and Overall Efficiency

Greater mechanical efficiency in doing work or performing physical activity results from the adaptive changes which occur in the human organism as a result of participation in regular, vigorous exercise. The physically fit person absorbs proportionately more oxygen from the air and delivers this oxygen to the tissues with less effort on the part of the heart and the muscles of respiration. He requires less oxygen than a poorly conditioned person in order to do a given task. He performs this task with an expenditure of energy that is relatively less than that expended by a poorly con-

EFFECT	RESULT
Circulatory System	
Increase in number of capillaries.	Increased local endurance.
Increased use of latent capillaries.	Increased local endurance.
Lowers resting heart rate.	
Increased stroke-volume of heart.	Increases in length of rest periods for heart.
Increase in number of red blood corpuscles.	Increased internal supply of oxygen.
More rapid return of heart rate and blood pressure to normal.	Quicker recovery from fatigue.
Respiratory System	
Some decline in rate and depth of breathing at rest.	Somewhat increased capacity.
Greater minute volume of ventilation possible during exhausting work.	Increased supply of oxygen and removal of carbon dioxide in lungs.
Lower oxygen consumption for a given amount of work.	Greater mechanical efficiency.
Muscular System	
Hypertrophy, increase in size of muscle fibers.	Increase in strength.
Nervous System	
Improvement in certain neuromuscular co-ordinations.	Increase in skill.
Skeletal System	
Some increase in size and thickness of bones.	Greater strength and resiliency.

Figure 3-1. Chronic effects of exercise.

ditioned individual. It must be concluded that regular participation in vigorous activity influences in a favorable manner, all components of the human organism.

The chronic effects of exercise—and the results of these effects in terms of physical performance—are summarized in Figure 3-1, which is presented to enable the reader to rapidly comprehend some of the important adaptations that occur. It should be pointed out that other minor chronic effects of exercise have not been discussed in this chapter.

Degeneration from Lack of Exercise

The adjustments made by the body to regular exercise will continue to occur only if the activity in which one participates is vigorous and becomes progressively more vigorous as time goes by. Once a person has attained a desired level of physical fitness, he no longer needs to increase the exercise load. However, if he wishes to maintain that degree of physical fitness, it is essential that he continue to exercise regularly.

If, for any reason, the person ceases to exercise regularly, the chronic adaptations to exercise reverse and, in time, are lost completely. When a muscle undergoes a period of disuse, it atrophies (decreases in size and strength). The process of muscle atrophy is evident in the muscles of a limb that has been confined by a cast for a period of time, or in a limb that has been paralyzed by polio.

Endurance is more rapidly lost than is strength during a period of physical inactivity. This is partially due to the rapid decrease in the number of red corpuscles in the blood. Also, many of the capillaries in the muscles cease to function, thus restricting the blood flow through the muscles. Similarly, the pulse rate at rest increases and the stroke volume of the heart decreases. At the same time, the lungs become less efficient in transmitting oxygen and carbon dioxide to and from the blood.

A lack of exercise acts in a negative fashion upon the body. Once a satisfactory degree of physical fitness has been developed, it is much easier to maintain that condition than it is to first lose that degree of physical fitness and then attempt to regain it.

4. the benefits derived from being physically fit

In the preceding chapter the changes that occur within the body, as it adapts to the demands of regular, vigorous exercise, were discussed. Are these changes beneficial? If so, what benefits are enjoyed by the physically fit person that are not shared by those who are not physically fit?

In the past, numerous claims have been made concerning the benefits that are derived from regular participation in vigorous physical activity, and from the improved physical fitness that results from such participation. Some examples of these claims are that (1) by exercising regularly, one can improve his resistance to specific diseases; (2) by exercising regularly, one can relieve his nervous tensions and worries; (3) by exercising regularly, one can increase his ability to think effectively; (4) by exercising regularly, one can maintain his normal body weight; and (5) by participating in games and sports, one can develop favorable personality traits and, thus, develop his character. Have any of these claims been proven? Has sufficient scientific research—carefully controlled and involving large groups of subjects—been conducted that adequately supports such claims?

Unfortunately, some of the statements made in the past concerning the values associated with exercising regularly—and with the improved physical fitness that results—have not been substantiated by scientific research and must be listed as extravagant claims for which little or no evidence has yet been established. However, during recent years considerable research that satisfies the criteria listed above, which also supports some of the claims mentioned, has been conducted by physical educators, physiologists, medical doctors, psychologists, and sociologists. An examination of the findings of this research provides a basis for determining the benefits that one can expect to gain if he develops and maintains a reasonable degree of physical fitness. Implicit in this examination is the fact that the maintenance of physical fitness requires regular participation in vigorous physical activities. It is difficult, if not impossible, to differentiate between the benefits that result from being physically fit, exercising regularly, and a combination of these two conditions.

The presentation of the findings and the conclusions from recent research concerning the benefits associated with regular, vigorous exercise is divided into two parts: The findings and the conclusions for which substantial supporting evidence is available are presented in Part I, and the findings and conclusions for which little supporting evidence is available are presented in Part II. The material presented in Part II is based primarily on expert opinion and empirical evidence.

The reader should be aware that it is extremely difficult to prove beyond a shadow of doubt that findings and conclusions for which substantial supporting evidence has been gathered are true. However, it can be demonstrated that the probability that the findings and the conclusions are valid is high, and that most authorities agree that such claims or generalizations can legitimately be made. The problem of obtaining solid, incontrovertible evidence is akin to proving that the taking of prescribed doses of oral polio vaccine or Salk vaccine will without exception prevent polio, and that the vaccines themselves can never be a cause of polio. So many variables are involved when millions of people are given the vaccines that not all of the variables can be controlled or all of the results attributed only to the effect of the vaccine. It can only be proven that, as indicated by past records, the probability of contracting polio after taking the vaccine is quite small. The problem is somewhat similar to an attempt to prove that because the sun has risen each day for countless years it will, without question, rise tomorrow morning. While past happenings indicate that this will occur, it is impossible to prove absolutely that the sun will rise tomorrow morning unless one waits until tomorrow morning for the proof.

One of the major problems encountered in attempting to demonstrate the beneficial effects of exercise is that the body may be influenced by many different factors each day. This creates the difficult problem of isolating such a single factor as exercise or physical fitness and proving that it alone is responsible for the effect under investigation. Such factors as diet, general state of health, degree of freedom from tension and worry, and climatic conditions may all play a role in bringing about or influencing a change. These and other factors are usually so interrelated that it is quite difficult to prove that one and only one is responsible for a given change, and that the other factors have

no effect. However, the role of exercise and physical fitness in bringing about certain beneficial changes in the body has been well established.

PART I: FINDINGS FOR WHICH SUBSTANTIAL SUPPORTING EVIDENCE IS AVAILABLE

Physical Activity Reduces Cardiovascular and Degenerative Diseases

Only recently has recognition been given to the role of exercise in preventing heart attacks and degenerative diseases, in lessening their severity, in minimizing the time required for recovery from them, and in reducing the fatalities resulting from them.

During the past sixty years the incidence of cardiovascular disease as a cause of death and as an incapacitating ailment with permanent crippling effects has increased drastically. Sixty years ago cardiovascular disease ranked well down (about tenth place) from the top in the list of the leading causes of death. At the present time cardiovascular disease causes more deaths, almost 1,000,000 deaths a year, than do all other diseases combined. Approximately 14,000,000 people in the United States suffer from serious heart disturbances, or from the clogging of blood vessels, which in turn leads to serious heart and coronary illnesses. The increase in heart ailments has come about partly because advances in medicine and disease prevention have increased the average life span; thus, older persons, who in earlier times would have been dead, are exposed to heart disease. However, a part of this increase is undoubtedly due to the physical inactivity which is characteristic of the way in which many of the citizens in the advanced nations of modern civilization live.

Regular participation in physical activity, suitable to the age and the degree of physical fitness of the participant, is not the only factor that is of importance in reducing or alleviating cardiovascular disorders, but it appears to be a very important factor in this regard. The amount of saturated fat consumed in one's diet, the amount of tension and stress one habitually encounters, one's hereditary background, and the degree to which one is overweight are other factors that also apparently influence the incidence of cardiovascular disorders.

RESEARCH CONCERNING DEGREE OF PHYSICAL ACTIVITY
AND INCIDENCE OF CARDIOVASCULAR DISEASE

During exercise, the blood flow in the veins—
particularly in the legs—is increased by the alternate contraction and relaxation of the muscles
which, in a sort of milking action, increases the
flow of blood through the veins. As the tone of
the muscles is improved by regular exercise, their
effectiveness in aiding the circulation also increases.
In this sense, increased circulation may be re-
garded as a long-term effect of exercise, as well
as an immediate effect. Thus, regular exercise
tends to reduce the possibility of a blood clot
(thrombosis) forming in a blood vessel. Such
clotting is extremely dangerous since the clot (em-
bolus), or a part of it, may break loose and lodge
in a vital area of the circulatory system, partially
or completely blocking the blood vessel. If this
occurs in the lung, a pulmonary embolism results,
if in the heart, a coronary thrombosis results, and if
in the brain, a stroke results.

Fatal heart attacks occur most frequently to
people engaged in sedentary occupations and least
frequently to people engaged in occupations requiring strenuous physical activity. As revealed
by the studies cited below, the incidence of cardiovascular disease apparently increases and the recovery rate apparently decreases in proportion
to the degree to which the occupation is sedentary.

British study. The occupations of 2,500,000 people
who had resided in Great Britain were classified
according to the amount of physical activity required in that occupation. For each type of occupation the percentage of deaths caused by coronary
disease was determined, and the percentages were
compared for various occupations. Those engaged
in sedentary occupations or occupations that required only light physical work had a much larger
percentage of deaths from coronary disease than
did those engaged in heavy physical work.

Indian study. A study of army personnel in India
showed that heart attacks occurred twenty-three
times more frequently among the officers, who led
physically inactive lives, than among the physically
active enlisted men.

Italian study. Less than 1 per cent of the cardiograms (recordings of the movements of the heart)
taken on 600 Italians and 600 inhabitants of the
island of Crete, who were quite active physically
and who did not own automobiles, indicated the
presence of coronary disease. Cardiograms taken
on Bostonians of Italian descent (most of whom
owned automobiles) indicated that 13 per cent had
some form of coronary disease.

Austrian study. An examination of four groups
of Austrians—highly active athletes, mountaineers,
Alpine soldiers, and people in sedentary or inactive
occupations—showed that a significant decline occurred in the heart-protecting mechanisms of the
members of the groups, in proportion to the decrease in the level of physical activity in which
the group regularly engaged.

Irish study. The incidence of coronary disease
among several hundred adult males living in Ireland was compared to the incidence of coronary
disease among their brothers who had migrated to
the United States and were living in Boston. These
Americans were found to have a much higher incidence of coronary disease than their brothers
in Ireland with the same hereditary background.
The Irish-Americans were also several pounds
heavier than their more physically active brothers,
even though the Irish males consumed a larger
number of calories each day than did the American
males.

Swiss study. The percentage of heart disease for
the adult residents of a Swiss mountain village was
compared to that for adult residents from the same
social background and culture who lived in the
Swiss town of Basel. The mountain villagers, who
climbed mountains and carried heavy loads as a
matter of daily routine, had a much lower percentage of heart disease than did the inhabitants
of the town which was not located in the mountains.

London bus employees. The health records of
31,000 double-decker bus workers in London were
studied a few years ago. The active conductors,
who frequently walked around the bus and climbed
the stairs, were found to have a lower mortality
rate and a markedly faster recovery rate from
heart attacks than did the bus drivers, who sat
throughout their working day.

English postal workers. Another investigation in
England showed that the percentage of heart attacks for postmen in England is significantly

smaller than the percentage of heart attacks for postal executives, whose work is much more sedentary.

Cambridge University graduates. For Cambridge University graduates who had been active in sports while in college, the mortality rate due to cardiovascular disease was less than for the graduates who had not been active in sports while in college.

South Dakota study. An investigation conducted by researchers at Purdue University indicated that the percentage of heart attacks for South Dakota farmers, whose work demanded considerable physical toil, was only one-half of that for their less active neighbors who lived in town.

Railroad employees study. The severity of cardiovascular disease among several thousand railroad clerks who performed little exercise in fulfilling their job requirements, railroad switchmen who performed an average amount of physical activity in fulfilling their jobs, and railroad section hands whose jobs required heavy physical activity, was recently investigated. For employees forty years of age and older, the death rate due to cardiovascular disease was higher for railroad clerks than for the other two groups. In this study the problem caused by people shifting from one occupation or type of employment to another was better controlled than is possible in some studies, because most railroad employees who are forty years of age or older have accumulated seniority in their jobs and ordinarily remain railroad employees until their retirement or death. Also, the amount of physical activity performed in each type of job is fairly constant, as railroad employees do little shifting from one type of job to another.

EXPLANATION OF THE RELATIONSHIP BETWEEN PHYSICAL ACTIVITY AND CARDIOVASCULAR DISEASE

Why does being physically fit as a result of regularly engaging in vigorous physical activity aid in reducing the amount and severity of cardiovascular disease? Within the past few years many studies have been made in which the role of exercise and diet in controlling heart disease has been investigated for various age groups and occupations. These studies have yielded findings that help to explain the relationship between lack of physical activity and cardiovascular disease.

Narrowing of arteries. Recently physicians, physi-

ologists, nutritionists, and other researchers, who have studied the inner walls of the arteries, have found that fatty deposits tend to collect there and, because the inside diameter of the arteries is decreased, impede the flow of blood. Apparently, a lack of physical activity, diets rich in cholesterol (which causes a waxy fat to form in the blood), and increased age are all related to the "rusting of the arteries."

Cholesterol-rich diets can cause the blood to contain more than the normal level of cholesterol (100 to 250 mg. is considered normal), which in turn often causes fatty deposits to form on the inside walls of the arteries. Dr. Dudley White, who attended former President Eisenhower during his heart attack, found, as a result of performing over 350 autopsies, that none of the males over 21 years of age had arteries that were free of fatty deposits. Autopsies performed on United States soldiers who were killed in combat during the Korean War indicate that over 70 percent had beginning signs of atherosclerosis (a narrowing of the arteries caused by fatty deposits on the inside walls, which reduces the elasticity of the arteries and produces degenerative changes). Coronary thrombosis (in which a blood clot lodges in a vessel in the heart, and decreases or cuts off blood flow to an area of the heart) occurs with the most frequency when atherosclerosis is most severe.

Recent investigations have demonstrated that regular vigorous exercise is effective in lowering the cholesterol level in the blood. The blood cholesterol of a group of rabbits was measured before and after they were strenuously exercised on a treadmill. Following the exercise, a significant decrease in cholesterol level was found. The serum cholesterol level of a group of inactive chickens was compared to a similar group of chickens that was exercised regularly and that was also fed a diet that tended to produce high cholesterol levels. The inactive chickens consistently maintained a higher cholesterol level than did the active chickens, even though the active chickens were fed a high cholesterol diet.

Experiments in the early 1950's showed that when adult human males have an above-normal caloric intake that is expended by vigorous exercise, the cholesterol level does not increase. When the exercise is of sufficient duration and intensity to cause obese subjects to lose weight, their cholesterol level also decreases.

Golding study. Dr. Larry Golding subjected forty-two middle-aged business men, who were low in physical fitness, to an exercise program in which they exercised each week day during the noon hour for several months. The serum cholesterol level for these men averaged 261 mg. at the time the exercise program was started. By the time the program ended, the average level of serum cholesterol was 191 mg., and some individuals had a drop in cholesterol level of nearly 150 mg. This drop in cholesterol level appeared to be caused by the increased physical activity, because the diet of the men was not restricted; actually, most of the men reported that they increased their caloric intake soon after starting the exercise program.

Dr. White's theory. Dr. Dudley White, the noted heart specialist, has advanced another reason why engaging in regular exercise is of value in reducing cardiovascular disease. He believes that the constant expansion and contraction of the muscles during exercise aids in preventing fat deposits from accumulating in the arteries.

EXERCISE RETARDS CLOTTING TIME OF BLOOD

Some studies have shown that the blood of persons who exercise regularly, or who frequently engage in severe physical activity, clots less rapidly than the blood of sedentary persons. A reduction in blood coagulation is highly important in the prevention of coronary accidents because such a reduction lessens the chance of a blood clot forming in the blood vessels of the heart, brain, or other vital area and thus creating a blockage of blood flow which leads to a heart attack or stroke.

EXERCISE DEVELOPS COLLATERAL CIRCULATION

Studies on dogs and humans have revealed that the collateral (secondary or accessory) circulation of the blood in the capillaries is developed as a result of the demands made on the circulatory system by the stress of exercise and physical activity. This added development is of extreme importance in the event that a coronary thrombosis impedes, or stops altogether, the regular circulation of the blood that supplies a portion of the muscle fibers of the heart. The added collateral circulation in the heart can rapidly assume part or most of the task of delivering blood to all parts of the heart, and thus minimize the damage to the heart cells that often occurs as a result of a coronary thrombosis.

In one experiment, certain arteries of a number of dogs were deliberately blocked. The dogs were then divided into two groups, one of which was exercised regularly. The other was kept inactive. The group that regularly exercised developed secondary circulation in the areas served by the blocked arteries much more rapidly than did the group of dogs that was not allowed to exercise. For patients that suffer a coronary thrombosis many physicians now prescribe mild exercise as soon as the symptoms disappear; in some cases, mild exercise is prescribed before the symptoms disappear.

ABILITY OF HEART TO WITHSTAND STRESS

At one time it was thought that the "overdeveloped" or "athlete's" heart caused by heavy training for athletics or exhausting physical labor endangered the health of the athlete or the worker. Now authorities recognize that this enlargement is a natural condition that results from such training, and is in fact a desirable condition. The heart is exercising constantly and under normal conditions is quite tough, as evidenced by its ability to withstand manual manipulation when emergency conditions sometimes require that the heart be directly massaged by hand. As noted in the previous chapter, consistent vigorous exercise is beneficial to the heart, causing it to become stronger with better muscle tone, and creating an increased blood supply which gives extra nourishment to the heart. The inadequate and degenerated "loafer's" heart is now recognized as an abnormal heart caused by the sedentary living associated with today's civilization. The "loafer's" heart is often unable to cope with the extra stress and strain placed on it in times of illnesses or in emergencies in which extraordinary physical effort may be required. For these reasons, many medical authorities prescribe physical activity—such as walking and, eventually, running—for the healing cardiac patient as a means of not only recovering his physical abilities but also building up a reserve against future cardiac attacks. Dr. Edward Bortz, a past president of the American Medical Association, has summarized the results of considerable investigation and observation by stating, "it begins to appear that exercise is the master conditioner for the healthy and the major therapy for the ill."

Physical Activity Controls Body Weight

There is considerable evidence that for most adults and youth regular participation in vigorous daily exercise is of value in keeping the body weight within the normal range. At one time most people believed that controlling the daily caloric intake was the only practical means of maintaining the body weight at a desirable level. In support of this belief, the amount of exercise needed to burn up one pound of fat (4,320 calories) was cited. Examples of the amount of exercise that a 150-pound person would have to perform to burn up one pound of body fat are (1) to run at a moderate speed for six hours, (2) to do approximately six thousand pushups, (3) to swim for twenty hours, (4) to walk at a fast pace for thirty-five hours, or (5) to walk at a slow pace for seventy hours. This mistaken belief that exercise is of little value in weight control, together with the erroneous belief that the reducing benefits derived from any increase in the daily exercise load would be more than offset by a corresponding increase in the appetite and the accompanying increase in food intake, has in the past prevented many persons from using exercise as a method of controlling body weight. That both beliefs are erroneous is shown in the review of several research studies which follows.

ILL EFFECTS OF OVERWEIGHT

Before considering the role of exercise in weight control, the question of whether or not obesity is a serious handicap—other than its detrimental effect on personal appearance—should be discussed. The mortality rates established by insurance companies indicate that the more overweight a person is the shorter is his life expectancy, compared to what it would be were he of normal body weight. The mortality rate of men who are 35 per cent or more overweight for their age and height is 150 per cent that of men of similar age and height who are normal in body weight. For those whose abdominal girth is two or more inches greater than the girth of the chest at full expansion, the mortality rate is 50 per cent above that for those with only an overweight condition. The overweight person suffers from a higher incidence of heart disease and re-lated ailments than does the person of normal weight because excess body fat places a large overload on his heart. The fat person also has a greater incidence of chronic and degenerative diseases than the person of normal weight.

CALORIC EXPENDITURE OF EXERCISE

It is true that the most strenuous exercise will expend only about 1,000 calories per hour. However, if each day a person walks for one-half hour he will burn up the equivalent of five pounds of body fat in a year. Hence, one-half hour of walking daily would, within a few years, prevent a considerable degree of obesity if no more than the usual amount of calories were consumed. If quite strenuous exercises were performed daily for one hour, the exerciser would burn up the equivalent of twenty-five to thirty pounds of body fat each year.

The fact that physical activity does expend a large number of calories is supported by the Recommended Daily Dietary Allowances issued by the United States National Research Council and similar agencies. The recommended daily dietary allowance varies from 2,400 calories for sedentary men to 6,000 calories for such extremely active men as athletes and heavy laborers. The more than 3,000 extra calories needed by physically active persons shows that exercise is exceedingly important in maintaining the daily energy balance without storing excess calories as body fat.

EXERCISE, APPETITE, AND FOOD INTAKE

Many adults who become obese often do so during the third or fourth decade of life. Does this indicate that they suddenly begin eating more food than usual during the weight-gaining period, which commonly extends over a period of several months or years? Studies of the eating habits and daily level of physical activity of adults, children, and animals who are overweight almost always reveal that the period of weight gain is one in which no more than the usual amount of food is consumed; instead, there is a definite decrease in physical activity which usually precedes, and accompanies, the weight gain. The logical explanation for the weight gain is that the period of decreased activity is not accompanied by a decrease in appetite; hence, the surplus calories consumed are stored as fat. Studies of obese children and children of normal weight in the same age classification indicate that most obese children consume no more food than do their contemporaries of normal weight. However, the obese children are quite inactive when compared to the children of normal weight.

Many people have the mistaken concept that an increase in the level of daily physical activity will cause a corresponding increase in appetite, and that the resultant increased food intake will negate the extra calories burned in performing the increased physical activity. During the past few years evidence has been gathered which refutes this belief. Nutritionists, physiologists, and others have discovered that with a daily increase in physical activity the appetite and food intake increases, but the increase in food intake is not large enough to make up for the calories expended by the increased physical activity. Therefore, a more-than-normal amount of physical activity carried on over a period of time will usually result in a loss of weight which continues until body adjustments have been accomplished, and the energy intake and the energy expenditure are balanced. On the other hand, if the daily living habits are changed and less physical activity than usual is performed, the appetite and food intake does not decrease a corresponding amount, and body weight is increased for a short period of time, until the body has adjusted to the decreased level of physical activity. For most adults, habitually performing from one to eight hours of physical activity daily will cause their appetite and food intake to be of the correct amount to supply the energy required for their basic needs. Consequently, their body weight remains stable.

People who perform heavy physical activity for long hours each day, or who are unaccustomed to doing strenuous exercises, tend to lose weight because they are working at the exhaustion level and until their bodies become adjusted to this level of physical activity their appetite will ordinarily not be sufficient to stimulate them to ingest as many calories as they expend daily. On the other hand, one hour of physical activity each day seems to be the minimum amount required to regulate the appetite to the caloric needs of the body. Many adults who fail to perform at least one hour of physical activity daily often discover that their desire for food causes them to consume too many calories, some of which are stored as excess body fat. Several studies have demonstrated that people who are sendentary consume more calories daily than people of the same body weight who get one to two hours of vigorous physical activity each day. The implication to be drawn here is that a normal amount of physical activity each day balances the caloric intake to the caloric expenditure, making special dietary consideration unnecessary.

We are seemingly trapped by the sedentary living habits engendered by the labor-saving devices of modern civilization. While man has easily adapted his living pattern to a life in which little physical activity is demanded of him, his body has not made the transition so quickly or so easily. Dr. Jean Mayer of the Department of Nutrition at Harvard University sums up our dilemma by stating that the avoidance of obesity requires either an increased amount of exercise or a feeling of hunger during most of adulthood.

Exercise Benefits Posture

Regular exercise definitely aids in improving the tone of the skeletal muscles which in turn helps to maintain a dynamic, erect body posture. On the other hand, the stooped, slumped body posture associated with sedentary living habits is frequently evident in adults. This poor posture is often caused by long-term fatigue brought on because of weak and easily fatigued muscles. Some physicians believe that poor posture is responsible for many of the so-called "minor ills" that frequently beset members of the inactive segment of the American population.

Exercise Relieves Low Back Pain

A lack of physical activity has been found to be the major cause for some cases of pain in the lower back. Low back pain may be caused by weakness of the ligaments which are attached to the vertebrae, thus causing the spine to be unstable; by weakened, stretched, or strained muscles in the abdominal or lower back area; by faulty posture; or by disease, pathological causes, or hereditary defects. Studies of normal people indicate that their back muscles are at least three times stronger than their abdominal muscles. Those people who suffer from low back pain generally have back muscles that are significantly less than three times as strong as their abdominal muscles. Most adults who suffer from low back pain are relieved of this pain by exercises that strengthen their back and abdominal muscles to the normal 3-to-1 ratio. Thus it has been concluded that exercise has both preventive and remedial value for low back pain.

Physical Activity Retards Ageing Process

Several physicians and physiologists have stated that continued participation in regular exercise of the proper amount and severity is of considerable value in postponing the deterioration that usually takes place as a person grows older. Regular physical activity can significantly delay the ageing process in a number of ways:

1. The decline in physical capacity of the circulatory and the muscular systems is slowed.
2. The physical deterioration that accompanies aging is retarded.
3. The incidence of degenerative diseases is decreased.
4. Energy and vigor are increased, providing increased enjoyment and interest in living and aiding in the prevention of chronic fatigue.
5. Obesity is controlled or prevented, which aids in retaining optimum physical appearance and in preventing many of the ailments induced by excess body fat.
6. Relaxation and recreation (that are otherwise sometimes difficult to achieve) are provided, which in turn, improves mental health and aids digestion.
7. There is some indication that long-term physical activity of a suitable nature is of value in increasing life expectancy.

Physical Fitness and Ability to Meet Emergencies

The argument is sometimes advanced that in our push-button civilization little strength or physical fitness is needed to operate the labor-saving devices available to us. Is this logic valid? Yes, for everyday living the body that is accustomed to only sedentary living habits can usually operate effectively even though it is operating at near-maximum effort. However, in emergency situations, or in unusual or unaccustomed circumstances, the physically-unfit body frequently is incapable of making an adequate response to the demands placed upon it. The amount of normal activity performed not only varies considerably from person to person, but

also the amount may change rapidly for an individual because of a change in jobs, in living habits, or in recreational pursuits. Other circumstances that require an abnormal expenditure of energy, or which place unusual demands on the reserve capacity and efficiency of the cardiovascular system are:

1. The suffering of an injury when one is in an isolated area—for example, prolonged containment in an automobile following an accident—without immediate outside help.
2. Prolonged, and heavy physical activity needed to cope with such catastrophes as floods, forest or home fires, being lost in an isolated area, falling fully clothed into deep water, or attempting to rescue another person who is unable to help himself.
3. Running to catch a public vehicle or to escape pursuit.
4. Being trapped in a confined area for a period of time.
5. Accidents, injuries, and operations that require most or all of the body's resources for recovery.

The person who is physically fit is in a much better condition to successfully cope with an emergency situation than is a person who is physically unfit.

Other Beneficial Effects of Exercise

Several other authenticated benefits that may be derived from regularly engaging in exercise are listed below:

1. Exercise favorably influences physical growth during childhood, youth, and even young adulthood in a number of ways. Aside from the obvious increase in the size of the musculature, there is an increase in vital capacity and in the size and composition of the skeletal bones.
2. Neuromuscular skill—the smooth, efficient coordination of the muscular and nervous systems—is improved as a result of regular participation in physical activity. As neuromuscular skill is increased, less energy is expended in physical performances, causing the physical performances to be less fatiguing and more enjoyable. Sensory perceptions and responses are also improved.

3. Not only the heart, but such internal organs as the lungs, the intestines, the liver, and the endocrine glands benefit from muscular activity.
4. Regular exercise promotes regularity of bowel movements and therefore is useful in preventing constipation.

PART II: FINDINGS FOR WHICH LITTLE EVIDENCE EXISTS

Physical Activity and Relief of Tension

Although it is difficult to objectively measure the amount of tension present in large numbers of people before and after engaging in strenuous physical activity, clinical and empirical evidence strongly suggest that exercise and physical activity are of value in reducing tension. Overactive minds in underactive bodies often need physical outlets for accumulated emotional and muscular tensions that seem to be relieved by action of the skeletal muscles. The widespread prevalence of hypertension supports the view that many people are unable to achieve a satisfactory degree of relaxation. Sports, games, and other physical activities provide acceptable outlets for emotions that ordinarily must be inhibited and restrained in our present-day culture. Muscular activity creates a sense of achievement and satisfaction that rapidly dissipates pent-up frustrations and stresses. The relaxing fatigue that follows vigorous exercise is a pleasant experience that may well be beneficial to mental health. The worries accumulated during the day often disappear as one concentrates on some physical exercise. Participation in physical activities also appears to aid in relieving a feeling of chronic fatigue and in improving a sense of well-being.

Games, Sports, and Improvement of Personality and Social Skills

If the rules are intelligently observed, participation in games and sports may aid in improving the personality and in developing desirable social skills, because the cooperative give-and-take demanded of the participants is not qualitatively different from that required of them in everyday living. Such traits as group loyalty, teamwork, realistic evaluation of self and others, leadership, cooperation, observance of rules, and perseverance

may be developed if knowingly practiced while engaging in games and sports. Several studies have indicated that persons with better-than-average physical skills have better personalities and are better adjusted than those with poor physical skills. During childhood, a lack of physical skills is a serious barrier to being accepted by playmates. Many lasting friendships are first established during play or sports participation. Studies of leadership traits indicate that the possession of better-than-average physical prowess plays an important role during childhood and youth in determining those who are selected as leaders; however, physical traits are less important to adults in this regard.

Exercise Aids Mental Ability

Because of the mental and physical relaxation that often results from physical activity, regular exercise is thought by many to be of considerable value in aiding the mental processes to function with increased efficiency. Several people with international reputations have attested that their mental work benefited as a result of participating in physical activities. Although most studies of grade-point averages earned by high school or college students show little or no difference in favor of male students with a high degree of physical fitness, in two studies it was found that students who improved in physical fitness during the semester also exhibited more of an improvement in their general academic work—and grade-point averages—than did students who did not improve in physical fitness.

Physical Fitness and General Health

At one time it was commonly believed that the possession of an optimum degree of physical fitness gave direct protection against specific diseases such as polio, small pox, diphtheria, and the like. Now it is known that such specific resistance as is acquired by vaccination is required to prevent the occurrence of these diseases if one is exposed to them. However, the physically fit person usually possesses a high degree of general resistance, which enables him to successfully avoid such minor illnesses as colds that otherwise could occur if he were in a run-down condition. One of the reasons sometimes ascribed for the low death rate of wounded American soldiers during World War II and the Korean combat is the high degree of physical fitness that they possessed.

A high relationship apparently exists between the degree of physical fitness and general health. Many physicians, health specialists, and physiologists have expressed the opinion that the physically fit person who exercises regularly can successfully withstand many of such common middle-aged ailments as headaches, postural diabetes, digestive upsets, constipation, breathlessness, kidney disorders, chronic fatigue, heartburn, and acidosis. This may in part be attributed to improved blood circulation, caused by the increased flow of venous blood induced by muscular activity. The biochemistry of the body is thus improved, which improvement aids in preventing discomfort and illnesses caused by an improper chemical balance in any of the systems of the body.

Exercise is frequently prescribed by medical doctors for a number of purposes. Among these are:

1. To improve or correct body mechanics by re-aligning or modifying the alignment of body segments.
2. To increase muscular strength and other components of physical fitness before and after surgery, and after childbirth.
3. To speed convalescence from the effects of various diseases and to promote complete recovery.
4. To ease the process of childbirth.
5. To promote the removal of kidney stones.

5. the overload principle

In Chapter 3 the physiologic changes that occur as the body adapts to the demands of regular, vigorous exercise are described. Collectively, these changes increase the capacity of the body to perform physical work. The reader should note that the body adapts *only* to the demands made upon it; if no demands are made, adaptations that result in improved physical fitness do not occur.

The overload principle is the basic tenet of any program of physical conditioning. It may be stated as follows: *When the body is regularly stimulated by a greater-than-normal exercise load, it responds by demonstrating an increased capacity to perform physical work.* Thus, to improve in physical fitness, the body must regularly be subjected to exercise that is more vigorous than that to which it is accustomed. After the body has adapted to the increased exercise load, the exercise load must again be increased to force the body to adapt further. This procedure must be repeated until the desired level of physical fitness is reached. Upon reaching the desired level, one must exercise regularly to maintain this level of fitness; but he need not continue to increase the exercise load.

APPLICATION OF OVERLOAD PRINCIPLE

In general, the exercise load may be increased (1) by increasing the resistance that must be overcome to do the exercise, (2) by increasing the duration of the exercise, or (3) by increasing both the resistance and the duration of the exercise. The resistance that must be overcome to do the exercise may be increased (1) by adding weight, as is done in weight training, (2) by increasing the speed with which the exercise is performed, thus utilizing inertia to increase the resistance, or (3) by increasing both the weight and the speed. The duration of the exercise may be increased (1) by increasing the number of repetitions of the exercise, as in weight training or calisthenics, (2) by increasing the distance over which the exercise is performed, as in running, or (3) by increasing both the number of repetitions and the distance over which the exercise is performed. Most of the conditioning activities described in this book may be utilized in the application of the overload principle. For purposes of illustration, three specific examples of such application follow.

Weight Training

In weight training to develop *strength*, relatively heavy weights are used in the performance of a few repetitions of each of a set of exercises. Ordinarily, the weight used is such that the performer can execute the movement involved in the given exercise at least six—but not more than ten—times in succession. When sufficient strength to perform more than ten repetitions of the exercise is developed, the weight used for the exercise is increased to a poundage with which the performer can again do at least six—but not more than ten—repetitions. (See Chapter 8.) This procedure is repeated until the desired level of strength is reached.

In weight training to develop *local muscle endurance,* relatively light weights (in comparison with the weights used for the development of strength) may be used in the performance of many repetitions of each of a set of exercises. The increase in the number of repetitions increases the duration of the exercise and thereby creates an overload. In actual practice, both increased repetitions and increased resistance are usually utilized to improve local muscle endurance.

Interval Training

Interval training was first used in the training of runners in track events. This method of training, however, has since been adapted for many other sports such as basketball, swimming, soccer, tennis, weight training, and wrestling.

Interval training is a type of physical conditioning that involves a period of vigorous activity followed by a brief interval of recovery from the immediate physiologic effects of the activity. The alternate periods of activity and recovery are repeated in the same manner a specified number of times.

In interval training for running, four variables are involved: (1) the distance that is run repeatedly, (2) the speed (pace) at which the distance is run, (3) the number of times the run is repeated, and (4) the time interval (recovery period) between runs. By holding some of these variables constant and systematically increasing (or decreasing) the remaining variables, an overload may be developed.

Although many combinations of these variables are possible, runners in training usually rely on two combinations: a combination in which the speed that they run is about the same speed that they plan eventually to run for the entire race and a combination in which the speed that they run is considerably faster than the speed that they can maintain for the entire race. In the first instance, the runner who hopes to condition himself to run the mile in 4 minutes, 30 seconds may, in the early stages of his training, use as his workout two 880-yard runs in 2 minutes, 15 seconds each, with a 5-minute recovery interval (during which he walks or jogs easily) between the runs. As his condition improves, he will systematically increase the number of runs to three, four, and five, and will keep the time for each run and the recovery interval the same as before.

For about every third workout, the runner will utilize the second combination—repeated runs at a speed faster than that which he can maintain for the entire race. For example, during the early part of the season he may run five 440-yard dashes in about 68 seconds each with 3 minutes of jogging between dashes. As his condition improves, he will, by increasing his speed, systematically reduce the time required for each dash until he can run the dashes in about 61 or 62 seconds each. He will keep the recovery interval between dashes the same as before.

A number of coaches believe that interval training in which short distances of 40 yards to 100 yards are utilized is best for developing local muscle endurance, whereas distances of 220 yards to 880 yards seem to be best for the development of circulorespiratory endurance.

The swimmer, by swimming instead of running, may effectively utilize interval training to increase his speed and endurance in swimming. The soccer player may adapt the interval training procedure by utilizing repeated sessions of intensive practice on fundamental skills (such as dribbling) with short recovery intervals between sessions. The tennis player, by hitting the ball against a wall repeatedly, may utilize the same procedure as the soccer player for such fundamental skills as forehand and backhand strokes. The weight lifter may utilize interval training by using various combinations of four variables: (1) the number of repetitions in each set of exercises, (2) the number of times each set of exercises is completed, (3) the recovery interval between sets of exercises, and (4) the magnitude of the weight used for each exercise.

Circuit Training

Circuit training is a type of training that involves participation in a variety of activities in rapid succession. (See Chapter 21.) *Circuit* is a term given to the group of activities. The activities of the circuit are conducted at various locations called *stations*. For example, a circuit may consist of a specified number of repetitions of the following activities: pull-ups, stair-climbing, sit-ups, and a flexibility exercise such as bending over and, while keeping the knees straight, touching the floor. Each activity is conducted as a different station: pull-ups, at a horizontal bar; stair-climbing, at a nearby stairway; sit-ups, on the floor; and flexibility exercise, on the floor. The performer completes the required number of repetitions at one station and then proceeds to the next station until he has passed through all of the stations one or more times, as required. The reader should note that the activities in the circuit are so arranged that the effort required of any one portion of the body is changed alternately from an active phase to a passive phase. In the circuit mentioned here, for example, the portion of the body used for the activity is varied with the exercise: the muscles of the shoulder girdle, in the pull-ups; the muscles of the legs, in the stair-climbs; the muscles of the hip area and the abdomen, in the sit-ups; and primarily the muscles of the back and legs, in the flexibility exercises. Also, the primary components of physical fitness that are developed vary from station to station: strength, in the pull-ups; cardiorespiratory endurance, in the stair-climbing; local muscle endurance, in the sit-ups; and flexibility in the flexibility exercises.

In circuit training, the overload is produced in the following ways: by increasing the number of stations in the circuit, by increasing the number of repetitions at each station in the circuit, by increasing the number of times the circuit is completed, or by so increasing the speed of performance at each station that the total time required to complete the circuit is decreased.

part 2

Specific Activities for Developing or Maintaining Physical Fitness

6. the selection and use of physical-fitness exercises and activities

There are many avenues through which physical fitness may be enhanced. By properly applying the basic overload principle described in Chapter 5, any vigorous physical activity may be utilized to improve or maintain one's physical fitness. However, circumstances often cause some types of activities and exercises to be much more suitable for this purpose than other types.

COMPETITIVE SPORTS AND PHYSICAL FITNESS

Because competitive sports play a rather spectacular role in schools and colleges, most boys in the process of growing up develop some knowledge and skill in at least one sport. Regular participation in a sport undoubtedly contributes to the physical fitness of the participant. In addition, many social, moral, and recreational values may be derived from such participation. However, to rely completely on a single competitive sport—or on several such sports—as a means of developing and maintaining one's physical fitness is unwise for several reasons.

Competitive Sports Are Seasonal

In the United States, most sports are played "in season." Football is played in the fall, basketball and volleyball in the winter, softball in the spring and summer, etc. If one relies on a single sport for regular exercise, he is seldom able to locate others who are willing to engage in the sport during the "off season." Further, the climate in most of the United States is not suitable for playing golf, tennis, and other outdoor sports throughout the year. Unless a field house or other specialized facilities are available, the person who can participate in only one sport will experience difficulty in participating in the sport throughout the entire year.

Competitive Sports Are Often Not Suitable for Adults

Many of the popular competitive sports are not suitable for most adults because for safe and enjoyable participation in such sports a high level of physical fitness is required. Most adults do not have the physical stamina required to play a regulation basketball game on a full-length court. Should they attempt to play basketball without previous conditioning, they would experience considerable discomfort and muscular soreness the next day. Similarly, without being properly conditioned, most adults would not consider running the mile in competition or playing a game of tackle football, not only because of the soreness and stiffness that would undoubtedly result, but also because of the danger of physical injury and the possibility of seriously endangering the heart.

Competitive Sports Require Special Facilities and Equipment

For a few sports, such as touch football and cross-country running, an open space is the only basic facility required for satisfactory participation. Most sports, however, require special facilities. To play basketball, a basketball goal, a smooth and level floor, and boundary lines are essential. Volleyball requires a large unobstructed space and a volleyball net placed in the proper position. To play tennis, a tennis court and net are needed; to play golf, a golf course is required. In addition, one must acquire certain basic equipment, such as balls, rackets or golf clubs.

Even though one has the basic equipment for the sport, the special facilities required for using such equipment may not be readily available. Golf courses and tennis courts are not often in a location that is convenient to the user; even on travelling to the facility one often finds that he must wait his turn to play. As a result, the special facilities that are required for participating in a competitive sport are often simply not available at the time one feels like "working out."

Competitive Sports Require Teammates and Opponents

Most of the traditional sports in which large numbers of American youth participate are team sports. Because it is often difficult to assemble a sufficient number of players to form two teams, one who is not a member of an established team that practices and competes in accordance with a formal schedule can participate in team sports only

on an irregular and infrequent basis—usually on weekends or holidays. Rarely does he have the opportunity to participate daily in team games.

For one to participate in dual sports such as badminton, tennis, squash rackets, or table tennis, at least one other player is required. Few players will go alone to the court to practice for the sake of improving their skills, and even fewer will participate alone to improve their physical fitness. When competition is absent, the joy of participation is diminished.

Because participation in both team and dual sports requires that two or more players are available and willing to play simultaneously, the average person who relies solely on such sports for exercise will experience considerable difficulty in arranging to exercise regularly.

The Body May Develop Unevenly

Another disadvantage of relying solely on sports to gain or retain physical fitness is that through such participation one may not develop all parts of the body equally. An unsymmetrical development of the musculature of the body can result. Also, participation only in sports often fails to develop sufficiently all the components of physical fitness. For this reason, most athletes supplement their regular training activities in a given sport with special training methods; for example, wrestlers perform distance running, swimmers engage in weight training, track men do calisthenics daily, and football players perform isometric exercises.

Sports Participation Is Time Consuming

Still another limitation of participation only in sports as an avenue to becoming and staying physically fit is that the time devoted to sports is often inefficiently expended. A more complete and vigorous workout can be obtained in fifteen minutes of participation in wisely selected conditioning exercises than in two hours of playing golf or softball, enjoyable as the latter activities may be. Because participation in sports is too time consuming for many busy adults, they are forced to consider activities and exercise methods that demand only a few minutes for maintaining a desired level of physical fitness.

NEED FOR LEARNING A VARIETY OF FITNESS ACTIVITIES

There are a great number of exercises and physical activities that may be used to supplement—or to replace—participation in sports as a means of fostering physical fitness. Just as one should acquire diversified interests and hobbies many years before retirement, one should learn while still young a variety of physical fitness activities, for use in later life. If proper exercise methods are utilized, these activities can be used successfully to maintain physical fitness at any stage in life.

Require No Specialized Equipment or Facilities

A large variety of exercises and activities have been devised that require no special facilities and little or no special equipment. For the most part, these exercises and activities can be performed either indoors or out-of-doors, and in a limited area; consequently, they are useful regardless of whether or not specialized sports and exercise facilities are available.

Require Little Time

Some exercise methods are more efficient in terms of time expended than are others. A person might prefer to spend at least one or two hours daily in physical activity but on occasion find it impossible to do so. If he is acquainted with highly efficient exercise techniques, he can obtain a complete, vigorous workout in a shorter period of time. Undoubtedly, everyone encounters situations in which the use of rapid exercise techniques are the only possible means for engaging in vigorous exercise.

Can Be Adapted to Age and Physical Condition

A large number of exercises and activities can be adapted to fit the exercise needs of persons of all ages and of varying degrees of physical fitness. Unlike competitive sports, the intensity of such exercises and activities can be made as mild or as vigorous as the user desires.

CRITERIA FOR SELECTING ACTIVITIES AND EXERCISES

The reader should learn the correct methods of utilizing a variety of exercises and activities in order that he may exercise regularly:

1. Without specialized equipment and facilities.
2. Regardless of where he is.
3. Regardless of the time that he has available.
4. Regardless of the number of players available.
5. Regardless of his age.

The exercises and physical activities described in Chapters 7 through 21 meet these limiting criteria admirably well. Included are exercises and physical activities from which may be selected those that meet the specific needs of the person concerned, regardless of his age or level of physical fitness. Further, exercises and physical activities may be selected to develop specific components of physical fitness—strength, endurance, agility, and the like. Most of the exercises and activities can be carried on by one person or by large groups simultaneously. For the person who understands the proper application of the overload principle and the principles involved in selecting a well-planned physical fitness program, no trained leader is needed. Some competitive activities are included for those who particularly enjoy pitting their talents against those of others. Many activities that may be engaged in strictly "for fun" are provided for those who wish to meet their exercise needs and recreational needs simultaneously. Moreover, the exercises and activities included are inherently without danger to the performer, and involve simple and uncomplicated physical skills which require little or no time to acquire.

SELECTING ACTIVITIES AND EXERCISES

What guides should be followed in choosing the activities and the exercises to be utilized for present and future use? Several criteria should be observed in making such a selection.

Develop All Components of Physical Fitness

The activities and exercises selected should, when considered in their entirety, develop or help to maintain all the components of physical fitness. However, some of these components are more important than others, and some require more time to develop than others; hence, increased effort should be devoted to such components.

Definitions of components of physical fitness. In order that the reader may understand the meaning given by the authors to the components of physical fitness, these terms are defined below.

Agility—The ability to change rapidly the direction or the position of the body or parts of the body.

Balance—The ability to maintain neuromuscular control of the body position.

Coordination—The ability to integrate movements of different parts of the body into a smooth, efficient, purposeful pattern or effort.

Endurance—The capacity of the human organism for sustained or continuous effort, sometimes termed the ability to withstand fatigue. There are two main types of endurance: *circulorespiratory* or *cardiorespiratory endurance*—the effectiveness of the heart, lungs, and circulatory system in supplying oxygen and energy-producing materials to working muscle groups and other areas of the body, and in expediting the removal of waste products from the body, for an extended period of time; and *local muscle endurance*—the ability of a muscle or muscle group to continue to exert force by submaximal muscle contractions against a load placed on these muscles over a period of time.

Flexibility—The ability to achieve a maximum range of movement at the various joints of the body.

Speed—The ability to make a movement or successive similar movements rapidly.

Strength—The ability of a muscle, muscle group, or muscle groups to exert maximum force in a single contraction.

Isolating components of physical fitness. As a rule, participation in a single exercise or activity contributes in some degree to the development of several components of physical fitness. When an exercise or activity is performed, rarely will only one component of physical fitness be developed or maintained and all other components be unaffected. This is true because the various components of physical fitness are related to one another. When pull-ups are regularly performed, for example, not only is the strength of the arm flexors increased, but the muscular endurance of these muscles is also in-

creased. Running fifty yards at full speed contributes to some extent to the development of cardiorespiratory endurance, speed, agility, and coordination. Thus, it is extremely difficult to select exercises or activities that contribute to only one component of physical fitness.

For the sake of simplicity and in order to allow the reader to plan his physical fitness exercise program with care, the component or components of physical fitness that are primarily developed by the exercises and activities described in the following chapters are listed at the beginning of each chapter, or for specific types of exercises. This listing will enable the reader to select a balanced program of activities, and to emphasize those activities that primarily affect the development or maintenance of the components of physical fitness in which he is particularly interested.

Exercise All Parts of the Body

It is important that all major muscle groups of the body are exercised when participating in exercises and activities designed to develop the various components of physical fitness. The program of exercise should contribute toward a symmetrical development of the body. In general, the following four main muscle groups of the body should be exercised during each exercise session:

1. The flexors of the trunk, which are primarily involved in such movements as sit-ups.
2. The extensors of the trunk, which are involved in such movements as back arches from a prone position or picking up an object from the floor.
3. The thigh and leg muscles, which are involved in such movements as running or squatting.
4. The shoulder and arm muscles, which are involved in such movements as push-ups or pull-ups.

A detailed explanation of how to determine which muscle groups are involved in various movements is given in Chapter 8.

Choose Variety of Activities

A variety of activities should be selected and practiced to insure that boredom and monotony do not occur with long-term use. If the activities selected are interesting and enjoyable, long-term participation in them will have recreational value rather than being an unpleasant duty. The exercise program should include activities in which participation may be mild or vigorous, as need and desire dictate. If an increase in the level of physical fitness is desired, the overload principle should be applicable to the activities and exercises selected.

FACTORS TO CONSIDER WHEN USING EXERCISES AND ACTIVITIES

Physical Examination

Before engaging in a regular exercise program, strenuous sports, or other vigorous physical activity, one should undergo a thorough physical examination and should obtain clearance from a physician, especially if the person has become accustomed to sedentary living. Specific information should be obtained from the examining physician as to whether certain movements or specific types of activities should be avoided. The physical examination should be repeated at least once a year, particularly after the age of thirty.

Warm-Up

Warm-up is the term given to the preliminary activity used to prepare the performer for participation in the main activity. The preliminary activity is generally a mild type of activity. A runner in a track event may use calisthenics as his warm-up, while a baseball pitcher may throw the ball several times for his warm-up.

The value of engaging in a mild warm-up activity before engaging in strenuous physical activity has been questioned by some authorities in physical education and physiology. However, until this controversy has been settled, it is considered advisable to engage in a warm-up before participating in a physical activity that calls for vigorous physical effort. Much of the usual warm-up activity is based on tradition rather than fact. However, there are basic principles related to the warm-up that, if applied, can aid in preparing the body for participation in vigorous activity. A knowledge of these principles enables one to differentiate between the traditional, superfluous types of warm-up and those that benefit the performer, saving considerable time

and energy that might otherwise be uselessly expended.

Warm-up activities are classified as either *formal* or *informal*. Informal warm-up activities have little or no relationship, in terms of the neuromuscular skills involved, to the activities that follow. Such warm-ups are exemplified by the previously mentioned warm-up of the runner—namely, calisthenics. Formal warm-up activities are, in terms of neuromuscular coordination, the same as or closely related to the activities that follow. The handball player is said to be using a formal type of warm-up when he throws the ball against the wall, because the neuromuscular skills of throwing and hitting the handball are quite similar.

Many authorities agree that the function of the formal warm-up is to improve neuromuscular coordination. There is, however, disagreement about the need for the informal warm-up. In this disagreement, two camps emerge—the traditionalists and the skeptics. The traditionalists claim the following functions for the informal warm-up: to increase the temperature of the muscle and to decrease the viscosity of the muscle, which in turn aids in preventing injuries to muscles and tendons; to increase the speed and the strength of muscle contraction; to reduce muscle soreness following strenuous activity; and to promote physiological economy during strenuous activity. The skeptics point out that some of the benefits (increased temperature of muscle, decreased viscosity of muscle) seemingly obtained from the informal warm-up would normally occur during the first few muscle contractions anyway, and that time spent in warming up before athletic contests is probably wasted unless a formal warm-up is utilized. In view of this disagreement, one might logically limit his informal warm-up activities to a few appropriate stretching exercises, and concentrate on formal warm-up activities.

Application of the Overload Principle

If the performer is interested in raising the level of his physical fitness, he should apply the overload principle in using the exercises and activities described in the succeeding chapters. The general methods that may be used to incorporate the overload principle when exercising are listed and explained in Chapter 5. Suggestions are given, where appropriate, for applying the overload principle to the various exercises and activities described in the following chapters.

Time of Day for Exercising

Setting aside a specific time in which to engage regularly in physical activity is important. A time of day should be chosen that is not likely to be canceled or interrupted for any reason other than illness. There appears to be no one time of day or night that is most suitable for improving physical condition. However, most authorities recommend waiting a minimum of one hour after eating before engaging in vigorous physical activity.

Duration of Exercise Period

The duration of the activity period depends upon the purposes, needs, and desires of the performer. This period should be at least thirty minutes in length, and if possible one hour or longer. The length of the exercise period, however, will vary with the time available from one's daily schedule, the type and nature of the exercises and activities participated in, and whether the performer wishes to increase his physical fitness or only to maintain it.

Equipment Needed for Exercises and Activities

Many of the exercises and activities described in the chapters that follow require no equipment. Some of the exercises and activities require simple equipment that is readily available in the home, while others require special equipment commonly found in gymnasiums and other exercise areas, but that can be obtained for use in the home.

Selection of Facilities

For the student, the choice is often between the physical education facilities of his school and his place of residence. If one is not attending school, the daily period of activity may be carried on at home, at work, or at a community agency such as the Y.M.C.A. The same facilities may be used each day, or the site of the activity can be varied as often as desired. Personal convenience is the main consideration when making a choice of facility.

There are several valid reasons for selecting one's home as the place in which to exercise. Community facilities could not begin to serve the general public if everyone wanted to participate in a daily program of physical activity. In the home, permanent facilities and inexpensive equipment that may be constructed easily can be developed and used for a variety of activities. Even the apartment dweller can develop a satisfactory physical-conditioning center. It is convenient to participate in physical-conditioning activities in the home because dressing and bathing facilities are available, no transportation is involved, and home exercise programs are not affected by inclement weather.

The exercise center may be developed in a recreation room, basement, or garage. Some of the physical activities that may be used in the home exercise center are weight training, calisthenics, isometric exercises, dual-resistance exercises, circuit training, rope skipping, grass drills, simple tumbling stunts, and hand balancing. Sports activities and games that are practical for use in the basement or garage include archery, deck tennis, golf driving, table tennis, hand tennis, shuffleboard, smash, and modified one- or two-wall games such as handball or paddleball. A multipurpose court may be constructed on the lawn if sufficient space is available. The following sport activities may be adapted to such a court: badminton, paddle tennis, deck tennis, newcomb, volleyball (such as two-man volleyball), cabinet ball, and lawn tennis.

Intensity of Exercises

How intensely should one exercise? Is there a simple but safe guide for determining the amount and intensity of exercise needed to obtain effective results and yet not endanger one's health? The present capacity of the body to tolerate exercise is determined primarily by the amount of physical activity to which the body has been accustomed in the past, because the present degree of physical fitness is proportional to the amount of physical activity to which the body has been regularly subjected. Obviously a miler with several months of training can safely and comfortably endure a much higher exercise load than can a person who has been leading a sedentary life.

Ordinarily, a built-in psychological limit operates to cause one to want to stop exercising before he reaches the initial state of exhaustion. This desire to rest usually causes one to stop the exercise far short of his physiological limit and well within the margin of safety. As the body undergoes regular physical stress, it gradually marshals its resources and adapts itself to that stress, thus increasing both the physiological and psychological limit. However, it is probably impossible for one to raise his psychological limit to that of his physiological limit.

One's present capacity for exercise is influenced much more by the intensity and quantity of habitual physical activity than by age. A man forty or forty-five years of age who regularly engages in strenuous physical activity can usually tolerate a much greater exercise load than a youth of seventeen or eighteen years of age who is not accustomed to doing any physical activity. Regardless of age, the amount of exercise in which one engages should be sufficient to tax the circulatory system and the respiratory system. The exercise should be of such vigor and duration that one perspires freely.

What progression in the exercise load is recommended? How rapidly should the intensity and duration of exercise be increased? When beginning an exercise program it is advisable to do the physical activity at a moderate pace and to perform with a relatively light exercise load during the first few periods of physical activity. This procedure will enable the various muscle groups being exercised to gradually adjust to the unaccustomed exercise movements with a minimum of soreness and stiffness. This period of training is sometimes referred to as the "toughening stage."

After an initial period of adjustment to physical activity, the exercise load or resistance should be progressively increased over a period of several weeks. This period is often called the "development stage." During this period, one should exercise five days of each week. A definite progressive improvement in physical fitness should be evident for a number of weeks. Eventually, a plateau will be reached—that is, it will become difficult to improve one's physical fitness further without increasing the exercise load a considerable amount in relation to the amount of gain in physical fitness that results. The attainment of this stage indicates that one is ready for a maintenance exercise program.

In order to maintain the level of physical fitness that has been attained, one does not need to engage in as strenuous an exercise program as was required during the improvement stage. The length of each exercise period and the number of exercise periods required each week will also be less than are required for improving physical fitness. Three training periods each week are the minimum recommended during the maintenance stage of physical conditioning.

Specific Training Effects

In selecting exercises and activities for a physical fitness program, one should bear in mind that a specific type of training tends to give a specific type of physical fitness. The highly trained basketball player is not in condition to play a strenuous game of tackle football. A well-trained swimmer is not in shape for a rigorous workout on the horizontal bar, nor is the highly conditioned baseball pitcher physically prepared to engage in an exhausting wrestling bout for nine minutes. Engaging regularly in weight-training exercises with heavy weights does not prepare one for running a mile. Running a mile each day does little to increase one's flexibility. Because the training effects are specific, one should engage in a variety of exercises and activities to insure a well-rounded development of physical fitness.

SIMILARITY OF EXERCISES AND ACTIVITIES

In reading about the various exercises and activities described in Part II, the reader should note that some exercises and activities appear under more than one general heading. This repetition is necessary because the same exercise or activity may be utilized in one or more methods of training. For example, the exercises and activities that are included in a circuit in circuit training may be selected from calisthenics, weight training, apparatus and tumbling activities, rope jumping, and the like. Exercises and activities that are utilized in more than one method of training are cross-referenced throughout the book.

The reader should also note that some of the exercises and activities are quite similar in nature to other exercises and activities. In some instances, the same type of resistance is employed in two different exercises or activities, but the manner in which this resistance is applied differs. This relationship is evident for weight training, isometric exercises, and dual-resistance exercises. Also, weight-training exercises and apparatus activities are closely related in that barbells and dumbbells of various poundage are used as the resistance in weight training whereas the performer's body (a fixed weight) is the resistance used in apparatus work and in tumbling. Rope jumping and some calisthenic exercises are quite similar in action, and both aid in developing or maintaining the same components of physical fitness. Except for the competitive element, dual-resistance exercises and combative activities are often quite similar.

7. calisthenics

There are several reasons for selecting calisthenics as a means for developing and maintaining physical fitness. Calisthenic routines are easy to learn and are relatively easy to perform. Calisthenics require no special equipment and very little space. Utilizing calisthenics, one can take a vigorous workout in a short period of time. By carefully selecting the exercises for the calisthenic routine, it is possible to exercise and to develop almost any muscle group or groups. Calisthenics can be performed by the person who desires to exercise alone, or by a group whose members enjoy participating together. The enjoyment of participating in calisthenics can be enhanced by performing the exercises rhythmically to music or in a progressively faster cadence. The chief limitation of calisthenics as a means for developing physical fitness is that a program of calisthenics, used extensively for a long period of time, may prove to be boring and monotonous to some people. Also, the types and amount of overload possible with calisthenics are limited.

USE OF CALISTHENICS

To achieve the maximum benefit from participation in a program of calisthenics, the following procedures should be employed:

1. Even though most calisthenic routines are performed in a definite rhythm or to a cadence count, the first time or two that each exercise is performed it should be done slowly and in good form. Frequent checks should be made to insure that each movement of the exercise is performed properly. During the initial stages of learning to perform an unfamiliar calisthenic routine, a leader or trained performer can be very useful in checking for errors in the execution of the exercises.
2. If maximum benefits are to be derived from performing calisthenics, correct form should always be the goal. This is particularly true for exercises of the stretching type.
3. To achieve an all-around development of the

37

body and to gain a balanced development of physical fitness, a variety of exercises should be learned and used in the calisthenic routine.

4. From ten to fifteen different exercises should be included in a complete calisthenic routine.

5. To enable the performer to regularly increase his exercise load, he should remember the number of times that he completes each exercise in the calisthenic routine. Most exercises in calisthenic routines are performed in a series of four movements. To keep a running count of the number of times each exercise is performed, the performer should silently or orally count the cadence in such a way that the last number in each cadence series is the total number of times that the exercise has been completed—for example, 1-2-3-1, 1-2-3-2, 1-2-3-3, 1-2-3-4, 1-2-3-5, etc.

6. As a general guide for establishing the initial exercise load in beginning a calisthenics program, it is recommended that each exercise in the calisthenic routine be completed five or six times. Ultimately, a maximum of twelve to twenty repetitions of each exercise should be performed by the experienced and well-conditioned calisthenics performer.

7. The performer should systematically increase the stress imposed by the calisthenics program by utilizing the overload principle in one or more of the following ways: by increasing the speed with which each exercise is performed; by increasing the number of repetitions of each exercise; by taking a decreased period of rest between each exercise; by resting only after performing two, three, four, or even the entire series of exercises.[1]

8. The beginner should perform the exercises in

---

[1] The *5BX Plan for Physical Fitness*, which was developed by the Royal Canadian Air Force for use by its members, is an excellent illustration of how the overload principle may be applied to calisthenics. The 5BX Plan includes six different charts of calisthenic routines, each of which contains five exercises. The five exercises are essentially the same on each of the six charts, but the exercises progressively increase in difficulty of execution from chart 1 through chart 6, chiefly because the number of repetitions for each exercise is increased while the time allotted for doing the repetitions remains the same as on previous charts. In additon, for each chart there are twelve levels of performance which range from D— to A+. For each level, the number of times each exercise should be performed within the given time limit is listed. On each chart, all five exercises for each level are to be completed in eleven minutes.

the calisthenic routine in a sequence that causes the various parts of his body to be exercised in turn; for example, if one exercise employs the arms, the next exercise should employ the legs. The advanced performer may concentrate on thoroughly exercising one area of the body through the use of several exercises before shifting to an exercise that brings into play another part of his body.

9. Persons with specific physical limitations or handicaps should avoid doing calisthenics that force movements of damaged joints beyond the limits of safety or that place excessive strain on a weakened area. If, in the exercises that follow, a specific exercise is inadvisable for a certain physical condition, attention is called to this fact.

CLASSIFICATION OF CALISTHENIC EXERCISES

Even though most exercises for calisthenic routines do not specifically develop only one component of physical fitness, they can generally be classified into one of three categories in terms of the component of physical fitness toward which the exercise contributes most. Some exercises can be considered to be quite specific with relation to the development of one component of physical fitness, even though the development of other components may, to some extent, occur as a result of engaging in the exercise. The three general categories into which calisthenics are classified in this chapter are (1) the circulorespiratory type, (2) the flexibility type, and (3) the muscle-endurance type.

The circulorespiratory type of calisthenics—sometimes called the warm-up type—involves rapid movements such as arm swinging and jumping, that increase the rate of the circulorespiratory processes. The flexibility type of calisthenics—sometimes called the stretching type—involves bending and stretching for the purpose of increasing the range of motion of various body levers at their respective joints. The muscle-endurance type of calisthenics—often called the fatigue type—involves repetitive movements with the body serving as a natural resistance. This type of calisthenics is beneficial in developing muscular strength; however, it should be noted that calisthenics are a relatively inefficient method of increasing strength.

In addition to the classification of calisthenics according to the component of physical fitness to which the exercises make primary contributions, calisthenics are sometimes classified according to the following categories:

1. Warm-up exercises, conditioning exercises, and ground exercises (for exercises performed while in a supine position).
2. Wand exercises, dumbbell exercises, rifle exercises, and exercises done without any special equipment.
3. One-man and two-man exercises.
4. Two-, four-, and eight-count exercises (the number refers to the number of counts or separate movements needed to complete one repetition of the exercise).

There are several hundred exercises suitable for calisthenic routines. The exercises described in this chapter include those that are commonly used, those that are easily learned, and those that can be used for the all-around development of the body. Since more than one name exists for some of the exercises, the most descriptive name for each exercise is listed. The descriptions given are for one complete movement of each exercise. Unless otherwise stated, each exercise should be considered to be a four-count exercise.

CIRCULORESPIRATORY-TYPE EXERCISES

Exercises of the circulorespiratory type are generally used as a warm-up or as an aid in adjusting the body to subsequent exercises of increased vigor and stress. Stationary running is probably the most common of this type of exercise. For this reason circulorespiratory-type exercises are usually the first type performed in a calisthenic routine. Two to four such exercises should be included in the routine. If a cadence count is maintained for jumping types of movements, the count is made during each jump.

Persons with such chronic shoulder joint difficulties as previous shoulder dislocations or separations should avoid flinging movements, especially those in which the arms are raised above the level of the shoulders.

DOUBLE HIGH JUMPER

The performer stands with his feet slightly apart, his legs flexed at the knees, his body bent forward, and his arms so thrust backward that his position is similar to that of a swimmer when in a position to do a racing start. To do the double high jumper, he swings his arms forward and upward and jumps vigorously from the floor. On coming down to the floor, he returns to the starting position. The exercise is repeated as often as is desired. This exercise is usually done as a four-count exercise with two complete jumps performed during each four cadence counts.

HIGH JUMPER

The starting position is the same as for the double high jumper. The performer swings his arms forward and jumps slightly off the floor. As soon as his feet again contact the floor, he swings his arms downward and backward and again jumps slightly off the floor. He then swings his arms forward and upward and jumps vigorously from the floor. As soon as he lands, he jumps slightly off the floor and returns to the starting position.

JUMPING, FALSE ROPE

The performer stands erect with his feet together and his arms at his sides. He jumps about two inches off the floor and at the same time makes a small circle with each arm as if he were swinging a jumping rope. Nearly all the footwork variations of rope jumping may be used for this exercise. (See "Rope Jumping," Chapter 14.) The total number of jumps performed is counted.

JUMPING, FORWARD HAND KICK (FIGURE 7-1)

The performer assumes a crouched position. From this position he springs off the floor. At the height of his jump he attempts to touch his toes to his hands by flexing the upper legs at the hips. He attempts to alight in an erect standing position with his legs slightly bent.

JUMPING, HEEL CLICK

From a crouched position the performer springs off the floor and attempts to click his heels together twice before landing in a semi-crouched position. The total number of jumps performed is counted.

JUMPING, HEEL SLAP (FIGURE 7-2)

From a crouched position the performer springs off the floor, flexes his legs at the knees, and, at the

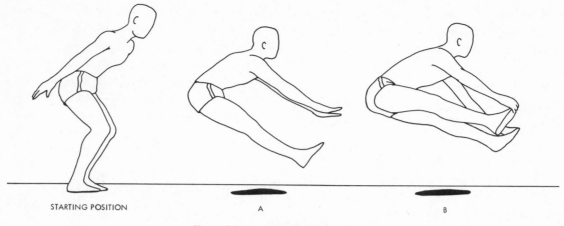

Figure 7-1. Jumping, forward hand kick.

height of his jump, attempts to slap his heels with his hands. He lands in a semi-crouched position.

JUMPING, SPLIT JUMP

From a crouched position the performer springs upward and spreads his legs apart, one leg in front of and one leg behind his body. He attempts to bring both feet in line and next to each other by the time he lands on the floor. On the next jump the position of the legs is reversed—that is, the leg that went behind the body now goes in front of the body and vice versa. The total number of jumps performed is counted.

JUMPING, TUCK JUMP (FIGURE 7-3)

From a crouched position the performer springs upward and raises his knees to his chest by flexing his thighs at the hips and his legs at the knees. At the height of his jump he clasps his shins with his hands. He lands on the floor in a semi-crouched position. The total number of jumps performed is counted.

JUMPING, VERTICAL WALL SLAP

The performer stands sideways and next to a wall. He crouches and then jumps upward while vigorously extending both arms upward. At the peak of the jump he attempts to slap the wall with the hand that is next to the wall. He then lands in a semi-crouched position. The total number of jumps performed is counted.

SIDE STRADDLE HOP

The performer stands in an erect position with his feet together and his arms at his side. He springs into the air, spreads his legs until they

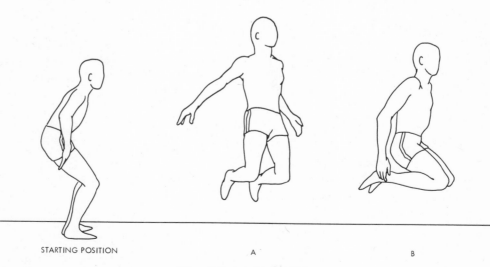

Figure 7-2. Jumping, heel slap.

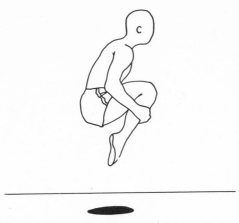

Figure 7-3. Jumping, tuck jump.

are shoulder distance apart, and, at the same time, swings his arms in a sideward arc until his palms touch together overhead. He alights on the floor in this position and then jumps up and returns to the starting position. One count is given during each jump.

FLEXIBILITY-TYPE EXERCISES

After the selected number of circulorespiratory-type exercises has been completed, flexibility-type exercises are usually performed next, although these may be mixed with exercises of the muscle-endurance type. Four to six exercises of the flexibility type should be included in the calisthenic routines.

ARM CIRCLING

The performer stands in an erect position with his arms raised sideward so that they are parallel to the floor. He then moves his arms in a circular motion with his hands moving in larger and larger circles until the maximum range of motion is attained. He then reverses the direction of the circular motion and repeats the process. A cadence count is not needed for this exercise; instead, the exercise is often performed for a specific period of time.

BEND AND REACH BEHIND

With his feet spread wider than the width of his hips, the performer stands in an erect position. His arms are together overhead. He flexes his legs at his knees and, at the same time, bends forward at his waist, reaches between his legs with his hands, and forces them as far behind his legs as possible. He then returns to the starting position.

BOTTOMS UP OR SQUAT BENDER (FIGURE 7-4)

From an erect standing position the performer squats, assumes a deep knee bend position, and touches his fingertips to his toes. Keeping his fingertips touching his toes, he straightens his legs, squats again, and returns to the starting position.

This exercise is contraindicated for people with chronic injuries of the knee joint.

HAMSTRING STRETCHER

With his legs spread as wide apart as possible, the performer sits on the floor. He flexes forward and, keeping his legs straight, attempts to touch his elbows to the floor, first touching between his legs, then by his right knee, and then by his left

Figure 7-4. Bottoms up or squat bender.

knee. Next he grasps his legs at the calves, pulls and flexes his trunk, and attempts to touch his forehead first to the floor area between his legs, then to his right knee, and then to his left knee. The exercise is done in eight counts.

HIGH KICK

From a position of attention the performer transfers his weight to his left foot and lifts his extended right arm to a position in front of his body parallel with the floor. He then swings his right leg forward and attempts to touch the palm of his hand with his right toes. He returns the kicking foot to the floor and performs three steps in place —right, left, right. On the third step in place (when the weight is transferred to the right foot), he kicks with his left foot and attempts to touch his toes to the palm of his left hand which is held in front of his left shoulder. This exercise may also be done without taking three steps in place between each kick.

LEG CIRCLING

The performer lies on his back and raises his legs until they are perpendicular to the floor. His arms are on the floor, palms down, and are extended at right angles to his body. Keeping his legs straight and his hands braced against the floor, he moves his feet, together, in ever-widening circles. When the maximum circumference of the circling movement is attained, the size of the circles is decreased until the starting position is regained. He may then circle his feet in the opposite direction. This exercise is ordinarily performed for a selected period of time.

LEG ROLL-BACK

The performer lies on his back with his arms at his sides. He slowly raises his extended legs over-

head and continues moving them until his toes touch the floor behind his head. He then returns his legs to the starting position.

MAD CAT (FIGURE 7-5)

The performer assumes a crawling position by placing his hands, knees, and toes on the floor. His back should be straight or arched downward toward the floor. He next humps his back, attempting to raise it as high as possible. He then lowers his back to the starting position.

SIDEWARD LEG RAISE

From a position of attention the performer shifts his weight to his right foot and raises his left leg sideways to his left as high as possible. He returns to the starting position and repeats the exercise, moving his right leg to his right while standing on his left leg.

SIDE STRETCHER

With his legs slightly apart, his arms extended overhead, and his hands interclasped, the performer stands in an erect position. He first moves his trunk to his left, bending sideward at the waist until he can go no farther. He returns to the starting position and stretches to his right as far as possible. If desired, two or three "bounces" may be taken when in the stretched position to either side, in which case the exercise is performed as an eight-count exercise.

SIDEWARD STRETCH

With his arms at his sides and his legs spread as wide apart as possible, the performer stands in an erect position. He bends his left leg, flexes his trunk to his left as far as possible, and, at the same time, presses down on his left knee with his left hand. He then returns to the starting position and

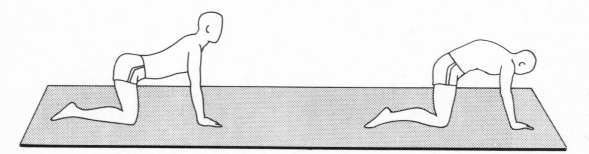

Figure 7-5. Mad cat.

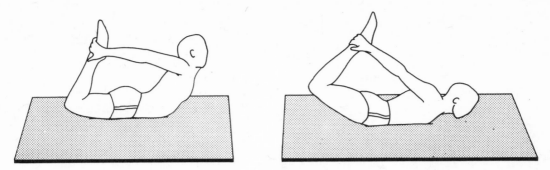

Figure 7-6. Stomach roller.

repeats the exercise by flexing his trunk to his right.

STOMACH ROLLER (FIGURE 7-6)

The performer lies in a face-down (prone) position with his legs flexed and his hands clasping his ankles. He pulls on his ankles and rocks back and forth on his thighs, stomach, and chest. This exercise is usually performed for a selected period of time.

TRUNK-STRETCHER

With his hands on his hips and his legs slightly apart, the performer stands in an erect position. He flexes his upper trunk as far forward as possible and then returns to the starting position. He then moves his upper trunk as far to his left as possible and returns to the starting position. He then repeats these movements to the rear and to his right. The exercise is performed to eight cadence-counts.

TURN AND BOUNCE

The performer stands in an erect position with his legs slightly apart and his arms extended and raised sideward until they are parallel to the floor. He so turns his arms and shoulders that his hands move in a counterclockwise direction as far as possible. If desired, two or three "bounces" may be taken after each initial movement. He then returns to the starting position and turns in a clockwise direction as far as possible.

WINDSHIELD WIPER

With his legs raised perpendicular to the floor, the performer lies on his back (supine position). His arms are on the floor, palms down, and are extended at right angles from his body. Keeping his legs straight and his arms braced against the floor, he moves his legs to his left as far as possible in an

attempt to lightly touch the floor with his left foot. He returns his legs to the starting position and repeats the exercise to his right.

MUSCLE-ENDURANCE-TYPE EXERCISES

In a calisthenic routine exercises of the muscle-endurance type are usually the last of the three types performed; they may, however, be mixed with exercises of the flexibility type. Four to six exercises of the muscle-endurance type are recommended for each calisthenic routine. The muscle-endurance-type exercises that follow are grouped according to the muscles that the exercise is designed to strengthen and, within each grouping, are listed in progressive order from the easy to the difficult. In terms of the muscular endurance required to execute the exercise, the exercises proceed from those in which a small amount of resistance is encountered to those in which a large amount of resistance is encountered.

Abdominal Progression

ABDOMINAL COMPRESSOR

With his arms at his sides the performer assumes a supine position on the floor. He exhales and then, by contracting his stomach muscles, pulls his abdominal area toward his backbone as hard as he can and holds for three counts. He then relaxes and inhales. This exercise is performed a selected number of times.

ABDOMINAL CURL

With his arms at his sides the performer assumes a supine position on the floor. He curls his upper trunk and head upward and forward while keeping his lower back in contact with the floor. He

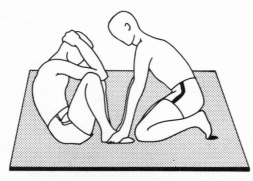

Figure 7-7. Sit-up with bent legs.

then slowly lowers his upper trunk and head to the floor.

ROWING ABDOMINAL CURL

The performer lies on his back with his arms extended overhead. Bringing his knees toward his shoulders, he sits up, curling his head, arms, and upper trunk toward his legs. At the completion of this movement he is in a sitting position with his knees next to his shoulders and his arms extended outside of his knees. He then returns to the starting position.

SIT-UP WITH BENT LEGS (FIGURE 7-7)

With his fingers interlaced and held behind his head, the performer lies on his back. His heels are placed near his buttocks; and his knees are together and above his feet, which are held to the floor by a partner or by an object. The performer sits up, attempts to touch his right shoulder to his left knee, and then returns to the starting position. He repeats the exercise to the other side.

LEAN BACK (FIGURE 7-8)

The performer sits on the floor with his fingers interlaced and held behind his head, and with his legs extended in front of him. Keeping his upper body in a semi-flexed position, the performer leans back until his legs are raised slightly off the floor and he is balanced on his buttocks. He holds the *V* position for three counts and then returns to the starting position. This exercise is usually performed a selected number of times.

Hip-Flexor Progression

SINGLE-LEG RAISE

With his arms at his sides and his legs extended, the performer lies on his back. He raises his left leg off the floor and swings it in an arc toward his head. He then lowers his left leg to the starting position and repeats the exercise with his right leg. He may repeat this movement several times with the same leg, or he may alternate the leg moved each time.

SIT-UP WITH STRAIGHT LEGS

With his arms at his sides and his legs extended and slightly spread, the performer lies on his back. His feet are held to the floor by a partner or are placed under a heavy object or non-movable support. The performer sits up, curling forward with his head and trunk until he can bring his head no closer to his legs. He then returns to the starting position.

SIT-UP WITH HANDS BEHIND HEAD

Starting from the same position as in the previous exercise, except with his hands clasped behind his head, the performer sits up, curls his body forward, and attempts to touch his right elbow to

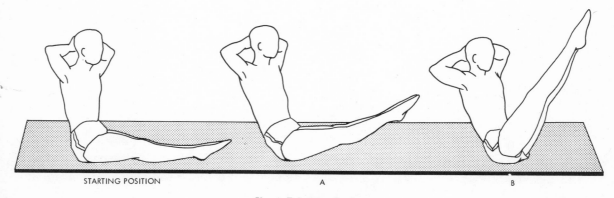

STARTING POSITION   A   B

Figure 7-8. Lean back.

Figure 7-9. Sit-up and leg raise.

his left knee. He returns to the starting position and repeats the exercise to the opposite side.

DOUBLE-LEG RAISE[2]

The performer lies on his back with his hands placed under his buttocks, and with his legs extended and together. He slowly lifts his legs until they are perpendicular to the floor, then returns them to the starting position.

SIT-UP AND LEG RAISE (FIGURE 7-9)

With his hands by his sides and his legs extended, the performer lies on his back. He sits up and, at the same time, raises his legs and touches his feet with his hands while balancing on his buttocks. He then returns to the starting position.

Push-up Progression

Exercises of the push-up variety may be performed in cadence, or a predetermined number may

---

[2] If the performer is able to slide his hands under the small of his back when his legs are off the floor, he should omit this exercise until his abdominal muscles are sufficiently strong to prevent his pelvis from tilting when his legs are raised from the floor.

be performed at the individual's own preferred pace.

WALL PUSH-AWAY

The performer stands facing a wall with his arms extended and his hands touching the wall at about chest height. He moves his feet backward approximately twenty-four inches, and he lowers his hands on the wall about six inches; the performer is now leaning against the wall. He flexes his arms until his face is one inch from the wall. He then extends his arms and pushes vigorously with his hands and fingers until his hands leave the wall and his body approaches an erect position. He then leans forward until his hands again touch the wall and repeats the push-up movement.

BACK ARCH PUSH-UP (FIGURE 7-10)

With his feet together and his hands underneath his shoulders, the performer lies in a prone position on the floor. He raises his upper body by extending his arms, keeping his legs and his abdomen on the floor at all times. He then lowers his upper body to the floor.

KNEE OR HALF PUSH-UP (FIGURE 7-11)

The performer lies in a prone position on the floor with his feet together, his knees and feet resting on the floor, and his hands underneath his shoulders. Keeping his knees and toes in contact with the floor, and keeping his body, from head to knees, in a straight line, he pushes up until his arms are fully extended. He then lowers his body to the floor.

TOE OR REGULAR PUSH-UP

The performer lies in a prone position on the floor with his feet together, his hands underneath

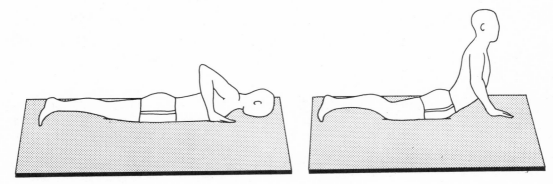

Figure 7-10. Back arch push-up.

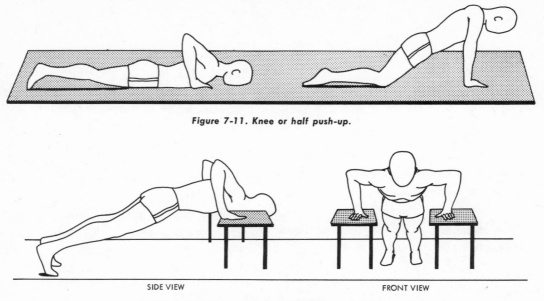

Figure 7-11. Knee or half push-up.

SIDE VIEW   FRONT VIEW

Figure 7-12. Hands-on-benches-or-chairs push-up.

his shoulders, and his toes and chest resting on the floor. By extending his arms, he does a push-up while so maintaining his body in a straight line that his body comes to a front leaning-rest position. He then lowers his body until his chest touches the floor.

ONE-LEG PUSH-UP

With his hands underneath his shoulders and one leg raised off the floor, the performer lies in a prone position on the floor. Keeping his raised leg off the floor, he does a push-up while maintaining his body in a straight line. He then lowers his body to the starting position. At the completion of each push-up the performer may alternate the leg that he raises.

HANDS-ON-BENCHES-OR-CHAIRS PUSH-UP (FIGURE 7-12)

The performer bends forward and places his hands on top of two benches or chairs, which are placed slightly more than shoulder-distance apart. Supporting his weight on his extended arms, he extends his legs and lower trunk until his body is in a straight line. He lowers his body, keeping it rigid and in a straight line, until he can lower it no further. He then returns to the starting position.

FEET-ON-BENCH-OR-CHAIR PUSH-UP

With his feet resting on a chair and his hands placed on the floor underneath his shoulders, the performer takes a front leaning-rest position. Keep-

ing his body straight, he lowers it until his chest touches the floor. He then returns to the starting position.

FEET-ON-WALL PUSH-UP (FIGURE 7-13)

Standing with his back to a wall and with his feet next to the wall, the performer assumes a front leaning-rest position. He then walks his feet up the wall while moving his hands toward the wall, until his hands are positioned three to five feet from the wall.[3] Keeping his body straight, the performer

---

[3] The more vertical the body position, the more difficult is the push-up movement.

Figure 7-13. Feet-on-wall push-up.

Figure 7-14. Side leaning-rest exercise.

lowers himself until his head touches the floor. He then returns to the starting position. This is a difficult push-up movement and requires considerable arm and shoulder strength.

SIDE LEANING-REST EXERCISE (FIGURE 7-14)

The performer takes a front leaning-rest position and so turns his body to the right that his weight is supported by his right foot and right hand. He raises his left arm sidewards until it is perpendicular to his body and, at the same time, raises his left leg as high as possible. He returns to the right side leaning-rest position and repeats the movements. The exercise can also be performed from the left side-leaning rest position.

ONE-ARM PUSH-UP: SIDE POSITION

The performer assumes either a right or a left side leaning-rest position. If he wishes, he may place his left foot approximately twenty inches in front of his right foot. He lowers his body until his shoulder touches his hand. He then returns to the starting position.

ONE-ARM PUSH-UP: PRONE POSITION (FIGURE 7-15)

The performer takes a front leaning-rest position with his feet spread several inches apart. He removes one hand from the floor and places it on the small of his back. He centers his weight over the other hand. Attempting to keep his body in a straight line, he lowers it until his chest touches the floor. He then returns to the starting position.

Side Arch Progression

SIDE ARCH ON FLOOR: HANDS ALONG BODY (FIGURE 7-16)

With his arms and hands positioned in front of his body, the performer lies on his side. His top leg is placed in front of his bottom leg, and his ankles are held to the floor by a partner or are placed under a restraining device. The performer flexes his head and trunk toward his uppermost side, raising his upper body as high as possible. He then returns to the starting position. This exercise may be performed with either side facing upward.

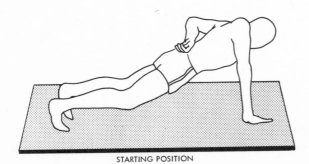

STARTING POSITION

Figure 7-15. One-arm push-up: prone position.

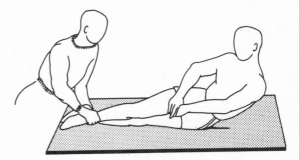

Figure 7-16. Side arch on floor: hands along body.

SIDE ARCH ON BENCH: ARMS AT SIDE

With his arms positioned at his sides, the performer lies on his side on a bench in such a position that the edge of the end of the bench is slightly below his waistline. His partner holds his feet. The performer attempts to touch the floor with the side of his head and then raises his upper body as high as possible. He then returns to the starting position.

SIDE ARCH ON BENCH: HANDS BEHIND HEAD

With a partner holding his feet, the performer assumes the same starting position as taken for the preceding exercise, except that the performer's fingers are interlaced and held behind his head. The performer raises his upper body as high as possible. He then returns to the starting position.

Squat Jump Variations

Contra-indication. Squat-jumping exerises should not be performed by anyone who has a history of a dislocated knee joint, who has a cartilage or ligament problem of the knee joint, or who has an unstable knee joint when in a deep knee-bend position.

FULL SQUAT JUMP

With his arms by his sides, his feet apart, and one foot slightly ahead of the other foot, the performer stands in an erect position. He squats, flexing his legs at the knees until his fingertips touch the floor. He then jumps off the floor, extends his arms overhead, and so changes the position of his feet in the air that he lands on the floor with the opposite foot in advance. This exercise may also be performed with the hands resting on top of the head throughout the exercise.

HALF SQUAT JUMP

The performer assumes the same initial position as was used for the preceding exericse. He squats, flexing his legs at the knees until the heels of his hands touch his knees. He then jumps off the floor, throws his arms overhead, and so changes the position of his feet in the air that he lands on the floor with the opposite foot in advance. This exercise can also be performed with the hands resting on top of the head throughout the exercise.

THREE-QUARTER SQUAT JUMP

With one foot slightly ahead of the other, the performer squats and flexes his legs at the knees until his hands touch the middle of his shins. He then jumps off the floor, swings his arms overhead, and so changes the position of his feet in the air that he lands on the floor with the opposite foot in advance. This exercise may also be performed with the hands resting on top of the head throughout the exercise.

Squat-Thrust Progression

Contra-indication. Squat-thrusting exercises should not be performed by anyone who has a cartilage or ligament problem at the knee joint or who has an unstable knee joint when the leg is flexed.

DOUBLE-LEG THRUST (FIGURE 7-17)

The performer squats and places his hands on the floor directly below his shoulders and outside of his knees. Supporting himself on his extended arms, he raises his feet off the floor and thrusts his legs backward to a front leaning-rest position. He then returns to the starting position.

ONE-LEG ARCH THRUST

The performer assumes the same starting position as for the preceding exercise. Supporting himself on his extended arms, he raises his feet off the floor and thrusts his legs backward to a front leaning-rest position, but with one leg raised off the floor. He then returns to the starting position and

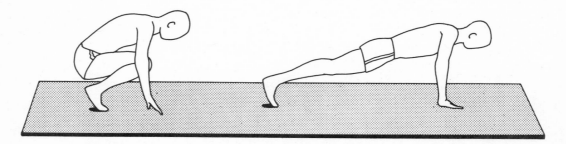

Figure 7-17. Double-leg thrust

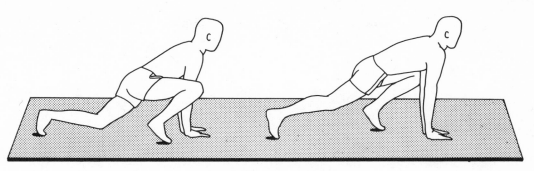

Figure 7-18. Treadmill with foot outside.

repeats the movement, but this time the opposite leg is raised.

REGULAR SQUAT THRUST

The performer stands erect in a position of attention. He then executes the following four movements: (1) squats and places his hands on the floor outside of his feet, (2) supports himself on his extended arms and raises his feet off the floor and thrusts his legs backward to a front leaning-rest position, (3) returns to the squat position, and (4) returns to the erect standing position.

DIAGONAL SQUAT THRUST

The performer stands erect in a position of attention and then performs the following four movements: (1) squats and places his hands on the floor outside of his feet, (2) supports himself on his extended arms, raises his feet off the floor, and thrusts his legs diagonally backward to his right, (3) returns to the squat position, and (4) returns to the erect standing position. He repeats the exercise, thrusting his legs diagonally backward to his left.

SQUAT ARCH THRUST

The performer stands erect in a position of attention and performs the following four movements: (1) squats and places his hands on the floor outside of his feet, (2) supports himself on his extended arms, raises his feet off the floor, and thrusts his legs backward to a front leaning-rest position, but with one leg raised off the floor, (3) returns to the squat position, and (4) returns to the starting position. He repeats the exercise, this time raising the other leg.

SQUAT THRUST WITH PUSH-UP

Squat thrust variations can be readily combined with the push-up variations by beginning one of the squat thrust exercises and then doing one of the push-up exercises while in the front leaning-rest position. At the finish of the push-up exercise, the squat-thrust exercise movement is completed. The most common combination is to do two push-ups while in the front leaning-rest position (eight-count push-up with squat thrust).

Treadmill Progression

TREADMILL WITH FOOT OUTSIDE (FIGURE 7-18)

The performer takes a front leaning-rest position, flexes his right leg, and moves his right foot in line with and outside of his right hand. Supporting himself on his extended arms, he changes the position of his feet so that his left foot is outside of his left hand and his right foot is in the front leaning-rest position. He then returns to the starting position and continues to alternate the position of his feet.

TREADMILL WITH FOOT INSIDE

The performer takes a front leaning-rest position and moves his right foot forward to a position between his hands. Supporting himself on his extended arms, he so changes the position of his feet that his left foot is between his hands and his right foot in the front leaning-rest position. He then returns to the starting position and continues to alternate the position of his feet.

TREADMILL WITH BOTH FEET OUTSIDE

The performer assumes a front leaning-rest position. Supporting his weight on his extended arms, he simultaneously moves both feet up to and outside of his hands. He then returns to the starting position.

Figure 7-19. Stretcher.

TREADMILL WITH BOTH FEET INSIDE

This exercise is performed in a manner similar to that of the preceding exercise, except that the feet are moved forward to a position between the hands.

STRETCHER (FIGURE 7-19)

The performer takes a front leaning-rest position. Supporting his weight on his extended arms and keeping his legs straight and together, he walks his legs forward as close as possible to his hands. He then returns to the starting position.

Additional Calisthenics

Additional exercises suitable for calisthenic routines may be found in Chapter 21, "Activities for Circuit Training."

Combining Exercises into a Calisthenic Routine

There are several advantages to be gained from combining selected exercises into a fixed daily routine for calisthenics. The fixed routine allows the important parts of the body to be regularly exercised and the chief components of physical fitness to be systematically developed. Moreover, a rapid workout can be had with no time wasted in deciding on the next exercise or in learning new exercises. Following the same calisthenic routine for a long period of time, however, can become boring;

hence, the routine should be changed from time to time. As examples of how exercises may be combined into a routine, the "Daily Dozen," taken from the *Army's Technical Manual No. 21-200: Physical Conditioning*, and the general types of exercises included in the Royal Canadian Air Force's *5BX Plan for Physical Fitness* are listed below.

DAILY DOZEN

1. High Jumper
2. Bend and Reach
3. Squat Thrust
4. Rowing Exercise
5. Squat Bender
6. Push-Ups
7. Side Bender
8. Body Twist
9. Squat Jumper
10. Trunk Twister
11. Stationary Run
12. Eight-Count Push-Up

5BX PLAN FOR PHYSICAL FITNESS

1. Toe-Touching (and back arches or trunk circling)
2. Sit-Ups
3. Back-Archers
4. Push-Ups
5. Stationary Running (and jumping exercises)

8. weight training

Since the time of the ancient Greeks, man is known to have lifted weights as a sport or for exercise. In the United States, the use of weight-training equipment to develop the strength and size of the muscles has greatly increased during the past two decades. The two main factors responsible for this increase have been the use of progressive resistance exercises (in which dumbbells, barbells, or pulley weights are used) in rehabilitation centers during and after World War II, and the favorable reports from research studies—completed in the 1940's and 1950's—that weight training is an efficient method of training athletes for increased performance.

DISTINCTION BETWEEN WEIGHT TRAINING, WEIGHT LIFTING AND BODY BUILDING

Exercises which primarily involve the lifting of weights are usually performed for one of three purposes: weight training, weight lifting, or body building.

Weight Training

Weight training is concerned with the development of increased physical capacity—that is, greater muscle endurance, greater strength, increased speed of movement, and greater power. This chapter is devoted to weight training, the development of increased physical capacity.

Weight Lifting

Weight lifting is concerned with how much weight the performer is able to lift overhead, using a certain type of lift. Usually competition is held for several different body-weight divisions, and the winner in each division is determined by the total poundage lifted with three different types of lifts. For many years weight lifting has been a competitive athletic event at the state, national, and international levels, including the Olympic Games.

Body Building

Body building is concerned with increasing the

51

size of the muscles and developing a well-proportioned body. Most "body builders" develop their physiques for aesthetic reasons. Contests are held regularly to determine the person with the best physique or best build, and the one with the most (muscularly) developed body. Such titles as Mr. California, Mr. America, and Mr. Universe are awarded the winners.

BENEFITS OF WEIGHT TRAINING

During the past twenty years a number of research studies have investigated the effects of weight training. These effects have been compared with the effects of engaging in other types of physical activity for an equal period of time. The majority of these studies have been conducted for periods of six weeks to a semester, with male college students serving as subjects. In the majority of these studies, a greater gain in overall strength occurred in weight-training groups than in control groups. In addition, the weight-training groups generally made a larger gain in the strength of selected muscle groups, in speed of movement, and in power. Other benefits have been found to accrue from engaging in a weight-training program. An increase in local muscular endurance is usually a concomitant of increased muscular strength. When weight-training exercises that stimulate an increased range of motion are included in the weight-training program, an increase in the flexibility of certain joints also results.

ADVANTAGES OF WEIGHT TRAINING

There are several advantages in including a program of weight training in the program of activities employed to enhance physical fitness. Among these advantages are the following:

1. Weight-training exercises involve essentially simple skills, and hence are easy to learn.
2. Only a minimum of basic weight-training equipment, which is fairly inexpensive and extremely durable, is needed.
3. A large variety of weight-training exercises can be included in a program, which permits the weight trainer to change his program of exercises as often as he desires to avoid monotony and boredom.

4. Weight-training exercises can be selected to develop specific muscles or areas of the body.
5. Engaging in a weight-training program can be very satisfying, because the weight trainer can easily observe the gains made in strength and muscular development by keeping a record of the amount of weight lifted for each exercise.
6. Despite rumors that were prevalent at one time, there has been no evidence that participating in weight training causes muscle-boundness (lack of flexibility and loss of coordination and timing).

DISADVANTAGES OF WEIGHT TRAINING

Participating only in a program of weight training does not develop all-around physical fitness. Specifically, cardiorespiratory endurance and the favorable body responses that accompany its development are not increased. Also, participation in weight training does little, if anything, to develop increased coordination, timing, or motor skills. Consequently, other activities should be combined with weight training to insure that these shortcomings are eliminated from the physical-fitness program. Running, swimming, games, and sports are excellent activities to supplement a weight-training program.

WEIGHT-TRAINING EQUIPMENT

Weight-training equipment ranges from inexpensive, homemade barbells—made by inserting the ends of iron pipes into cement-filled cans or buckets—to the special precision-machined, chrome-plated equipment available in privately owned gymnasiums or studios. The weight trainer should be familiar with the weight-training equipment described below.

Bar

The bar is a steel bar from one to one-and-one-eighth inches in diameter, ranging from four to eight feet in length (five and six feet are the most common lengths). With collars attached, the five-foot bar weighs approximately 25 pounds and the six-foot bar weighs approximately 30 pounds. The middle section of the surface of the bar is usually knurled to provide increased friction for the one-hand and two-hand grip.

Plates

Plates are iron or semi-steel discs with a center hole of sufficient diameter to accommodate the insertion of the bar. The weight of the plate is generally imprinted on each side of the plate. Plates are usually available in the following poundages: 1¼, 2½, 5, 7½, 10, 12½, 15, 20, 25, 35, 50, 75, and 100 pounds.

Collars

Four metal collars (two inside and two outside collars) usually encircle each bar and are used to hold the plates in place on the bar. Most collars contain set screws for securing them to the bar.

Barbell

The bar with collars and plates attached makes up the barbell, which is the only essential piece of weight-training equipment. The poundage on most barbells can be adjusted by changing the plates.

Dumbbell

The dumbbell can best be described as a short barbell, eight to eighteen inches in length. Most dumbbells are cast in one piece and have round or hexagonal-shaped ends. The poundage of this type of dumbbell is fixed. Fixed-weight dumbbells are available in poundages ranging from 3 to over 75 pounds.

Iron Boots

Iron boots are attached to the feet with straps. Each boot contains a center hole through which a short metal bar is inserted and to which plates are attached in order to increase the weight of the boot to the desired poundage. Iron boots are generally used for exercises designed to strengthen the muscles controlling leg movements at the knee or hip joints.

Head Strap

The head strap is a device made of canvas webbing, which is worn like a cap around the top of the head. Plates are attached to a chain that is fastened to the head strap. The head strap is used to develop the muscles of the neck.

Benches

Padded metal or wooden benches are commonly from twelve to sixteen inches in height, ten to sixteen inches in width, and four to six feet in length. The weight trainer lies on the bench in order to perform certain weight-training exercises.

Other Special Equipment

Standards. For convenience in performing certain exercises, metal standards are used to support the barbell at a desired height from the floor.

Leg-press machine. The leg-press machine is used for developing the extensor muscles of the legs.

Lat machine. The lat machine enables the weight trainer to bring his arms downward against resistance from an overhead position. This exercises the latisimus dorsi muscles, the development of which creates a broad upper back.

Incline and decline boards. Incline and decline boards are padded boards which support the weight trainer's body at an angle sloping upward or downward from a horizontal position.

COMMON WEIGHT-TRAINING TERMS

The terms listed below are commonly used in weight training. A knowledge of these terms will enable the reader to better understand instructions concerning the principles, techniques, and rules of weight training.

Load

The actual poundage lifted during each movement of a weight-training exercise.

Repetitions

One repetition of a weight-training exercise is executed each time a complete movement is performed. When engaging in a weight-training workout, the poundage and the number of repetitions are generally indicated for each exercise.

Ten-Executions Maximum

The term refers to the maximum number of repetitions of an exercise that the weight trainer can perform with a specified poundage. *Ten-executions maximum* means that the weight trainer cannot perform more than ten repetitions using a given poundage. A corollary to this term is *six-executions minimum,* which indicates that the poundage for an exercise should be such that the weight trainer can do at least six repetitions.

Sets

Sets refers to the number of times (or bouts) that a fixed number of repetitions of an exercise is performed.

Spotters

Spotters (usually two) are persons who stand near the performer for the purpose of quickly supporting the barbell to prevent accidents, or to give assistance if the weight trainer loses control of the barbell.

PRINCIPLES OF WEIGHT TRAINING

The following principles of weight training have for the most part been empirically derived. Only a few formal studies have been undertaken in an effort to substantiate them. However, most authorities support the principles listed below, especially as they apply to the beginning weight trainer.

Number of Repetitions

Strength development. Six-executions maximum of an exercise has been found superior to two- or ten-executions maximum for the development of strength. To develop strength rapidly, for each exercise the beginner should perform three sets of six repetitions each.

Local muscular endurance. A minimum of fifteen-executions maximum seems to be required for the effective development of local muscular endurance, although thirty-executions maximum is sometimes used. To develop local muscle endurance rapidly, the beginner should perform fifteen to twenty-five repetitions of each exercise.

Number of Sets

Three sets of each weight-training exercise are recommended for the beginner who wishes to achieve maximum gains in strength.

Frequency of Workout

For beginners, performing weight-training exercises every other day produces more effective results than working out every day or only once or twice a week. Beginning weight trainers profit most if they have approximately forty-eight hours of rest between weight-training workouts.

RULES FOR WEIGHT TRAINING

Preliminary Conditioning

The beginning weight trainer should use a lighter-than-normal exercise load during the first five weight-training workouts, to permit his body to adjust to unaccustomed movements and to avoid the muscular soreness and stiffness that might otherwise result. This preliminary conditioning period will also allow him to learn the correct form for performing the weight-training exercises before he begins to exercise with a maximum load.

Warm-Up

If not already warmed up as a result of participating in some other vigorous physical activity, before lifting heavy poundages the weight trainer should warm up by using a light weight to exercise most of the major muscle groups of his body.

Safety

The beginning weight trainer, especially, should lift only an exercise load that he is certain he can control. He should not exercise with heavy weights without first practicing the exercises for several weeks with a load that he can handle easily. When in doubt as to his ability to safely handle a weight, the weight trainer should ask a spotter to assist him. When straining for several seconds to lift a maximum load, it is essential that the weight trainer does not hold his breath by closing his glottis; in rare cases this action has resulted in a momentary loss of consciousness. If other persons are near the weight trainer while he is performing an exercise, he should check that the outside collars on his barbell are securely fastened, because a loose collar will permit the plates to slide off the bar. The weight trainer himself is in no danger of the plates dropping on his own feet, if he retains his grasp on the bar at all times.

Body Position When Exercising

When lifting a heavy weight, the weight trainer should: (1) keep his back as straight as possible, or even slightly arched, to let the stronger muscles of the legs do the work, and thus avoid straining the weaker muscles of the back; (2) keep the bar as close to his body as possible when lifting the barbell to his chest (beginners have a tendency to stand too far from the bar because of a groundless fear that the bar will strike the body when it is lifted); (3) keep his feet flat on the floor for better balance and to spread the load over a wider area of support (if the ankle joints are not sufficiently flexible to permit the feet to remain flat on the floor during a squatting movement, the heels should be placed on a board one or two inches high); (4) keep his feet spread approximately shoulder width in order to maintain a comfortable stance and good balance while performing an exercise.

Correct Form in Performing Exercises

For maximum gains, and to avoid the possibility of injury, it is recommended that the beginner make certain that he uses correct form when engaging in weight-training exercises.

Control Over Exercise Movements

During all phases of a weight-training exercise, whether working against or with gravity, the weight trainer should forcefully control his movements.

Order of Exercises

The beginning weight trainer should perform the exercises in a sequence that causes first one area of the body to be exercised, then another, and so on.

Number of Repetitions

The amount of weight used for weight-training exercise will depend on the performer's strength and the number of repetitions he wishes to perform. To effectively develop both strength and local muscular endurance, it is recommended that for most exercises the beginning weight trainer employ a load with which he can perform from seven to eleven repetitions. The beginner can establish this

training load for each exercise by trial and error during his first few workouts.

Number of Sets

The beginning weight trainer should do only one set of each exercise during the first few workouts. During succeeding workouts, he should attempt to do a minimum of two sets. If time permits, three sets of each exercise are preferable.

Overloading

When the desired number of repetitions of an exercise can be performed during the first set, the poundage used for that exercise should be increased by approximately 3 to 5 per cent for the next workout.

Duration of Workout

Depending upon the amount of rest taken between exercise bouts, the number of exercises and sets included in each workout, and the number of persons with whom the equipment is shared, the beginning weight trainer can usually complete his workout in from thirty to sixty minutes. As his strength, the exercise load, and the length of rest periods increase, the weight trainer may require as long as two hours to complete the workout.

TECHNIQUES OF WEIGHT TRAINING

In this section are listed the most important basic techniques of weight training.

Basic Stance

The basic stance employed when performing weight-training exercises from the standing position is a stance in which the head is held erect, the back straight, and the feet are aligned flat on the floor and spread about hip width.

Grips

When grasping the barbell, the hands should be placed approximately shoulder-width apart on the bar and spaced an equal distance from the inside collars.

REGULAR OR PRONATED GRIP (FIGURE 8-1)

The regular grip is used when performing most

Figure 8-1. Regular or pronated grip.

barbell exercises. For this grip, the palms of the hands face down and back when grasping a bar resting on the floor. At all times the thumbs are adjacent to each other and are wrapped around the bar in a direction opposite to that in which the fingers are pointing.

REVERSE OR SUPINATED GRIP (FIGURE 8-2)

The reverse grip is used for only a few barbell exercises. For this grip, the palms of the hands face upward and forward when grasping a bar resting on the floor. The fifth or little fingers are adjacent to each other, and the thumbs are wrapped around the bar in a direction opposite to that of the fingers.

COMBINATION OR ALTERNATE GRIP (FIGURE 8-3)

The combination grip is frequently used to lift a heavy barbell off the floor because this grip prevents the bar from turning in the hands. For the combination grip, the regular grip is taken with one hand and the reverse grip is taken with the other.

Body Position

CROUCH OR DEAD-LIFT POSITION (FIGURE 8-4)

The crouch position is used when lifting a heavy barbell from the floor. In this position, the bar, the hips, and the feet are in line with the weight trainer's shoulders. The body is crouched, the knees and hips are flexed, the back is straight, the neck and head are extended slightly backward, and the eyes are focused straight ahead.

FRONT-HANG OR FRONT-THIGH REST POSITION (FIGURE 8-5)

With the body erect and the arms held straight,

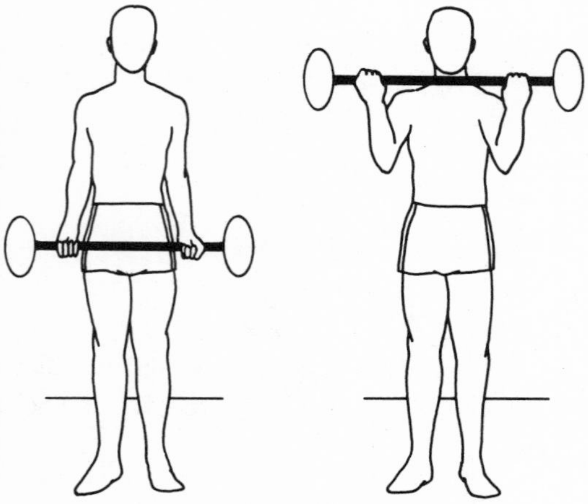

Figure 8-2. Reverse or supinated grip.

Figure 8-3. Combination or alternate grip.

Figure 8-4. Crouch or dead-lift position.

Figure 8-6. Chest-rest position.

the barbell is held in front of and resting against the thighs.

CHEST-REST POSITION (FIGURE 8-6)

In the chest-rest position, the bar is in contact with the chest, the arms are flexed, and the forearms are under the bar.

SHOULDER-REST POSITION (FIGURE 8-7)

In the shoulder-rest position, the barbell is behind the weight trainer's neck, resting on his shoulders and upper back, and his hands are located on the bar several inches on either side of his shoulders.

SUPINE POSITION

When the weight trainer is lying on his back in a horizontal position, he is in the supine position.

Movements

The two primary movements used in weight-training exercises are flexion and extension.

Flexion. Flexion is a movement, at one or more joints, in which the two parts of the body connected at the joint are brought closer together.

Extension. Extension is the straightening or unfolding of two parts of the body after they have been flexed upon each other.

IDENTIFICATION OF EXERCISED MUSCLES

For the specific weight-training exercises described in this chapter, no attempt will be made to identify all the muscles that function when a movement is performed. Instead, only the primary muscle groups will be identified. Two methods by which the weight trainer may identify the muscle groups involved in an exercise are: (1) The muscles that

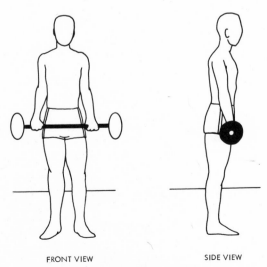

FRONT VIEW   SIDE VIEW

Figure 8-5. Front-hang or front-thigh rest position.

Figure 8-7. Shoulder-rest position.

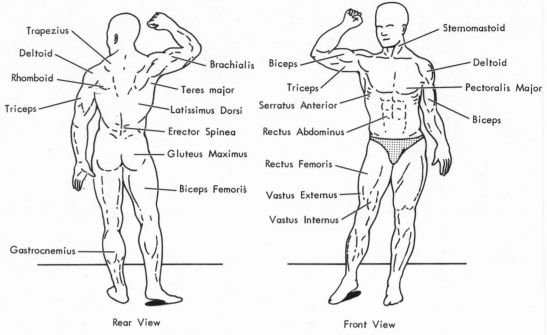

Rear View   Front View

Figure 8-8. Major surface muscles of the body.

cause movement to occur at a joint are usually located adjacent to and above the joint, toward the center part of the body. For example, when the forearm is flexed or extended at the elbow joint, the muscles responsible for these movements are located between the elbow joint and the shoulder joint. (2) By having someone resist his movement in any direction, the weight trainer may feel his surface muscles near the joint where movement occurs. The hard muscles are the contracted, working muscles, and those that are yielding are the relaxed, nonworking muscles.

As a further aid in muscle identification, the weight-training exercises in this chapter are arranged according to the muscle groups that are primarily exercised. The charts in Figure 8-8, on which the major surface muscles of the body are identified, may be of value in locating the major muscles developed by weight-training exercises.

WEIGHT-TRAINING EXERCISES

When all the variations of the same type of exercise are included with all the various type of exercises possible, there are literally hundreds of weight-training exercises. However, the number of *basic* weight-training exercises is considerably less.

Only those weight-training exercises that are commonly used, and whose value has long been demonstrated, are included in this chapter. The selection includes exercises that may be used to develop all of the major muscle groups of the body.

Two or more names exist for many of the weight-training exercises. For most such exercises the most descriptive or the most common name is listed; but for a few of these exercises, more than one name is given. Wherever the regular grip should be used, the type of grip to be used for an exercise is not specified.

Warm-Up Exercise with Barbell

Starting position. Crouch position.

Exercise movements. In one slow, continuous motion, the weight trainer straightens his body and legs, and with his arms raises the barbell overhead to an extended-arms position. He then slowly lowers the barbell, returning to the starting position.

Muscles of the Forearm that Flex the Wrist and Fingers

WRIST CURL

Starting position. The performer sits on a bench and rests his forearms on his thighs, with his wrists

Figure 8-9. Regular curl with barbell.

extended beyond his knees. He holds a dumbbell in a reverse grip in each hand.

Exercise movement. Without moving his forearm, he flexes his hands upward as high as possible. He then lowers the dumbbells to the starting position.

Variations. The regular grip may be used for this exercise. A barbell may be substituted for the dumbbells.

Muscles of the Upper Arm that Flex the Forearm (*Biceps Brachii, Brachialis, Brachioradialis,* and *Pronator Teres*)

REGULAR CURL WITH BARBELL (FIGURE 8-9)

Starting position. Front hang position with a reverse grip.

Exercise movement. By keeping his elbows at his sides and flexing his forearms, the weight trainer raises the barbell through an arc until the bar touches his chest. He then lowers the barbell to the starting position.

Variation. When the regular grip is used, this exercise is known as the reverse curl. Dumbbells may also be used for this exercise.

PULL-UP WITH WEIGHT

Pull-ups (chins) are performed in the usual manner, except that overloading is obtained by resting a barbell behind the knees while the legs are maintained in a flexed position. The overload may also be obtained by chaining plates to a belt fastened around the waist. A variation of this exercise is to thrust the head forward and touch the back of the neck to the bar as the pull-up is being completed.

Muscles of the Upper Arm That Extend the Forearms (Triceps)

MILITARY PRESS

Starting position. Chest-rest position.

Exercise movement. Looking straight ahead throughout the exercise, being careful not to bend his back or legs, the weight trainer presses the barbell to an overhead position in which his arms are completely extended.

Variation. The starting position may be the shoulder-rest position, in which case the exercise is then called the "press behind the neck."

SUPINE PRESS ON BENCH (FIGURE 8-10)

Starting position. Supine position with the barbell held at arms length above the chest. If desired, the hands can be spaced considerably more than shoulder-width apart.

Exercise movement. The weight trainer lowers the barbell to his chest and then pushes (presses) it back to the starting position.

Variation. Similar exercises may be performed on inclined or declined boards, or with dumbbells.

FOREARM EXTENSION FROM BEHIND NECK (TRICEPS PRESS) (FIGURE 8-11)

Starting position. Using a reverse grip, the weight trainer assumes the basic stance and then supports the barbell in a position behind his neck. His elbows point overhead.

Exercise movement. Without moving his upper arms, he extends or raises his forearms overhead. He then reverses the movement of the barbell and lowers it to the starting position.

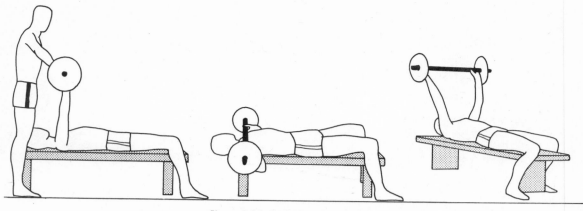

Figure 8-10. Supine press on bench.

Variation. This exercise may be performed with a dumbbell in each hand, or it may be performed from a sitting position or a supine position on a bench.

DIP WITH WEIGHT

Stationary dips are performed on the parallel bars (see Chapter 12) in the usual manner, except that an overload is attained by placing a barbell behind the knees and flexing the legs to hold it in place, placing a barbell across the top of the feet and flexing the feet upward to hold it in place, or fastening a weighted chain to a belt worn around the waist.

Muscles Surrounding the Shoulders That Move the Upper Arms (Deltoids, *Pectoralis Major, Latissimus Dorsi,* and *Teres Major*)

Exercises that develop the muscles of the shoulders also usually develop the muscles of the upper back, the chest, and the upper arms. Persons who have experienced difficulty with a shoulder joint should be cautious in performing the exercises described in this section. Such persons, including those who are subject to chronic shoulder dislocations, should not do exercises involving the shoulder joint until they have obtained approval from their physician.

UPRIGHT ROWING WITH BARBELL (FIGURE 8-12)

Starting position. Front-hang position with both hands placed near the middle of the bar and within a few inches of each other.

Exercise movement. Keeping his elbows higher than the bar throughout the exercise, the weight

trainer raises the barbell until it is in line with or touches his chin. He then lowers the barbell to the starting position.

Variation. Dumbbells may be used for this exercise.

FORWARD RAISE WITH BARBELL

Starting position. Front-hang position.

Exercise movement. Keeping his arm straight throughout the exercise, the weight trainer raises the barbell forward and upward through an arc until the weight is overhead. He then slowly lowers the barbell through the same arc, returning it to the starting position.

Variations. The weight may be raised only to shoulder height. Dumbbells may be used, in which case the arms may be alternately raised.

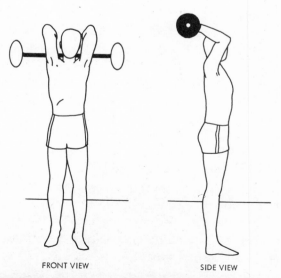

FRONT VIEW   SIDE VIEW

Figure 8-11. Forearm extension from behind neck (triceps press).

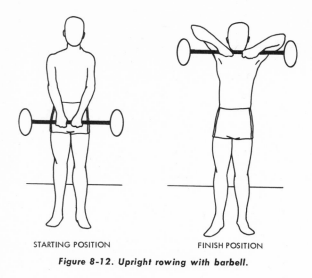

STARTING POSITION   FINISH POSITION

Figure 8-12. Upright rowing with barbell.

LATERAL RAISE WITH DUMBBELLS

Starting position. Standing in the basic stance, the weight trainer holds a dumbbell to the side of each thigh.

Exercise movement. Keeping his arms straight, he raises his arms sideward (laterally) and upward until the dumbbells are overhead. He then lowers the dumbbells through the same arc to the starting position.

Variation. The dumbbells may be raised only to shoulder height.

LATERAL RAISE WITH DUMBBELLS WITH TRUNK FLEXED

Starting position. The trunk is flexed forward until it is approximately parallel to the floor. A dumbbell is held in each hand, and the extended arms are hanging directly below the shoulders.

Exercise movement. The weight trainer raises the dumbbell sideward and outward to at least shoulder height. The dumbbells are then slowly lowered to the starting position.

OTHER SHOULDER EXERCISES

The military press, supine press on bench, and dips on the parallel bars are useful for developing the muscles of the shoulders.

Muscles of the Upper Back That Move the Shoulders, Shoulder Girdle (Scapula), or Upper Arms (*Trapezius, Latissimus Dorsi,* Rhomboids, and *Teres Major*)

BENT-OVER ROWING WITH BARBELL

Starting position. The weight trainer assumes the basic stance, flexes his trunk forward so that it is parallel to the floor, and grasps the barbell, which is resting on the floor below his shoulders.

Exercise movement. Remaining in the bent-over position, the weight trainer raises the barbell to his chest and then lowers it to the starting position. He attempts to keep his head and upper trunk stationary during the exercise.

Variations. Instead of the barbell being moved in a straight up-and-down motion, it may be moved in a circular motion. This exercise may be performed with a dumbbell held in one hand while the other hand rests on a bench.

SHOULDER SHRUG (FIGURE 8-13)

Starting position. Front-hang position.

Exercise movement. Keeping his arms straight, the weight trainer lifts the barbell by raising his

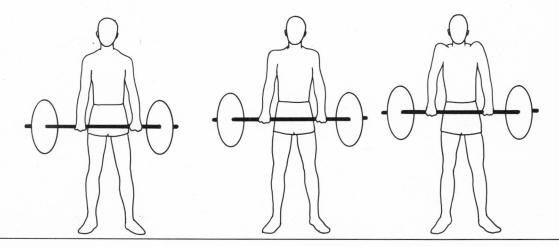

Figure 8-13. Shoulder shrug.

Figure 8-14. Bent-arm pull-over.

shoulders as high as possible, attempting to touch his shoulders to his ears. He then lowers his shoulders to the starting position.

Variation. Instead of up-and-down movements, circular movements—either clockwise or counterclockwise—may be performed. Dumbbells can also be used for this exercise.

BENT-ARM PULL-OVER (FIGURE 8-14)

Starting position. Supine position on a bench with the back of the head resting on the edge of the bench, below which a barbell is placed on the floor. With his arms flexed at about a 90-degree angle, the weight trainer reaches over his head and toward the floor. He then grasps the barbell, with his hands spaced only a few inches apart.

Exercise movement. The weight trainer raises the bar overhead in an arc, maintaining his arms in a flexed position throughout the movement. After the bar passes over his face and touches his chest, the weight trainer reverses the movement and returns the barbell through the original arc to the floor.

Variation. This pull-over may be performed with the arms extended throughout the exercise.

OTHER UPPER BACK EXERCISES

Pull-ups, upright rowing, and the forward raise are also somewhat beneficial in developing the muscles of the upper back.

Muscles of the Chest That Move the Upper Arms (*Pectoralis Major* and, Indirectly, *Serratus Anterior*)

SUPINE LATERAL RAISE WITH DUMBBELLS

Starting position. Supine position on a bench with the arms straight and extended sideward in line with the shoulders, so that the dumbbells rest on the floor.

Exercise movement. Keeping his arms straight, the weight trainer raises the dumbbells upward and over his chest until they touch, then lowers them to the starting position.

Variations. After the dumbbells are raised over the chest, the original arm movements can be continued until the arms are crossed and the dumbbells touch the opposite sides of the chest. This exercise may also be performed with the arms bent at an angle of about 120 degrees.

OTHER CHEST EXERCISES

The bent-arm and straight-arm pull-over, supine press on bench, dip on parallel bars, and pull-up effectively contribute to the development of the muscles of the chest.

Muscles of the Neck

Exercises for the specific purpose of developing the muscles of the neck are infrequently included in a weight-training program. Extension, flexion, and circular movements of the head—when plates are fastened to a chain that is attached to the front or back of a head strap—are effective exercises for developing the muscles of the neck. Pull-overs or supine presses from the wrestler's-bridge position are sometimes used for this purpose.

Muscles of the Lower Back and Hips That Extend the Trunk or Thighs (Extensors of the Trunk and Thighs: *Erector Spinea* and *Gluteus Maximus*)

Anyone with a history of low-back pain or difficulty with a knee joint should not do the exercises in this section without prior approval from his physician.

REGULAR DEAD LIFT

Starting position. Crouch position. Either a regular or a combination grip may be used.

Exercise movement. Keeping his arms and his back straight throughout the exercise, the weight trainer comes up to an erect standing position. He then returns to the starting position.

Variations. The barbell may be straddled during the dead lift, in which event the lift is called the straddle or Jefferson lift. If a light poundage is lifted, the legs may be kept straight throughout the exercise and the movement of the trunk created by flexion or extension of the lower back. This exercise, called the stiff-leg dead lift, is an excellent developer of the lower back and hips.

Comment. The regular dead lift is considered by many to be one of the best single weight-training exercises, since it develops many muscle groups including those of the legs, upper back, shoulder, forearms, and hands.

FLAT-FOOTED SQUAT WITH BARBELL

Starting position. Shoulder-rest position with a wide grip. The heels may rest upon a board of one or two inches in thickness, to insure that the heels are supported throughout the exercise.

Exercise movement. The weight trainer, keeping his back straight and head erect, squats by flexing his legs and lowering his hips until his thighs are parallel with the floor. He then returns to the starting position.

Variations. Deep squats, in which the buttocks are lowered until they touch the heels, can be performed. Some authorities take the view that this movement may have a detrimental effect upon the knee joint, as may the walking squat. However, squatting movements, in which the body is lowered to a sitting position on a bench, are highly recommended. Squat jumps, in which a dumbbell is held in each hand and a jump is taken after each squatting movement, can be also performed.

Comments. Since heavy poundages are often used for squatting exercises, the weight trainer may wish to place padding on the back of his neck and shoulders before resting the barbell on that area. Squatting movements require considerable energy. For this reason, some authorities recommend scheduling them among the first few exercises in the weight-training program.

Abdominal and Other Muscles of the Lower Trunk That Flex the Trunk or Thighs (Flexors and Rotators of the Trunk: *Ilio-Psoas, Rectus Abdominus,* Internal and External Obliques)

SIT-UP ON INCLINED BOARD

Starting position. Supine position with the feet held in place by straps and a dumbbell or plate held with both hands behind the head.

Exercise movement. The weight trainer comes to a sitting position by flexing or curling his trunk, touches an elbow to the opposite knee, and returns to the starting position. Each knee should be alternately touched.

Variations. Sit-ups may be performed on a level surface, or with the hips resting crossways on a bench. They also may be performed without holding a weight behind the head.

Comment. If sit-ups are performed with the legs straight, the hip flexors often do more work than do the abdominal muscles. For this reason, sit-ups with the legs held in a bent or partially flexed position are recommended, particularly for those whose lower back curves considerably when they do a sit-up with their legs straight. Many weight-training instructors recommend that a minimum of twenty executions of the sit-up movement be performed to develop the endurance and definition of the abdominal muscles.

SIDE BEND

Starting position. Shoulder-rest position with the barbell grasped in a wide grip. A wider-than-usual stance.

Exercise movement. Bend the trunk directly to one side as far as possible and then return to the starting position. Repeat the movement to the opposite side.

Variation. The above movements may be performed while holding a dumbbell in one hand. After performing the desired number of repetitions, the dumbbell is then held in the other hand.

Comment. A minimum of twenty repetitions is recommended for this exercise, if the weight trainer wishes to slim his waistline.

Muscles of the Hips and Thighs That Flex the Thigh (*Ilio-Psoas* and *Rectus Femoris*) and Extend the Lower Leg ((Quadriceps)—*Vastus Internus, Vastus Intermedius, Vastus Externus,* and *Rectus Femoris*)

FORWARD LEG RAISE WITH IRON BOOT

Starting position. Supine position on an inclined board, or a hanging position from a horizontal bar or from the stall bars.

Exercise movement. Keeping the legs straight, they are raised until they are at right angles to the trunk. They are then slowly lowered to the starting position.

Variation. One leg at a time may be raised and lowered in alternate order.

Comment. The forward leg raise is also an excellent exercise for developing the flexor muscles of the trunk and hips.

LOWER LEG EXTENSION WITH IRON BOOT

Starting position. Sitting position on a padded table with the lower leg of the booted foot hanging down just past the edge of the table.

Exercise movement. Raise the lower leg until it is in line with the thigh and the entire leg is straight. Slowly lower to starting position.

OTHER EXERCISES

The flat-footed squat, with all its variations, and the regular dead lift are particularly useful exercise for developing the quadriceps muscles.

Muscles of the Hips and Thighs That Extend the Thigh (*Gluteus Maximus* and Hamstrings) and Flex the Leg (Hamstring Muscles—*Biceps Femoris*)

LEG CURL WITH IRON BOOT

Starting position. Standing position on the foot on which the iron boot is not secured. For increased balance, a support may be grasped.

Exercise movement. The booted foot is raised backward and upward until the heel touches or almost touches the buttock. The leg is lowered to the starting position. The exercise is then repeated with the other leg.

Variation. Both feet can be exercised simultaneously if leg curls are performed from a prone position on a bench or inclined board.

OTHER EXERCISES FOR DEVELOPING THE THIGH EXTENSORS

Squat exercises aid the development of the extensor muscles of the thigh.

Muscles of the Leg That Extend the Foot (Calf Muscle—*Gastrocnemius*, and *Soleus*)

RISE ON TOES (HEEL RAISE)

Starting position. Shoulder-rest position with a wide grip and with the balls of the feet resting on a board two inches in height.

Exercise movement. The weight trainer raises his heels off the floor as high as possible. He then lowers his heels to the floor.

Comment. Since heavy poundages are often used for this exercise, the weight trainer may, for increased comfort, wish to place padding between the bar and his upper back and shoulders.

OTHER EXERCISES FOR THE LOWER LEG

Squat jumping with dumbbells, or straddle hops performed with a barbell placed in the shoulder-rest position, help in developing the muscles of the lower leg.

WEIGHT-TRAINING PROGRAMS FOR BEGINNERS

Reproduced on the following pages are two weight-training exercise charts developed at the State University of Iowa for use by students who are beginning a weight-training program.

Station Number _____

Weight Training Exercise Chart
for Beginners

Name _____

Section Number _____

1. As a rule, the range of repetitions (reps) for most weight-training exercises is: minimum, 7 times; maximum, 11 times. However, to lose bodyweight, do 15 to 20 repetitions (reps).
2. Do 30 repetitions for heel raises (10 with toes pointed inward, 10 with toes pointed outward, and 10 with toes pointed straight ahead).
3. The fraction listed for each exercise is the percentage of your body weight that, in pounds, should be the weight of the barbell used for that exercise during your first workout.
4. When the maximum number of repetitions is achieved, encircle the poundage used in that exercise and increase the barbell weight by 5 pounds for that exercise in the next training period.
5. With collars attached, the six-foot bar weighs 30 pounds and the five-foot bar weighs 25 pounds.
6. The first exercise (warm-up exercise) should be omitted from your work-out if you have just performed calisthenics or are thoroughly warmed up.

EXERCISE	WT.	REPS.	WT.	REPS.	WT.	REPS.	WT.	REPS.	WT.	REPS.	WT.	REPS.	WT.	REPS.
1. Warm-up Exercises 1/4														
2. Ordinary two-arm Curl 1/3														
3. Military Press 1/3														
4. Flat-footed Squats 1/3														
5. Pull-over on Bench 1/10														
6. Bent over Rowing 1/2														
7. Heel Raising (30 reps) 1/2														
8. Regular Dead-Lift 1/2														
9. Supine Press on Bench 1/2														
10. Inclined Sit-ups (20 reps)														

REMEMBER: REGULAR WORKOUTS ARE THE KEY TO SUCCESS

Platform Number _____

Weight Training Exercise Chart
for Elementary Course

Name _____

Sec. # _____ Instructor _____

1. As a general rule, the range of continuous executions (reps) for most weight-training exercises is: minimum, 6 times; maximum, 15 times (6 for strength; 15 for endurance).
2. When the maximum number of executions is achieved, encircle the poundage used in that exercise and increase the barbell weight by 5 pounds for that exercise in the next training period.
3. With collars attached, the six-foot bar weighs 30 pounds and the five-foot bar weighs 25 pounds.

EXERCISE	WT.	REPS.	WT.	REPS.	WT.	REPS.	WT.	REPS.	WT.	REPS.
1. Warm-up Exercise (High Pullup)										
2. Regular two-arm Curl										
3. (a) Squat (b) Squat Jump										
4. Military Press										
5. Bent-over Rowing										
6. Supine Press										
7. Stiff-leg Dead-Lift										
8. Forward Rise										
9. Pullover										
10. Exercise To Be Selected By Student										

REMEMBER: REGULAR WORKOUTS ARE THE KEY TO SUCCESS

9. isometric exercises

In the 1920's and 1930's Charles Atlas, through his system of "Dynamic Tension," was probably the first person to promote a form of isometric exercise for the development of strength. His claims, however, were not based upon scientific investigation. The scientific verification of the value of isometric exercises was the result of studies performed by two German physiologists, Dr. Th. Hettinger and Dr. Eric A. Muller. The findings of their initial investigation, which was conducted in the early 1950's, have forced a revision of some of the prevalent concepts of the development of strength. The two physiologists reported that to increase muscular strength at a rate of approximately 5 per cent a week, it is necessary only to contract a muscle at two-thirds of its maximum force for six seconds once each day. In other words, the stimulus necessary for the development of the strength of a muscle, according to the findings of Hettinger and Muller, is a single, less-than-maximum contraction of the muscle each day.

These findings imply that when isometric exercises are engaged in daily for a year, gains in strength of 100 to 150 per cent may be expected. The amount of gain, however, is dependent upon the beginning level of strength. A person with a low initial level of strength can be expected to show a greater percentage gain in strength than one who starts with a high level of strength. The two physiologists suggest that after the first year it is necessary to use isometric exercises only once a week to maintain the increased strength that was developed during the first year of training.

LATER STUDIES OF EFFECTS OF ISOMETRIC EXERCISES

The Hettinger and Muller study has been criticized on a number of points. The chief criticisms are that only nine subjects were used, that a large number of different muscle groups were investigated, that several variables were studied simultaneously (the contractions were held for different time periods and varying percentages of maximum effort were exerted), and that the duration of the training periods varied—the maximum being twenty-four weeks.

Since the publication of Hettinger and Muller's findings, many investigations of the effects of isometric exercises have been undertaken. While the findings resulting from these investigations do not agree in all respects, the consensus of the findings indicates that greater strength gains result when the muscular contraction is held for a period longer than six seconds—ten to twelve seconds is the time period most frequently recommended. When two or more sets of isometric exercises are performed, greater strength gains have been recorded than when only one set of each exercise is performed. Some investigators have also found that a maximum contraction produces greater strength gains than does a two-thirds-maximum contraction. In one study it was demonstrated that increased speed of movement resulted when isometric exercises involving the muscles used in the movement were practiced. However, scientifically conducted studies of the effect of regularly performing isometric exercises have failed to demonstrate the validity of some of the other claims for isometric exercises (such as an increase in the size of the exercised muscles or a reduction of fatty deposits).

The amount of strength gained by the exercised muscles when isometric exercises and weight-training exercises are performed the same number of times each week, and for the same number of weeks, by two groups of subjects has been compared in several studies. However, the variable that has been difficult to control or equate in these studies is the amount of time spent in performing the two types of exercises. In some of the studies, the group that engaged in weight-training exercises showed superior gains in strength. In many of the studies, no significant differences were found in the increase in strength demonstrated by the two groups. In one or two of the studies, the group that engaged in isometric exercises had superior gains in strength.

ADVANTAGES OF USING ISOMETRIC EXERCISES

There are several advantages of using isometric exercises as one phase of a physical-fitness program. Isometric exercises may be effectively used for the development and maintenance of muscular strength. The time required for the activity is quite short, because a complete program of isometric exercises, once learned, can be completed in less than five minutes. No special equipment or facilities are needed for performing isometric exercises. They can be performed at any time of the day in about any type of wearing apparel, since doing the exercises does not soil one's clothes or cause sweating. Finally, isometric exercises are not physically tiring.

DISADVANTAGES OF ISOMETRIC EXERCISES

The chief disadvantages of isometric exercises are that the performer may experience a sudden rise in blood pressure if he holds his breath while making a forceful muscular contraction, and such exercises contribute little to the development of circulorespiratory endurance or to the development of local muscle endurance.

ISOMETRIC EXERCISE EQUIPMENT

Although no equipment is required for performing isometric exercises, several commercial products that can be useful in performing isometric exercises have been marketed. These devices increase the number and variety of isometric exercises that can be performed. Isometric exercise equipment ranges from a piece of rope and an accompanying exercise chart to sophisticated devices that automatically lock a handle at any desired distance from the platform on which the exerciser stands, and that have dials which indicate the force being exerted at any given time and the maximum force that was exerted during the performance of the exercise.

DIRECTIONS FOR PERFORMING ISOMETRIC EXERCISES[1]

The isometric exercises that follow are direct applications of the findings of Hettinger and Muller and of other investigators of isometric exercises.

---

[1] Some of the isometric exercises contained in this chapter were developed by the late Dr. C. H. McCloy of the State University of Iowa.

Movement is not involved in any of the exercises, despite the fact that the muscle contraction should always be quite vigorous. For this reason, the exercises are given such names as *isometric, static, tension,* or *motionless exercises.* However, the exerciser should always attempt to make a maximum contraction each time that he performs an isometric exercise.

In order to develop maximum muscular tension, it is recommended that the exerciser hold each contraction for ten seconds. This length of time can be approximated by counting slowly to ten. If the exerciser wishes a rapid workout, he should hold each contraction for at least six seconds. Two sets of each exercise should be performed if maximum gains are desired, although the performance of only one set should produce satisfactory results. For best results, isometric exercises should be performed five days a week; three times a week is the minimum number of workouts that should be taken. Eight to fifteen isometric exercises should be included in the isometric exercise program.

The exerciser should engage in a variety of isometric exercises to insure the development of strength in all the major parts of the body. The regular user of isometric exercises may wish to select a new program of exercises every few weeks. Since training effects are specific, it is recommended that, for those isometric exercises in which the body, arms, or legs are flexed, the exerciser so vary the amount of flexion in these parts that strength is developed throughout the complete range of motion of each movement.

To enable the exerciser to develop tension in certain muscles, a rope similar to a jump rope is needed for several of the exercises. By using a rope or a strap to hold one or two metal bars in position for use by the hands and the feet, most weight-training exercises can be done as isometric exercises. To add variety, some of the isometric exercises are performed while the exerciser sits in a chair.

To aid the exerciser in selecting isometric exercises that will be of most value to him, the exercises are grouped according to the part of the body most benefited by the exercise. Descriptive names have been given to the exercises for ease in recognizing and learning them. With some imagination and resourceful thinking, the reader can easily add to the list of isometric exercises presented in this chapter.

MUSCLES OF THE FOREARMS THAT FLEX THE WRIST AND FINGERS

Hand Squeeze

Starting position. With the palms in front of his body and facing each other, the performer grasps each hand with the other thumb, hand, and fingers.

Exercise. He squeezes each hand as forcefully as possible.

Backward Neck Push

Starting position. The performer places his fingers on his forehead.

Exercise. He pushes backward with his fingers and arms, and resists the force with his head and neck.

Variations. The palms of the hands can be placed against the forehead. The exercise can also be performed from a sitting or supine position.

Forward Neck Pull (Figure 9-1)

Starting position. With fingers interlaced, the performer places his hands on the back of his head.

Exercise. Emphasizing a wrist-flexion action, he pulls forward with his hands and resists the force with his head and neck.

Variations. The exercise can also be performed from a sitting or a supine position.

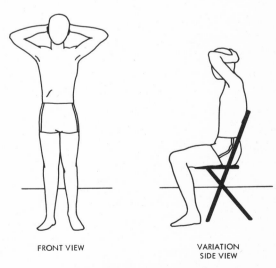

FRONT VIEW   VARIATION SIDE VIEW

Figure 9-1. Forward neck pull.

Figure 9-2. Raise with back.

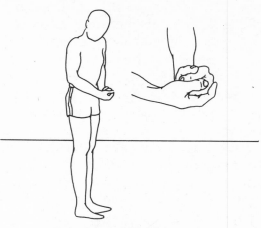

Figure 9-3. Body builder's stance.

MUSCLES OF THE UPPER ARM THAT FLEX THE FOREARM (BICEPS BRACHII, BRACHIALIS, BRACHIORADIALIS, AND PRONATOR TERES)

Static Arm Curl

Starting position. Standing in an erect position with his feet hip-distance apart, the performer stands on the loop of a rope, holding an end of the rope tautly in each hand. His upper arms are perpendicular to, and his forearms parallel with, the floor.

Exercise. The performer pulls upward on the rope with his hands.

Raise with Back (Figure 9-2)

Starting position. With his legs straight and his feet hip-distance apart, the performer stands on the loop of a rope. He bends forward at the waist until his trunk is at a 110-degree angle with the floor. He holds the ends of the rope in his hands with his upper arms at his sides and his forearms parallel with the floor.

Exercise. Using the muscles of his back, he pulls upward on the rope, while maintaining his arms in a flexed position.

Forearm Forcer

Starting position. The performer sits in a chair. His right forearm rests on his right thigh, and his left fist is held in his right hand.

Exercise. He presses his left forearm downward and tries to raise his right forearm. He repeats the exercise, changing the position and action of the arms.

Body-Builder's Stance (Figure 9-3)

Starting position. While in a standing or sitting position, the performer places his flexed right arm against his side and holds his right forearm across his body and parallel with the floor. His left arm is held against his body, and his left fist is placed in his right palm.

Exercise. He pushes down with his left fist while resisting with his right arm. He repeats the exercise, changing the positions and actions of the arms.

MUSCLES OF THE UPPER ARM THAT EXTEND THE FOREARM (TRICEPS)

Standing Press

Starting position. With his arms partially bent overhead, the performer stands in a doorway, pressing against the top of the door frame with his hands.

Exercise. He pushes against the top of the door frame, exerting as much force as possible with his arms.

Triceps Press with Towel or Rope (Figure 9-4)

Starting position. Grasping a towel or rope in both hands, the standing performer places his right upper arm against the side of his head and so flexes the arm that his right hand is just above his right shoulder. The left arm is alongside the left side of his body and is so flexed that his left hand is near the small of his back. The towel or rope is stretched taut.

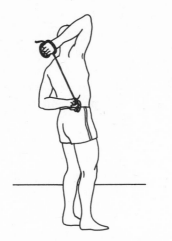

Figure 9-4. Triceps press with towel or rope.

Exercise. He attempts to extend both arms by trying to raise the right hand and lower the left hand. He repeats the exercise, changing the position and action of the arms.

Variations. This exercise may also be performed from a sitting or a prone position.

Horizontal Arm Press

Starting position. The standing performer loops a rope around his back and grasps one end in each hand. His forearms are perpendicular to his upper arms and his hands are in line with his shoulders.

Exercise. He attempts to extend his arms by moving his hands forward.

Variations. The distance of the hands from the shoulders may be varied by varying the positions of the arms from one in which the hands practically touch the shoulders to one in which the arms are almost straight. This exercise can also be done from a sitting or a supine position.

Figure 9-5. Bent-over raise to the rear.

Bent-Over Raise to the Rear (Figure 9-5)

Starting position. With his feet spread hip-distance apart, the performer stands on the loop of a rope. He bends forward at the waist and moves the rope behind him until both his arms and body are parallel to the floor and the rope is taut. He grasps one end of the rope in each hand.

Exercise. Keeping his arms straight and his hands behind his buttocks, he attempts to raise his hands.

Arm Push

Starting position. Flexing his arms and positioning his hands immediately in front of his chest, the standing performer places the palm of one hand against the fist of the other.

Exercise. He pushes his hands against each other.

Variations. This exercise can also be performed with the hands held overhead, in front of the face, or in front of the abdomen. This exercise may be performed while in a sitting or a supine position.

Archer's Exercise

Starting position. The performer stands with a rope held in his hands. His arms are in the position of an archer drawing a bow—that is, his left forearm is partially extended, and his right arm is so flexed that his right hand is under his chin.

Exercise. He attempts to move his hands away from each other. He then reverses the position of his arms and repeats the exercise.

Variation. This exercise may be performed from a sitting position.

Knee Push-down

Starting position. The performer, with his legs flexed, bends forward and, keeping his arms slightly flexed and his shoulders above his knees, places his hands on his knees.

Exercise. He pushes downward against his knees.

Variations. The performer may keep his arms straight while performing this exercise. By placing his elbows on his thighs approximately six inches above his knees, the performer can do this exercise while in a sitting position.

Other Exercises Previously Described in Chapter

Forearm Forcer.
Body-Builder's Stance.

MUSCLES SURROUNDING THE SHOULDERS THAT MOVE THE UPPER ARMS (DELTOIDS, *PECTORALIS MAJOR, LATISSIMUS DORSI* AND *TERES MAJOR*)

Shoulder Flexor

Starting position. The standing performer clasps his hands, interlaces his fingers, and places his hands and arms against the lower part of his rib cage.

Exercise. He pulls his hands and arms against his body.

Variation. The exercise may be performed while sitting.

Arm Pull

Starting position. The standing performer clasps his hands together and holds them in front of his chest.

Exercise. He pulls to the side with each arm.

Variations. This exercise can also be done with the hands held overhead, in front of the face, or in front of the abdomen. This exercise may be performed while in a sitting or a supine position.

Bent-Over Raise to the Side

Starting position. With his feet hip-distance apart, the performer stands on the loop of a rope. He bends forward at the waist and grasps one end of the rope in either hand at a height about two feet above his feet. He moves his extended arms sideward until the rope becomes taut.

Exercise. Keeping his arms straight, he attempts to raise his arms sideward.

Forward Raise (Figure 9-6)

Starting position. The standing performer so positions the rope that it passes behind and under his buttocks. He so holds the rope in his hands that his arms are straight and parallel with the floor.

Exercise. He attempts to raise his extended arms.

Variations. The hands may be positioned higher or lower than indicated in the above directions. This exercise may be performed while in a sitting position.

Sideward Raise

Starting position. The performer either stands on the loop of a rope or places it under his buttocks. With his arms straight, he so holds the rope in his hands that his arms are extended to either side and are parallel with the floor.

Exercise. He attempts to raise his extended arms.

Variations. This exercise may be performed with the arms above or below shoulder level and while in a sitting position.

Side Neck Push

Starting position. With his upper arm parallel with the floor and pointing directly to his right, the performer places his right hand on the right side of his head.

Exercise. He pushes sideward with his right hand and resists the movement with his head and neck. He repeats the exercise with the left hand placed on the left side of his head.

Variations. This exercise may be performed while in a sitting or a supine position.

Other Exercises Previously Described in Chapter

Backward Neck Push.
Forward Neck Pull.
Standing Press.
Arm Push.
Archer's Exercise.

MUSCLES OF THE UPPER BACK THAT MOVE THE SHOULDERS, SHOULDER GIRDLE (SCAPULA) OR UPPER ARMS (TRAPEZIUS, *LATISSIMUS DORSI, RHOMBOIDS,* AND *TERES MAJOR*)

Shoulder Shrug with Rope

Starting position. With his feet spread shoulder-width apart and his arms extended at his sides, the performer stands on a loop of rope and holds one end in each hand.

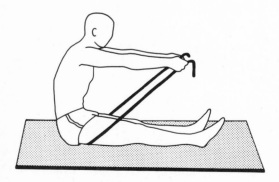

Figure 9-6. Forward raise.

Exercise. Keeping his arms straight, he attempts to raise his shoulders as high as possible.

Variation. By grasping the sides of the chair, he may perform this exercise while sitting in a chair.

Sitting Lift

Starting position. The sitting performer flexes his body and places both hands under his thighs near his knees, grasping one of his wrists.

Exercise. He attempts to lift his legs by extending his trunk; at the same time, he pushes down with his legs.

Variation. This exercise can be performed from a squat position.

Other Exercises Previously Described in Chapter

Bent-Over Raise to the Rear.
Shoulder Flexor.
Arm Pull.
Bent-Over Raise to the Side.
Sideward Raise.

MUSCLES OF THE CHEST THAT MOVE THE UPPER ARM (*PECTORALIS MAJOR* AND, INDIRECTLY, *SERRATUS ANTERIOR*)

Arms Forward

Starting position. Standing under a doorway, the performer, with his arms completely extended, grasps the top of the doorframe with his hands.

Exercise. The performer attempts to move his arms forward.

Variation. If the feet are placed approximately three feet from the wall, this exercise can be performed with the hands against a wall.

Other Exercises Previously Described in Chapter

Backward Neck Push.
Forward Neck Push.
Sideward Neck Push.

MUSCLES OF THE LOWER BACK AND HIPS THAT EXTEND THE TRUNK OR THIGHS (EXTENSORS OF THE TRUNK AND THIGHS: *ERECTOR SPINEA* AND *GLUTEUS MAXIMUS*)

Regular Dead Lift

Starting position. With his feet spread about hip-width and standing on a rope, the performer flexes his trunk slightly forward, so bends his legs that his thighs are parallel with the floor, and, with his arms straight and extended downward, grasps each end of the rope with his hands.

Exercise. He attempts to straighten his trunk and legs.

Variations. The degree of trunk flexion and leg bend can be varied over a considerable range.

Back Arch

Starting position. With his hands on the floor beside his head, the performer lies on his back and points his elbows upward.

Exercise. He raises his body from the floor, supporting himself on his hands, head, and heels.

Other Exercises Previously Described in Chapter

Raise with Back.
Sitting Lift.

ABDOMINAL AND OTHER MUSCLES OF THE LOWER TRUNK THAT FLEX THE TRUNK OR THIGHS (FLEXORS AND ROTATORS OF THE TRUNK: *RECTUS ABDOMINUS*, INTERNAL AND EXTERNAL OBLIQUES)

Abdominal Compressor

Starting position. The performer lies on his back.

Exercise. He exhales and then compresses his abdomen, contracting his abdominal muscles as though he would push his muscles through his backbone. He then relaxes and inhales.

Variations. This exercise can be performed from a standing or sitting position.

Abdominal Curl

Starting position. The performer assumes a supine position with his arms at his sides.

Exercise. He attempts to curl his trunk upward and forward while keeping his lower back on the floor.

Variation. This exercise can be performed from a standing position.

Side Push-Down

Starting position. The performer stands with his feet spread wide apart, his left leg straight, and his right leg so flexed that his right thigh and right leg form a 90-degree angle at the knee joint.

Exercise. Inclining his upper body forward and to the right, the performer pushes his right hand down and sideways on his right thigh. He then straightens his right leg, flexes his left leg, leans forward and to the left, and pushes his left hand down and sideways on his left thigh.

Other Exercises Previously Described in Chapter

Knee Push-Down.
Tensor.

MUSCLES OF THE HIPS AND THIGHS THAT FLEX THE THIGH (ILIO-PSOAS AND RECTUS FEMORIS) AND EXTEND THE LEG (QUADRICEPS—VASTUS EXTERNUS, VASTUS INTERMEDIUS, VASTUS INTERNUS, AND RECTUS FEMORIS)

One-Leg Squat

Starting position. The performer stands next to a wall. He raises his left leg and extends it forward, and so squats down on his right leg that his right leg and thigh form a 90-degree angle. If necessary, he places a hand against the wall to help retain his balance.

Exercise. He holds this position without lowering his trunk. He then reverses the position of the legs and repeats the exercise.

Legs Flexed—Push and Pull

Starting position. The performer lies on his back and raises his knees to a position above his hips. His lower legs are parallel with the floor and are crossed at the ankles.

Exercise. He forces his ankles against each other, pulling down with the top ankle and pushing up with the bottom ankle. He repeats the exercise with the ankles crossed in the opposite direction.

Variation. This exercise can be performed from a sitting position.

Comment. In the leg pushing up, the quadriceps are exercised; and in the leg pushing down, the *biceps femoris* is exercised.

Other Exercises Previously Described in Chapter

Regular Dead Lift.
Tensor (this exercise is described later in the chapter).

MUSCLES OF THE HIPS AND THIGHS THAT EXTEND THE THIGH (GLUTEUS MAXIMUS AND HAMSTRINGS) AND FLEX THE LEG (HAMSTRING MUSCLES— BICEPS FEMORIS)

Thigh-Leg Forcer

Starting position. The performer stands with his back toward a wall with one foot about twelve inches from the wall and the heel of his other foot against the wall.

Exercise. He pushes backward with the heel that is placed next to the wall. He then repeats the exercise with the other leg.

Variation. This exercise can be performed from a supine position.

Other Exercise Previously Described in Chapter

Legs Flexed—Push and Pull.

MUSCLES OF THE HIPS AND THIGHS THAT ABDUCT AND ADDUCT THE THIGHS (ABDUCTORS AND ADDUCTORS OF THIGHS)

Legs Apart: Thigh Abductor

Starting position. With his legs extended and crossed at the ankle, the performer lies on his back on the floor.

Exercise. He attempts to force his feet (which are engaged with each other) away from each other.

Variations. The legs can be flexed at various angles. This exercise can be performed while in a sitting position.

Legs Together: Thigh Adductor

Starting position. With his legs extended and together, the performer lies on his back.

Exercise. He forces his legs against each other.

Variations. The legs can be flexed at various angles, and the exercise can be performed while in a sitting position.

MUSCLES OF THE LEG THAT EXTEND THE FOOT (CALF MUSCLE—GASTROCNEMIUS, AND SOLEUS)

Heel Raise

Starting position. With his hands above his head, the performer stands on his right foot in a doorway and presses against the top of the door frame, keeping his arms as straight as possible. His left foot is raised off the floor.

Exercise. He raises his right heel off the floor, and, by extending his foot at the ankle joint, he pushes against the door frame with his hands.

Foot Pusher

Starting position. The performer assumes a sitting position and places his right thigh against his chest. He holds the ball of his right foot, which is flexed at the ankle, with both hands.

Exercise. While pulling up with his hands, he extends or pushes his right foot down, attempting to make the movement at the ankle joint. He repeats the exercise with his left leg and foot.

Variation. Instead of extending the foot, it can be flexed upward at the ankle joint while pushing down with the hands; a different set of leg muscles is then exercised.

AN ISOMETRIC EXERCISE PROGRAM FOR THE "BUSY PERSON": THE EFFICIENT FOURTEEN

This set of isometric exercises is designed for the person who believes that he is "too busy to exercise"—for example, the harried student, business man, or professional man. There are fourteen exercises in this set. If each exercise position is held while the exerciser counts slowly to six, the total exercise time will be 1 minute, 24 seconds. If the exercises are learned to the point where the performer needs no more than two or three seconds to change positions, then the total exercise period should not exceed two minutes. Almost anyone can spare two minutes from even the busiest of schedules.

All the exercises except one—the Tensor—are performed while the exerciser sits in a chair. No equipment other than a chair is required, so the exercises can be performed at any time that the performer is sitting.

Arm Push and Pull

Starting position. The performer clasps his hands together and holds them in front of his face.

Exercise. He pulls with both hands and then pushes with both hands. He may repeat the exer-

cise with his hands held over his head or with his hands held in front of his chest.

Arm Push-Down

Starting position. The performer flexes his forearms and rests his upper arms against the back of the chair.

Exercise. He presses his arms inward and backward against the back of the chair.

Shoulder Forcer

Starting position. The performer spreads his knees approximately a foot apart and, with his arms extended, places his hands on top of his knees.

Exercise. He presses his hands and knees against each other.

Shoulder Raiser

Starting position. The performer grasps the front of the chair seat.

Exercise. He pulls upward on the front of the chair seat. The performer may, instead, pull upward on the side of the chair seat.

Forward Neck Pull

Starting position. The performer places the interlocked fingers of his hands on the back of his head.

Exercise. He pulls forward with his hands and resists the movement with his head and neck.

Backward Neck Push

Starting position. The performer places the palms of his hands on his forehead.

Exercise. He pushes backward with his hands and resists the movement with his head and neck.

Tensor

Starting position. The performer stands in an erect position.

Exercise. He tenses as many muscles as possible by attempting to perform the following actions: (1) squeezes his buttocks against each other, (2) pulls his chin downward and inward while attempting to move his head backward, (3) lifts his shoulders, (4) tenses the arm muscles by extending his arms to the maximum, (5) pulls his stomach in,

(6) tenses his leg muscles by extending his legs to the maximum, and (7) raises his heels off the floor as high as possible.

Forearm Press-Down

Starting position. The performer rests his elbows on his thighs about six inches from his knees.

Exercise. By attempting to curl his body forward he presses his elbows against his thighs.

Abdominal Compressor

Starting position. The performer sits in a chair.

Exercise. He compresses his abdomen, pulling as though he would pull his abdominal muscles through his backbone.

Leg Flexed: Push and Pull

Starting position. The performer crosses his legs at the ankles.

Exercise. He forces his ankles against each other, pulling down with the top ankle and pushing up with the bottom ankle. Crossing his ankles in the opposite direction he repeats the exercise.

Thigh Spreader

Starting position. The performer leans forward, wraps his arms around his thighs, and grasps one of his wrists.

Exercise. He forces his legs outward against his arms.

Thigh Squeezer

Starting position. The performer's fists are held side by side between his knees.

Exercise. He presses his knees against his fists.

Foot Pusher

Starting position. The performer places his left thigh against his chest. He holds the ball of his left foot, which is flexed at the ankle, in both hands.

Exercise. While pulling up with his hands, he extends or pushes down with his foot. He repeats the exercise with the right foot.

10. dual-resistance exercises

Dual-resistance exercises are exercises in which a partner supplies the resistance against which the exercising person works. In such exercises the parts of the body being exercised may be allowed to move, so that isotonic muscle contractions are performed in much the same manner as in weight-training exercises. Dual-resistance exercises, in which the parts of the body being exercised are not allowed to move, may also be performed, in which case strength is developed by means of isometric contractions, as in isometric exercises.

ADVANTAGES AND DISADVANTAGES OF DUAL-RESISTANCE EXERCISES

A number of advantages and disadvantages of including dual-resistance exercises in a physical fitness program may be cited.

Advantages

1. Exercises of this type are valuable for developing the muscular endurance and strength of specific areas of the body, or for the overall development of muscular endurance and strength.
2. No equipment is necessary for performing dual-resistance exercises.
3. Special exercise areas or special types of facilities are not required.
4. Dual-resistance exercises provide vigorous muscular activity for pairs of performers.
5. A group of any size can participate in this type of activity.

Disadvantages

1. Except for muscular endurance and strength, the performance of dual-resistance exercises does little to develop the various components of physical fitness.
2. There is no objective way to determine the amount of resistance encountered in each exercise.
3. Gains in muscular strength and in muscular endurance must be measured by some method other than the performance of the exercises.

4. The motivation that results from visual signs of progress may be lacking.

DIRECTIONS FOR USING DUAL-RESISTANCE EXERCISES

In this chapter twenty-five dual-resistance exercises are given. For ease in learning the exercises and associating them with the correct names, the names given are descriptive. The reader should note that these exercises represent only a few of the many different types and variations of dual-resistance exercises. By studying Chapters 8 and 9, the reader should be able to devise many other dual-resistance exercises.

When performing dual-resistance exercises, the partners should be as closely matched in muscular strength as is possible. Since the performers work in pairs, it is necessary to distinguish between the two partners. The person who performs the exercise is hereafter referred to as the exerciser; his partner, who supplies the resistance for the exercise, is termed the resister. For each exercise, it is suggested that the partners change roles and repeat the exercise. Because the dual-resistance exercises described in this chapter are of the isotonic type, the resister should not resist the exerciser's movement so vigorously that no movement occurs, but should slowly yield to the force exerted by the exerciser. The resistance offered by the resister should be such that from eight to ten seconds are required for the exerciser to complete the full range of movement. For each exercise, it is suggested that the exerciser perform three repetitions. Overloading is accomplished by having the resister gradually increase—in proportion to the strength gained as a result of the exercises—the resistance offered to the exercises.

When selecting dual-resistance exercises for a physical-fitness program, exercises that strengthen all parts of the body should be chosen, unless the exerciser wishes to strengthen only specific parts of his body. The dual-resistance exercises presented in this chapter are categorized according to the area of the exerciser's body that is benefited by the exercise. It should be noted that, when resisting the exerciser, the resister derives considerable benefit, but often to an area of his body different from that of the exerciser's.

MUSCLES OF THE FOREARM THAT FLEX AND EXTEND THE HAND

Wrist Curl

Starting position. The partners face each other. The exerciser squats and places his forearms on his thighs with his hands extending past his knees. His palms face upward, his fingers are extended, and his hands are flexed backward so that his fingers point downward. The resister bends forward and places his palms, fingers pointing outward, in the palms of the exerciser.

Exercise. The exerciser slowly flexes his hands, raising them as high as possible, while the resister supplies sufficient resistance to permit the movement to proceed slowly throughout the range of motion. When the exerciser's hands are flexed as far as possible, the resister slowly forces the exerciser's hands back to the starting position.

Variations. The resister may place his palms on the back of the exerciser's hands, whose palms are facing the floor. This exercise may be performed with the exerciser sitting in a chair or with his forearms resting on a table top.

MUSCLES OF THE UPPER ARM THAT FLEX THE FOREARM (*BICEPS BRACHII, BRACHIALES, BRACHIORADIALIS, AND PRONATOR TERES*)

Forearm Curl (Figure 10-1)

Starting position. The partners face each other. The exerciser stands with his arms against his

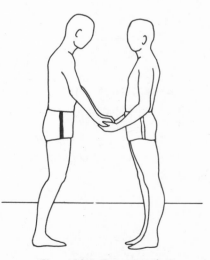

Figure 10-1. Forearm curl.

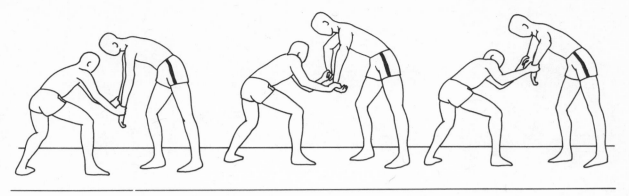

Figure 10-2. Bent-over rowing.

sides and with the palms of his hands facing forward and upward. The resister places his fist in the open hands of the exerciser.

Exercise. Keeping his upper arms against his sides throughout the exercise, the exerciser forcefully raises his hands through an arc and toward his shoulders. The resister supplies sufficient resistance to allow movement to proceed slowly throughout the range of motion. When the exerciser's hands touch his shoulders, the resister forces them down to the starting position.

Variation. The exerciser's palms may face the floor or each other and the resister grasps the backs of the exerciser's hands or his wrists.

Bent-Over Rowing (Figure 10-2)

Starting position. The partners face each other. The exerciser bends forward so that his trunk is parallel to the floor, and allows his arms to hang down. With his head to one side of the exerciser's

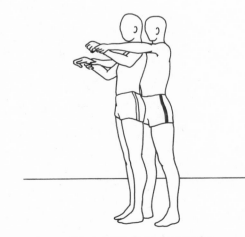

Figure 10-3. Forearm extender.

head, the resister leans forward and grasps each of the exerciser's wrists.

Exercise. Keeping his elbows pointing sideways and away from each other, the exerciser slowly pulls his hands to his chest while the resister supplies sufficient force to cause the movement to proceed slowly. After the exerciser's hands touch his chest, the resister slowly forces them back to the starting position.

MUSCLES OF THE UPPER ARM THAT EXTEND THE FOREARM (TRICEPS)

Forearm Extender (Figure 10-3)

Starting position. The exerciser stands with his hands in front of his shoulders, and with his elbows by his sides. Standing behind the exerciser, the resister reaches around the exerciser's body and grasps the exerciser's wrists.

Exercise. Keeping his hands at shoulder height, the exerciser forces his hands directly forward as far as possible. The resister permits slow movement of the exerciser's hands until the resister's arms are completely extended. The resister then forces the exerciser's hands back to the starting position.

Supine Press (Figure 10-4)

Starting position. The exerciser assumes a supine position with his arms flexed, elbows against his sides, and his hands, palms up, near his shoulders. The resister stands directly behind the exerciser's shoulders. Flexing his legs and trunk, the resister leans forward and grasps the exerciser's palms.

Exercise. Keeping his hands directly above his

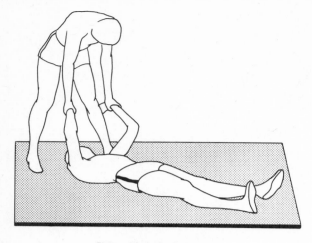

Figure 10-4. Supine press.

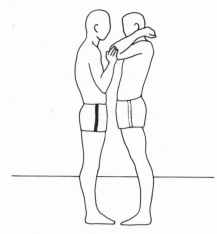

Figure 10-5. Upper-arm push-down.

shoulders, the exerciser slowly forces his hands upward until his arms are completely extended. The resister then forces the exerciser's hands back to the starting position.

Variation. In order to supply increased resistance, the resister may stand in the same location but facing away from the exerciser. The resister then places the back of his hands on his buttocks and squats down until he can place his palms in the exerciser's palms. The resister must be careful not to lose his balance.

Other Exercises Previously Described in Chapter

Forearm Curl.
Bent-Over Rowing.

MUSCLES SURROUNDING THE SHOULDERS THAT MOVE THE UPPER ARMS (DELTOIDS, *PECTORALIS MAJOR*, *LATISSIMUS DORSI*, AND *TERES MAJOR*)

Upper-Arm Push-Down (Figure 10-5)

Starting position. The partners face each other. The exerciser places his hands on his shoulders and points his elbows toward the resister. With his fingers pointing toward the exerciser's shoulders, the resister places the palms of his hands under the the exerciser's elbows.

Exercise. The exerciser forces his elbows downward toward the sides of his body. When the exerciser's elbows reach his sides, the resister slowly forces the exerciser's elbows back to the starting position.

Upper-Arm Lift

Starting position. The partners face each other. The exerciser flexes his forearms and squeezes his upper arms against his sides. With the fingers of his hands pointing toward each other, the resister places his hands on the exerciser's forearms just below his elbows.

Exercise. The exerciser forces his elbows forward and upward as high as possible. When this movement is completed, the resister forces the exerciser's elbows back to the starting position.

Lateral Arm Pull (Figure 10-6)

Starting position. With his arms extended at shoulder height, the exerciser touches the backs of his hands together. Facing the exerciser, the resister places his fist in the exerciser's hands.

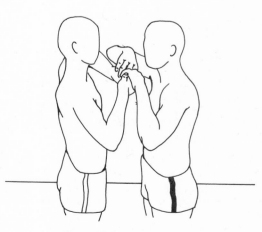

Figure 10-6. Lateral arm pull.

Exercise. The exerciser forces his hands apart as the resister permits slow movement. When the exerciser's hands are four to five feet apart, the resister slowly forces his fists together while the exerciser vigorously resists the movement.

Variation. The exerciser may have his arms flexed and his elbows pointing toward the floor throughout the exercise.

Lateral Arm Push

Starting position. With their arms flexed and their forearms parallel to the floor, the partners face each other. The exerciser's hands are spaced about forty inches apart and his palms face each other. The resister places his fists in the exerciser's hands.

Exercise. The exerciser slowly forces his hands together. When the resister's fists meet, he slowly forces them apart while the exerciser resists the movement.

Variation. The exerciser may have his arms extended throughout the exercise.

Lateral Arm Raise

Starting position. The exerciser stands with his arms at his sides. The resister stands behind the exerciser and grasps the exerciser's wrists.

Exercise. The exerciser keeps his arms straight and forces them sideward and upward. The resister permits the exerciser to move his arms until the back of the exerciser's hands are together. The resister then slowly forces the exerciser's arms back to the starting position.

Variation. The exerciser may sit while performing this exercise.

Other Exercise Previously Described in Chapter

Supine Press.

EXERCISES FOR THE MUSCLES OF THE UPPER BACK THAT MOVE THE SHOULDERS, SHOULDER GIRDLE (SCAPULA) AND/OR UPPER ARMS (*TRAPEZIUS, LATISSIMUS DORSI,* RHOMBOIDS, AND *TERES MAJOR)*

Shoulder Shrug

Starting position. With his hands resting on his knees, the exerciser sits on the floor with his legs flexed. The resister stands with one leg immediately behind the exerciser and with the other leg about two feet behind the exerciser. The resister leans forward and places his hands on the outermost part of the exerciser's shoulders.

Exercise. While the resister permits slow movement, the exerciser raises his shoulders as high as possible. The resister then slowly pushes the exerciser's shoulders back to the starting position.

Lateral Arm Depressor

Starting position. The exerciser stands with his arms extended overhead and touching. The resister stands behind the exerciser and grasps the exerciser's wrists.

Exercise. Keeping his arms straight, the exerciser slowly forces them laterally downward. When the exerciser's arms touch his sides, the resister slowly forces them back to the starting position.

Variation. The exerciser can perform this exercise while in a sitting or supine position.

Other Exercises Previously Described in Chapter

Upper-Arm Push-Down.
Lateral Arm Push.

EXERCISES FOR THE MUSCLES OF THE CHEST THAT MOVE THE UPPER ARMS (*PECTORALIS MAJOR* AND, INDIRECTLY, *SERRATUS ANTERIOR*)

Exercises Previously Described in Chapter

Supine Press.
Upper-Arm Push-Down.
Lateral Arm Pull.
Lateral Arm Depressor.

MUSCLES OF THE LOWER BACK AND HIPS THAT EXTEND THE TRUNK OR THIGHS (EXTENSORS OF THE TRUNK AND THIGHS: *ERECTOR SPINEA* AND *GLUTEUS MAXIMUS*)

Hump Back

Starting position. The exerciser kneels, places his hands on the floor, and assumes an all-fours position. His hands are placed directly below his shoulders, and his knees are located directly below his hips. The resister sits on the middle portion of the exerciser's back.

Exercise. The exerciser slowly raises his back as high as possible.

Straight-Leg Back Lift

Starting position. The standing exerciser flexes forward at the waist, keeping his legs straight, and positions his trunk so that it is parallel with the floor. Facing the exerciser and standing near his head, the resister squats, flexes his arms, and places his interlaced fingers on the back of the exerciser's neck.

Exercise. By extending his body, the exerciser slowly raises his trunk until he attains a standing position. The resister then forces the exerciser back to the starting position.

Prone Arch

Starting position. With his legs together, the exerciser lies on the floor in a prone position. Kneeling beside the hips of the exerciser, the resister places the palm of one hand on the upper back of the exerciser and the palm of the other hand on the back of the exerciser's ankles.

Exercise. The exerciser slowly arches his body as much as possible. The resister then slowly forces the exerciser's chest and feet to the floor.

MUSCLES OF THE LOWER TRUNK THAT FLEX THE TRUNK OR THIGHS (FLEXORS OF THE TRUNK: *ILIO-PSOAS*, *RECTUS ABDOMINUS*, AND INTERNAL AND EXTERNAL OBLIQUES)

Bent-Leg Sit-Up

Starting position. The exerciser lies on the floor in a supine position, with his legs together and heels drawn up toward his hips, so that his thighs and lower legs form a 90-degree angle. Kneeling to one side of the abdomen of the exerciser, the resister places one hand on the exerciser's chest and the other hand on the exerciser's knees.

Exercise. The exerciser slowly curls his upper body upward until his trunk comes to an erect position. The resister than slowly forces the exerciser back to the starting position.

Comment. The resister should apply the majority of his force to the knees of the exerciser.

Thighs Up

Starting position. The exerciser lies on the floor in a supine position with his legs together. Kneeling to one side of the abdomen of the exerciser, the resister places one hand on the exerciser's chest and the other hand on the upper portion of the exerciser's knees.

Exercise. Flexing his legs as he proceeds, the exerciser lifts his thighs and pulls them toward his chest as far as possible. The resister then forces the exerciser's legs to their original position on the floor.

Comment. The resister should apply the majority of his force to the chest of the exerciser.

Side Raise (Figure 10-7)

Starting position. Standing with his feet spread about three feet apart, the exerciser bends as far as possible to one side. Facing the side toward which the exerciser is bent, the resister stands and flexes his arms and places his intertwined fingers on the upper side of the exerciser's neck.

Figure 10-7. Side raise.

Exercise. The exerciser slowly straightens his body until he comes to an erect position. The resister slowly forces the exerciser back to his starting position. The exerciser then flexes his trunk toward the opposite side, repeating the side-raise exercise.

MUSCLES OF THE HIPS AND THIGHS THAT ABDUCT AND ADDUCT THE THIGHS (ABDUCTORS AND ADDUCTORS OF THIGHS)

Legs Apart

Starting position. The exerciser reclines on the floor in a supine position with his legs extended and touching. The resister kneels in front of the exerciser's feet and grasps the outside portion of his ankles.

Exercise. The exerciser slowly forces his legs apart. The resister then slowly forces them back together.

Variation. This exercise may be performed while the exerciser is in a prone position.

Legs Together

Starting position. With his legs extended and spread as far apart as is comfortable, the exerciser reclines in a supine position on the floor. The resister kneels in front of the exerciser's feet and grasps the inside portion of the exerciser's ankles.

Exercise. The exerciser slowly forces his legs together. The resister then slowly forces them back to the starting position.

Variation. The exerciser may lie in a prone position when performing this exercise.

MUSCLES OF THE HIPS AND THIGHS THAT FLEX THE THIGH (*ILIO-PSOAS* AND *RECTUS FEMORIS*) AND EXTEND THE LOWER LEG (*QUADRICEPS*)

One-Half Squats

Persons with knee ailments should not perform this exercise without prior approval from their physician.

Starting position. The exerciser stands with the resister mounted on his back. With the resister's legs wrapped around the exerciser's waist, he rests his upper arms on top of the exerciser's shoulders and clasps his hands together.

Exercise. The exerciser slowly does a knee bend, going down to a one-half squat position. He then returns to an erect position.

Variations. The exerciser may squat to a sitting position on a bench. If the exerciser has sufficient leg strength he may do a three-quarter squat.

Leg Raise

Starting position. The exerciser reclines on the floor in a supine position with his legs extended. The resister kneels near one of the exerciser's ankles and places his hands on it.

Exercise. While the resister permits slow movement of the legs, the exerciser keeps his leg as straight as possible and forces it upward until it is perpendicular to the floor. The resister then slowly forces the exerciser's leg back to the floor, and the exercise is performed with the other leg.

MUSCLES OF THE HIPS AND THIGHS THAT EXTEND THE THIGH (*GLUTEUS MAXIMUS* AND *BICEPS FEMORIS*) AND FLEX THE LOWER LEG (HAMSTRING MUSCLES)

Leg Lower

Starting position. The exerciser reclines on the floor in a supine position with his legs extended, one leg resting on the floor and the other pointing directly overhead. The resister kneels by the exerciser's foot that is on the floor and grasps each of the exerciser's ankles.

Exercise. The exerciser slowly forces the leg that is in a perpendicular position down to the floor. The resister then slowly forces the exerciser's leg back, and the exercise is then performed with the other leg.

Leg Curl (Figure 10-8)

Starting position. The exerciser lies in a prone position with his legs together. Kneeling to one side of one of the exerciser's thighs, the resister grasps the back of one of the exerciser's ankles with one hand and places the other hand on the back of the exerciser's thigh.

Exercise. While the resister keeps the exerciser's thigh on the floor and resists the movement, the exerciser slowly curls his lower leg upward and toward his thigh. The resister then slowly forces the

Figure 10-8. Leg curl.

exerciser's leg back to the starting position, and the exercise is then performed with the other leg.

Variation. The exerciser may exercise both legs at the same time.

MUSCLES OF THE LEG THAT EXTEND THE FOOT (CALF MUSCLE—*GASTROCNEMIUS,* AND *SOLEUS*)

Heel Raise

Starting position. With the resister mounted on his back, the exerciser stands on one leg. The toe of the exerciser's other foot may rest lightly on the floor as an aid in maintaining balance. The resister's hands are on the exerciser's shoulders, and the resister's legs are wrapped around the exerciser's waist.

Exercise. The exerciser slowly raises his heel from the floor by extending his foot as far as possible. Standing on the opposite foot, the exerciser then repeats the exercise.

Comment. For increased balance while performing this exercise, the exerciser may place his hands against a wall.

11. combative-type activities

Combative-type activities are a natural physical activity in which youths often engage spontaneously because of the sheer fun and enjoyment they derive from combative contests. Combative-type activities, in which one matches his strength, balance, agility, wiles, and wits against another, appear to have an instinctive appeal to most youths and adults. Combative activities provide vigorous and highly concentrated activity for the participants; but, because of the challenge and fun element inherent in them, the participants are usually oblivious to the amount of physical effort that they are exerting. Most combative-type activities require no special equipment.

With the exception of circulorespiratory endurance, participation in combative-type activities contributes to the development and maintenance of all the components of physical fitness—namely, muscular strength, muscular endurance, speed of movement, agility, balance, flexibility, and coordination. Because participation in combatives does little to develop circulorespiratory endurance, it is recommended that the contestant also engage in swimming or running activities during the exercise period.

COMPOSITION AND ORGANIZATION OF COMBATIVE-TYPE ACTIVITIES

Combative-type activities are traditionally classified as (1) dual combatives, in which one person is pitted against an opponent, as in a regular boxing match, (2) team combatives, in which one team composed of two or more persons is pitted against another team, or (3) mass combative, in which several persons compete against one another, usually to determine an individual winner. The combative-type activities presented in this chapter are described as dual combatives, but most of them may also be engaged in as team or mass combatives.

To avoid as much as possible the element of danger and the possibility of accidents, the combative activities presented in this chapter are mostly of the wrestling type. Only a few of the boxing combatives have been included. The combative activities have been arbitrarily placed into six categories. The activities in each category are listed in approximate order of difficulty—that is, in each category the activity that is the least difficult for most contestants to perform is listed first, and the activity that is the most difficult for most contestants is listed last. According to the vigorousness or strenuousness of effort required of participants, the activities in each of the six categories are classified into one of the following four classifications: light activity, moderately vigorous activity, vigorous activity, extremely vigorous activity.

When engaging in combative activities regularly as a means of developing physical fitness, an overload may be attained in many of the activities by (1) selecting opponents of progressively increased size or strength, (2) systematically increasing the number or the length of bouts, or (3) resting for decreased periods of time between bouts.

The name given to each combative activity either decribes the activity or is the name most commonly applied to the activity.

DIRECTIONS FOR ENGAGING IN COMBATIVE-TYPE ACTIVITIES

1. The contestants should not wear rings, wrist watches, bracelets, chains around the neck, or eye glasses when engaging in combatives. The wearing of safety-rim eye glasses equipped with a safety strap is permissible.
2. The room or area should have sufficient open space that there is no danger of striking or falling on obstructions or on other contestants.
3. Those activities in which there is danger of falling or striking the floor forcibly should be performed on a floor covered with mats or on a soft, grassy area.
4. Before engaging in a combative activity, the contestants should understand the rules, how to perform the activity, and when the activity should be terminated.
5. The two contestants (or teams) should be evenly matched on the basis of size and strength.
6. Before engaging in combative activites, the contestants should first warm up by performing mild physical activity.
7. To start a contest one of the partners says,

"Ready, go." Upon this starting signal, both partners simultaneously and rhythmically count aloud to 3. The combative activity starts as soon as the count of 3 is sounded. A leader or instructor may start team or mass combative activities with a signal of "Ready, Begin."

8. The contest should be terminated as soon as one of the contestants has lost the bout, after an agreed-upon period of time has elapsed, or when only one contestant or team remains in the contest.
9. During the period of participation, the contestant should proceed from less complicated to more complicated combative activities.
10. During the period of participation, the vigorousness of the combative activities should be varied.
11. The combative activities engaged in during the session should be selected from several of the six categories.
12. The number of bouts included in each contest of a combative activity is usually one, three, or five. The winner of the contest is the person or team winning the majority of the bouts.

SLAPPING OR STEPPING COMBATIVES

Slapping or stepping combative activities involve touching—by slapping or stepping—some portion of the opponent's body while avoiding contact by the opponent.

PINK HANDS—LIGHT ACTIVITY

The object of the contest is to slap the backs of the hands of the opponent who is on defense. The contestants face each other with their elbows at their sides and their forearms and hands extended out in front of their bodies. The contestant on offense places his outstretched hands, palm up, under the hands of his opponent. With his palms facing down, the contestant on defense rests his hands lightly on the palms of his opponent. The contestant on offense attempts to slap the back of one, or the backs of both, of the hands of his opponent. The contestant on defense attempts, by moving his hands in any direction desired, to avoid being slapped. The contestant on offense may feint a slap only if the palm of his hand does not lose contact with the palm of his opponent's hand.

A defensive foul occurs if the contestant on defense moves his hand away from contact when the offensive man does not attempt a slap, or if the defensive man holds his opponent's hands. The penalty for committing a defensive foul is that the defensive contestant must remain on defense. An offensive foul occurs if the contestant on offense (1) turns his hands over to feint a slap, (2) loses contact with his opponent's hands, but does not attempt a slap, (3) holds one of his opponent's hands, or (4) misses his opponent's hand when the slap is attempted. The penalty for committing an offensive foul is that the contestant on offense must assume the defensive role.

The contestants change roles when (1) the contestant on offense commits a foul or attempts, but fails, to slap one of his opponent's hands, (2) the contestant on offense makes ten slaps in succession, or (3) fifteen seconds have elapsed. A bout is completed after two minutes or when one of the contestants has pink hands.

STEPPING ON TOES—MODERATELY VIGOROUS ACTIVITY

The object is to step on the opponent's toes. The contestants face each other and grasp each other's wrists. At a signal, each contestant attempts—by jumping, hopping, or thrusting with either leg—to step on his opponent's toes. It is a foul and loss of a bout to kick the opponent. A match equals three out of five bouts.

KNEE SLAP—MODERATELY VIGOROUS ACTIVITY

The object is for the contestant to slap his opponent's knees and, at the same time, avoid having his own knees slapped. The contestants face each other and place both hands on each other's shoulders. By employing such techniques as lunging, feinting, and circling, each contestant attempts to gain a favorable position from which to slap one of his opponent's knees. The opponent may be held at a distance by pushing against his shoulders or by shoving him away, but he may be contacted only with the hands or the arms. A bout is won when the contestant slaps one of his opponent's knees. A match equals three out of five bouts.

DODGING AND SHIFTING COMBATIVES

Dodging and shifting combative activities involve moving around the body of an opponent in order to gain an advantage or a specific hold while preventing him from gaining the same hold or advantage.

WESTMORELAND WRESTLING—EXTREMELY VIGOROUS ACTIVITY

Westmoreland wrestling should be conducted on a mat, a dirt floor, or soft, grassy area. The object is to force the opponent to touch the mat with three points of his body. The contestants face each other. At a signal, each contestant grasps his opponent and attempts to force him off balance and to cause him to touch the mat with three points of his body. Two feet and one hand, two feet and one knee, or two hands and one foot are all considered to be three points of the body. A match equals one bout or two out of three bouts.

ADVANTAGE WRESTLING—VIGOROUS ACTIVITY

The object is to go behind the opponent's back and grasp him around the waist with both hands. The contestants face each other. At a signal each contestant maneuvers for position. Each contestant attempts to get behind his opponent's back and to grasp his opponent in a waist hold. A match equals one bout or two out of three bouts.

LIFT-UP WRESTLING—EXTREMELY VIGOROUS ACTIVITY

The object is to lift the opponent's feet off the floor. The contestants face each other. At a signal, each contestant circles his opponent, maneuvering for a favorable position. Each contestant attempts, with a rear or front waist hold, to grasp his opponent and lift his feet off the floor. One bout or two out of three bouts constitute a match.

BUTTING OR BATTERING COMBATIVES

Butting or battering combative activities involve jostling some portion of the body of an opponent, who is also in motion, in order to cause him to lose his balance and fall to a position of defeat.

KANGAROO FIGHT—MODERATELY VIGOROUS ACTIVITY

The object is to force the opponent off his feet, or cause him to drop a small card held between his ankles. With their arms folded across their chests, the contestants stand five feet apart and face each other. Each contestant holds a card, approximately 5-by-8 inches in size, between his ankles. Each contestant, using a double-footed hop, hops forward and jostles or shoulders his opponent, attempting to win the bout by forcing his opponent off balance or by causing him to drop the card. A match equals two out of three bouts.

ROOSTER FIGHT—MODERATELY VIGOROUS ACTIVITY

This contest should be held on mats, a dirt floor, or a soft, grassy area. The object is to make the opponent lose his balance and fall, or to cause the opponent to lose the special position that he must maintain throughout the bout. The contestants face each other and assume any one of the following variations of the starting position: (1) they fold their arms across their chests and raise their left feet off the floor; (2) they raise their left feet to the rear and grasp their left ankles with their left hands; or (3) they raise their left feet in front of their bodies, and with both hands grasp their left ankles. A variation on (1), in which each contestant reaches behind his back with his right hand and grasps his left elbow, is sometimes used. Each contestant should hold the same position during the bout. The contestant moves toward his opponent and, by butting with his shoulders, side-stepping, or feinting, attempts to make his opponent lose his balance or leave the special position that must be maintained during the bout. The use of the elbows is not permitted; a violation of the rules is penalized by the loss of the bout. A match equals two out of three bouts.

DRAKE FIGHT—MODERATELY VIGOROUS ACTIVITY

Persons with knee trouble or a history of knee injuries should not engage in drake fights unless they are given permission by a physician or an orthopedist. The object of the contest is to force the opponent to release his grip on his ankles or to force him to lose his balance and fall. The contestants face each other. Each bends forward and with both hands grasps his own ankles. In a variation, each grasp the rear of his own ankles. Each contestant attempts to so bump or jostle his opponent that he either falls off balance, touches his hand or body to the floor, or releases his grasp on his ankles with at least one hand. A match equals two out of three bouts.

CRAB FIGHT—VIGOROUS ACTIVITY (FIGURE 11-1)

The object is to force the opponent to touch his buttocks to the floor. With their hands on the

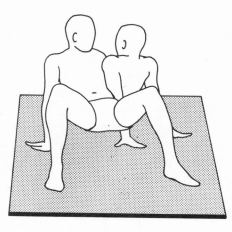

Figure 11-1. Crab fight.

floor behind them, the contestants sit facing each other on the floor. Each raises his buttocks from the floor, moves alongside his opponent, and attempts to jostle and bump him and force him to touch the floor with some part of his body other than his hands and feet. The contestants should avoid butting with their heads. A match equals two out of three bouts.

LEG HOOK—VIGOROUS ACTIVITY (FIGURE 11-2)

The object is to so force the opponent off balance that both of his feet touch the ground. Standing on their left feet, the contestants face each other and raise their right legs in the air and hook their right ankles. Hopping on his left leg, each attempts to force the other off balance by hooking or pushing with his right foot or leg. They may contact each other only with their feet. The contestants stand on their right feet for the second bout and on

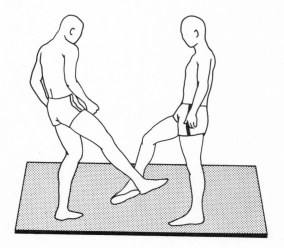

Figure 11-2. Leg hook.

Figure 11-3. Arm-link break.

their left feet for the third bout. A match equals two out of three bouts.

TUGGING OR JERKING COMBATIVES

Tugging or jerking combative activities involve forcing an opponent to move, by tugging or jerking him, from the starting position to the finishing or losing position.

BOXER'S STANCE AND PUSH—VIGOROUS ACTIVITY

The object is to move the opponent off balance or cause him to move his feet. Either of the following variations of starting position may be used: (1) the contestants take a boxer's stance, with the toe of the front foot of each touching the toe of the front foot of his oponent, or (2) they place both feet in a toe-to-toe position with their feet aligned. The contestants place their hands on each other's shoulders. By pushing, tugging, or jerking, each attempts to break his opponent's hold or to force him to move his feet. A match equals two out of three bouts.

ARM-LINK BREAK—VIGOROUS ACTIVITY (FIGURE 11-3)

The object is to break the opponent's grip. The contestants face each other and link arms together by grasping each other's upper arms. Each attempts to win the match by twisting or tugging on his opponent's linked arms, thus breaking his opponent's grip on his own upper arm. A match equals two out of three bouts.

NECK AND ELBOW WRESTLING—EXTREMELY VIGOROUS ACTIVITY (FIGURE 11-4)

The object is to force the opponent to move his feet, to lose his hold, or to lose his balance and fall. The contestants face each other and place their right hands on the back of their opponent's neck and their left hands on the rear of their opponent's elbow. By tugging and jerking his opponent, each attempts to win the match by breaking his opponent's hold, forcing him to move his feet, or forcing him to touch a part of his body other than his feet on the ground. A match equals two out of three bouts.

TOP-MAN WRESTLING—EXTREMELY VIGOROUS ACTIVITY (FIGURE 11-5)

Top-man wrestling should be conducted on wrestling mats. The object is to remain in the top posi-

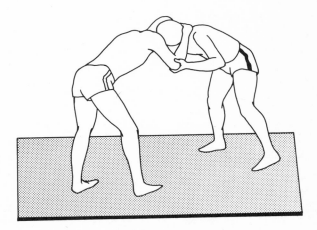

Figure 11-4. Neck and elbow wrestling.

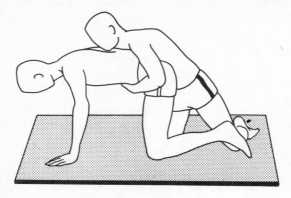

Figure 11-5. Top-man wrestling.

tion and in control of the opponent for thirty seconds. The contestants kneel side by side on the mat. The top man loosely places his inside arm around the bottom man's trunk, and with the outside hand grasps the bottom man's near arm just above the elbow. The bottom man tries to escape from the top man's hold, and the top man attempts to remain on top and in control of the bottom man for thirty seconds. If the bottom man escapes within thirty seconds, he wins the bout; if the top man successfully holds the bottom man for thirty seconds, he wins the bout. The contestants should switch positions after each bout. A match equals two out of three bouts or three out of five bouts.

PUSHING AND PULLING COMBATIVES

Pushing and pulling combative activities involve forcing an opponent to move, by pushing or pulling him, from the starting area to the finishing area, which is located across a line some distance from the starting area.

WRIST PULL—VIGOROUS ACTIVITY

The object is to pull the opponent across a line. Standing midway between two goal lines, which are ten feet apart, the contestants face each other. The contestants grasp each other's wrists in such a way that the heels of their hands are in contact. Each contestant attempts to win the bout by pulling his opponent across the goal line that is behind the puller. A match consists of two out of three bouts.

CATCH AND PULL—VIGOROUS ACTIVITY

The object is to pull the opponent across the line. The contestants face each other, and each stands an equal distance behind a line that runs between

them. The contestant attempts to grasp any part of his opponent's body and pull him over the line. Grasping the opponent's head or his clothing is not permissible, and is penalized by the loss of the bout. A match consists of two out of three bouts.

DRAG OUT OF THE GAP—EXTREMELY VIGOROUS ACTIVITY

The object is to force the opponent across the goal line that is behind him. The contestants face each other midway between two goal lines that are ten feet apart. The contestants attempt to push, pull, or carry their opponents across the goal line opposite the direction that the opponent initially faced. Grasping the opponent's head or his clothing is not permissible and is penalized by the loss of the bout. A bout consists of two out of three matches.

BACK-TO-BACK ELBOW PULL OR CARRY—EXTREMELY VIGOROUS ACTIVITY (FIGURE 11-6)

The object is to pull or to carry the opponent across a goal line. Standing midway between two goal lines that are ten feet apart, the contestants stand back-to-back and hook elbows. Each contestant attempts to pull or carry his opponent across the goal line. The elbow-linked position must be maintained throughout the contest. The contestants may not turn around, but must always face their goal lines. A match equals two out of three bouts.

BACK-TO-BACK PUSH—VIGOROUS ACTIVITY

The object is to push the opponent across the goal line. Situated halfway between two goal lines spaced ten yards apart, the contestants sit back-to-

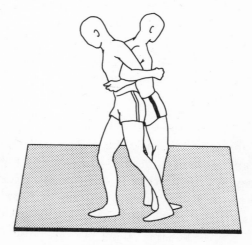

Figure 11-6. Back-to-back elbow pull or carry.

back on the floor with their arms interlocked. The contestants raise their buttocks off the floor, keep their backs and heads in contact with each other, and attempt to push their opponents backwards. The contestants should maintain an erect or semi-erect position throughout the contest. Lifting or carrying the opponent is not permitted. The contestant may not turn around, but must always face the opponent's goal line. A match equals two out of three bouts.

BACK-TO-BACK WRIST PULL—VIGOROUS ACTIVITY

The object is to pull the opponent across a goal line. Located midway between two goal lines spaced ten feet apart, the contestants stand back-to-back. Each contestant bends forward, places his right hand between his legs, and grasps his opponent's right wrist in an interlocking grasp. Each contestant attempts to pull his opponent across the goal line. They may not turn around but must always face their own goal lines. Neither may they release their grasp on each other's wrist; nor should they fall down. At the beginning of each succeeding bout, they alternate the hands used for grasping. A match equals two out of three bouts.

HOP WITH WRIST PULL—MODERATELY VIGOROUS ACTIVITY

The object is to pull the opponent across the goal line that he is facing. Standing midway between two goal lines that are ten feet apart, the contestants face each other. Each contestant raises one foot from the floor and grasps one of his opponent's wrist in an interlocking wrist-to-wrist grasp. A variation of the starting position is for the contestant to grasp both of his opponent's wrists, one in each hand. While hopping only, each contestant attempts to pull his opponent across the goal line that the opponent is facing. A contestant loses the bout if he touches his raised foot to the floor or if he releases his opponent's wrist(s). After each bout the contestants should change the foot on which they hop. A match equals four out of seven bouts.

SQUAT PULL—MODERATELY VIGOROUS ACTIVITY

Persons who have weak or unstable knee joints should not engage in this contest. The object is to force the opponent to move out of a squat position or to cause him to lose his balance. Either of the following variations in the starting position may be used: the contestants grasp their opponent's right hand, which is held at arm's length; or they may grasp opposite ends of a rope that is approximately six feet long. Each contestant attempts to over-balance his opponent by pulling and jerking his opponent's hand (or the rope). The contestant loses the bout if he does not remain in a squat position, falls to the floor, touches his free hand to the floor, or releases his grasp. A match equals three out of five bouts.

CIRCLE TUG—VIGOROUS ACTIVITY

This is a mass combative in which eight to ten contestants grasp hands and form a circle outside of a circle that is four feet in diameter. The object is to eliminate members of the group by forcing them to step into the circle. At a signal the contestants push and pull, attempting to force one another to step into the circle. Anyone who is forced to touch any of the area inside the circle must withdraw from the group, as do those contestants who release their grasp. The last man remaining outside of the circle wins. The eliminated contestants may engage in another combative activity while the circle tug contest is being concluded.

KING OF THE CIRCLE—EXTREMELY VIGOROUS ACTIVITY

This is a mass combative in which from five to twenty-five contestants start the activity from a position within a large circle, such as the free-throw circle on a basketball court. The object is to eliminate members of the group by forcing them to place both feet outside of the circle. At a signal, the contestants push, pull, or carry one or more of the other contestants outside of the circle. The contestants may "gang up" on other contestants. The eliminated contestants may immediately engage in another combative activity. The last man to remain inside the circle is "king of the circle."

COMBATIVES INVOLVING SUSTAINED MUSCULAR EFFORT

Sustained combative activities involve forcing an opponent, through the application of sustained muscular effort, to move to a defeated position.

LINKED-FINGERS FORCE-DOWN—MODERATELY VIGOROUS ACTIVITY

The object is to force the opponent to his knees. With their arms extended overhead and with their

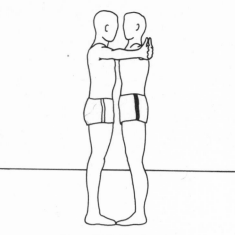

Figure 11-7. Hand push.

fingers interlaced, the standing contestants face each other. Each contestant slowly lowers his hands forward and toward his opponent. As he lowers his hands, he attempts to bend his opponent's wrists backward in order to force him to his knees and thus win the bout. A match equals two out of three bouts.

HAND PUSH—LIGHT ACTIVITY (FIGURE 11-7)

The contestants should have approximately equal arm spans. The object is to force the opponent to move a step backward. With their feet slightly spread, the contestants stand toe-to-toe. They extend their arms sideward at shoulder level and place the palms of their hands against the opponent's palms. Gradually increasing the intensity of the push, each contestant pushes against the hands of his opponent, attempting to make him step backwards and thus lose the bout. A match consists of three out of five bouts.

BACK-TO-BACK LIFT—VIGOROUS ACTIVITY

The object is to lift the opponent off the floor. With elbows interlocked, the contestants stand back-to-back in an erect position. Upon the starting signal, each contestant bends foward and attempts to lift his opponent's feet off the ground. A match consists of two out of three bouts.

WRESTLE ON KNEES—VIGOROUS ACTIVITY

The object is to force the opponent off balance. Facing each other, the contestants kneel on a large mat and clasp their opponent's hands. At a signal, each contestant, by pulling and pushing with his hands, attempts to win the bout by forcing his op-

ponent to touch some part of his body other than his knees to the mat. A match equals two out of three bouts.

INDIAN HAND WRESTLING—MODERATELY VIGOROUS ACTIVITY

The object is to force the opponent to move one or both feet from the starting position, or to touch a hand or any part of the body to the floor. The contestants face each other and grasp their opponent's right hand. Either of the following variations in starting position may be used: the outside edges of the contestants' right feet are placed alongside each other, with the contestants' left feet placed a comfortable distance behind them; or the contestants stand only on their right feet while holding their left feet off the floor. Each contestant attempts to maneuver or manipulate the hand of his opponent and force his opponent to move one of his feet. The contestant may not touch the floor with any part of his body or his hand (or his free foot if the second variation is used). After each bout the contestants should grasp with their opposite hands and reverse the position of their feet. A match consists of four out of seven bouts.

FOREARM WRESTLE, STANDING—MODERATELY VIGOROUS ACTIVITY (FIGURE 11-8)

The object is, without raising the elbow, to bend the opponent's right arm to his right (backward) an angle of 45 degrees from the vertical. The contestants face each other, clasp each other's right hands and grasp each other's right elbow with their left hand. With their forearms held in a verti-

Figure 11-8. Forearm wrestle, standing.

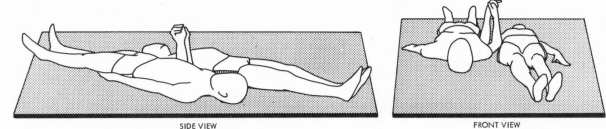

SIDE VIEW   FRONT VIEW

Figure 11-9. Forearm wrestle, supine.

cal position, each contestant attempts to force his opponent's forearm to his right until the forearm is at a 45 degree angle from the vertical. The contestant's left hand that is holding his opponent's elbow can be used for a fulcrum but not for applying force. The contestants clasp their opposite hands for each succeeding bout. A match equals two out of three bouts.

FOREARM WRESTLE, SUPINE—MODERATELY VIGOROUS
ACTIVITY (FIGURE 11-9)

The object is to force the opponent's forearm against the contestant's side. With their right sides adjacent to their opponent's right side and their feet pointing in opposite directions, the contestants lie on their backs with their heads in line with their opponent's waist. Keeping their right elbows on the floor and their forearms perpendicular to the floor, they clasp their right hands. Each contestant attempts to push his opponent's forearm to the left and against the contestant's side. After each bout the contestants alternate the hand clasped. A match equals two out of three bouts.

FOREARM WRESTLE, PRONE—MODERATELY VIGOROUS
ACTIVITY

The object is to so force the opponent's hand to the side that the back of the opponent's hand rests on the floor. Facing each other the contestants lie in a prone position on the floor. They clasp their right hands and block their opponent's right elbow by placing their left hands on the outside of the elbow. A common variation of this position is for the partners to sit in chairs that are placed on opposite sides of a small table. Each contestant attempts to push his opponent's forearm to the side until the back of his opponent's hand touches the floor or table. The contestants' right elbows must always be resting on the floor or on the surface of the

table. For succeeding bouts the contestants alternate the arms with which they push. A match equals two out of three bouts.

CUMBERLAND OR AMERICAN WRESTLING—EXTREMELY
VIGOROUS ACTIVITY (FIGURE 11-10)

The object is to lift the opponent off the floor. With chests touching, the contestants face each other. They place their left arms over their opponent's right shoulder, their right arms around their opponent's left side at waist level; and they clasp both hands. Upon the starting signal, each contestant attempts to lift his opponent's feet completely off the floor and thus win the bout. A match equals two out of three bouts.

SHOULDER PUSH-DOWN—VIGOROUS ACTIVITY

The object is to force the opponent's shoulder to the floor. With their arms and elbows interlocked, the contestants sit back-to-back on the floor. The right arm of each contestant is inside the left arm of his opponent. At the signal, each contestant attempts to force his opponent's left shoulder side-

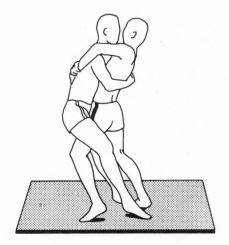

Figure 11-10. Cumberland or American wrestling.

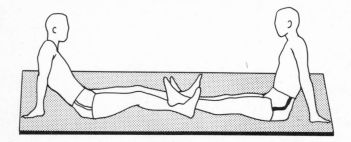

Figure 11-11. Leg force-up.

ways to the right until it touches the floor. For succeeding bouts the contestants alternate the position of their arms and the direction in which they apply force. A match equals two out of three bouts.

SEAT PUSH—VIGOROUS ACTIVITY

The contestants should wear rubber-soled shoes for this contest. The object is to stand up while preventing the opponent from standing up. With their legs bent, the heels of their feet placed near their buttocks, and the soles of their feet flat on the floor, the contestants sit back-to-back on the floor. Each contestant attempts to stand up and, at the same time, to push against his opponent's back in order to prevent him from standing up. A match equals two out of three bouts.

LEG FORCE-UP—MODERATELY VIGOROUS ACTIVITY
(FIGURE 11-11)

The object is for the contestant to lift the opponent's leg while preventing him from lifting the contestant's leg. With their feet spread and interlocked at the ankles—that is, with one ankle on top of the opponent's leg and with one ankle underneath the opponent's other leg—and with their hands placed on the floor behind their hips, the contestants sit on the floor facing each other. Each contestant attempts to lift his under-leg off the floor and simultaneously tries to prevent his opponent from doing the same thing. The contestants' arms may be used only to brace their trunks. A match equals two out of three bouts.

INDIAN LEG WRESTLING, SUPINE—VIGOROUS ACTIVITY

As a warm-up for this combative, the contestants should practice performing backward rolls and rocking-chair rock-ups from a prone position. The object is to force the opponent's leg down behind him, thus forcing him to roll over backwards. With their hips opposite one another and their heads

in opposite directions, the contestants lie side-by-side on the floor and interlock their right arms and elbows. Counting aloud to 3 and rhythmically raising and lowering their legs to the count, each contestant raises the leg nearest his opponent to a position slightly past a vertical position. When their legs are raised the third time, the contestant locks with his leg the heel or calf of his opponent's raised leg and attempts to push it to the floor, thus rolling the opponent over backward. The contestants change positions and alternate the leg raised for each succeeding bout. A match equals two out of three bouts.

FOOT PUSH—VIGOROUS ACTIVITY

The object is to extend the legs while preventing the opponent from straightening his legs. The contestants sit on the floor and face each other. They bend their legs at the knees, place the bottoms of their feet against those of their opponents, and place their hands on the floor adjacent to their hips. If the floor is slippery, the contestants may grasp each other's wrists. Each contestant attempts to straighten his legs while preventing his opponent from straightening his legs. A match equals two out of three bouts.

TUG-OF-WAR WRESTLING—VIGOROUS ACTIVITY
(FIGURE 11-12)

The object is to raise the opponent's body completely off the floor. The contestants sit facing each other on the floor and, with knees bent, place the soles of their feet against those of their opponents. They lean forward and clasp hands in an interlocking grasp. At a signal each contestant straightens his legs, pulls on his opponent's arms, and attempts to raise his opponent's buttocks off the floor. A match equals two out of three bouts.

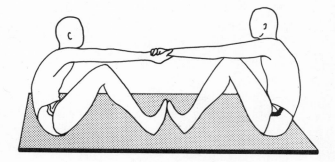

Figure 11-12. Tug-of-war wrestling.

12. apparatus and tumbling activities

The widespread inclusion of gymnastics in programs of physical education and the growing popularity of gymnastics competition attest to the value of gymnastics as a means of attaining or maintaining physical fitness, as well as to its wide appeal as a competitive event. Its appeal as a spectator sport is demonstrated by the fact that over 100,000 spectators periodically witness outdoor gymnastics exhibitions held in Europe. One of the probable reasons for the popularity of apparatus and tumbling activities is succinctly stated by the physical educator who wrote, "Gymnastics appeal to the monkey in our ancestry."

It is a common observation that most gymnasts possess remarkably well-developed physiques. Since the gymnastics performer's body serves as the resistance to his movements, he must manipulate a large load each time he performs a stunt and, hence, he regularly works against this large overload. Not only does regular participation in gymnastics develop the ordinarily neglected upper area of the body—especially the musculature of the arms and shoulder girdle—but vaulting, tumbling,

and trampolining activities develop the musculature of the legs as well.

Because of the large number and variety of gymnastics stunts, the enthusiast is continually challenged to learn new stunts. Thus, a sense of achievement is always present. If reasonable safety precautions are observed, little danger is involved in practicing most apparatus and tumbling activities. The small risk that is present alerts the performer to the possibility of an accident and adds significantly to the challenge of practicing and performing gymnastics activites.

Some of the gymnastics activities included in this chapter are not included in gymnastics competition. However, activities performed on such equipment as climbing poles, low horizontal bars, horizontal ladders, peg climbers, climbing ropes and traveling rings, as well as participation in balancing stunts and side horse vaulting, aid in developing a high degree of physical fitness.

For ease in planning a diversified program for all-around development, the activities contained in this chapter are grouped under one of three categories. The reader should understand that these are in part categories of convenience to aid him in planning his gymnastics workout, and that while the activity best belongs under the category in which it is placed, some of the stunts in any given category could be listed under one or both of the other categories.

1. Hanging-type activities.
2. Support-type activities.
3. Activities for developing legs and circulorespiratory endurance.

Under each of these categories, three or more different kinds of apparatus and tumbling activities are listed.

To provide a complete workout, stunts performed from both the supporting and hanging positions, stunts that require extensive use of the muscles of the legs, and stunts that place demands on the circulorespiratory mechanisms should be included in the gymnastics workout. A complete gymnastics workout will particularly aid in developing and enhancing the following qualities of physical fitness: strength, muscular endurance, flexibility, neuromuscular skill, agility, and balance. In addition, circulorespiratory endurance and speed of movement may be developed to a more-than-average degree. However, activities other than gymnastics that specifically and primarily aid in the development of these components of physical fitness should not be neglected in the workout.

The stunts that are listed under each activity are placed in the approximate order of difficulty of performance, according to the amount of timing and coordination required and the complexity of the movements involved. The easiest stunts are presented first and the most difficult ones are presented last. Stunts for which strength alone is the primary requisite to successful performance are not listed according to difficulty. If one is sufficiently strong, a one-arm pull-up or chin is easy; otherwise it is impossible.

The directions for performing stunts that can be done in more than one way are given for a right-handed and right-footed performer. The left-handed or left-footed performer should reverse the directions. The most common or the most descriptive name has been given to each stunt. For practically all apparatus stunts, the thumbs-around grip, in which the thumb encircles the apparatus in a direction opposite to that of the fingers, should be used.

SAFETY IN GYMNASTICS

The performer should practice the simple apparatus and tumbling stunts before attempting the stunts of increased difficulty. Gaining a mastery of the elementary stunts will prepare the performer for those that demand increased strength, timing, coordination, and an understanding of how to perform them. Before performing hazardous or strenuous gymnastics stunts, the performer should warm up by performing a few exercises and easier stunts.

Since certain apparatus and tumbling activities can be hazardous during the learning stage, or when they are performed hurriedly or carelessly, spotters should be available to assist and safeguard the performer during their execution.

Before performing stunts on gymnastics apparatus, the performer should rub the palms of his hands with carbonate of magnesium chalk, in order to avoid the possibility of their becoming moist from sweat, which makes it extremely difficult for him to retain his grasp during his performance. Carbonate of magnesium chalk also provides the correct amount of friction for the grip, and thus minimizes the possibility of tearing the skin of the palms when tightly gripping the apparatus. Loose clothing, especially loose-fitting sleeves or pants legs, should not be worn, because they may wrap around the apparatus during circling stunts or get in the way of the hands and cause an accident.

HANGING-TYPE ACTIVITIES

Hanging-type activities not only help to develop the musculature of the upper arms, shoulders, and chest, but also aid in developing the *lastisimus dorsi* muscles that contribute to a V-type appearance of the upper back. Mats should always be placed under the apparatus on which hanging-type activities are performed.

Climbing Rope

Rope climbing promotes the development of a strong grip. When climbing the rope, one must climb down as well as up, because sliding down the

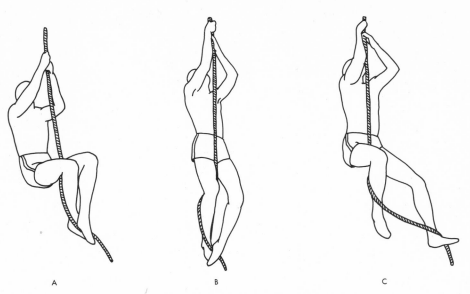

Figure 12-1. Leg wrap-around climb using leg lock.

rope will produce painful burns on the palms and fingers. Therefore, the rope climber should not overestimate his climbing ability, and should stop his ascent before he becomes overly fatigued. To increase the overload, the rope climber may climb at an increased speed, for an increased distance, an increased number of times, or without using his legs.

LEG WRAP-AROUND CLIMB USING LEG LOCK (FIGURE 12-1)

Grasping the rope with both hands in an overhead position, the performer stands with the rope between his legs. The rope is wrapped around his right leg and rests on top of his right instep. He flexes at the hips and knees and raises his legs, allowing the rope to glide around his right leg and foot. With the sole of his left foot he steps on the rope where it crosses his right instep. He straightens his body and flexes his arms. Then, one hand at a time, he transfers his hands to an overhead position. He continues to repeat the climbing procedure until he has climbed to the desired height. He reverses this procedure when climbing down the rope.

STIRRUP CLIMB USING FOOT LOCK (FIGURE 12-2)

Facing the rope, the performer stands with the rope alongside his right side, outside his right leg,

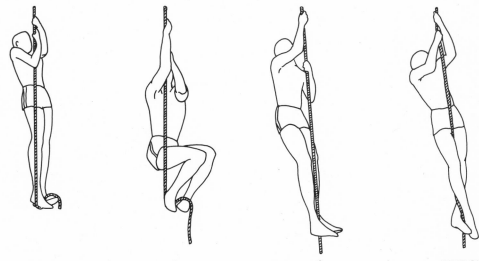

Figure 12-2. Stirrup climb using foot lock.

passing underneath his right foot, and over the instep of his left foot. He grasps the rope with both hands in an overhead position. He does a pull-up on the rope and, by flexing at his hips and knees, raises his legs—keeping them out in front of his body—allowing the rope to glide over his left foot. He then squeezes the sole of his right foot against the rope and the instep of his left foot in order to apply the foot lock. He shifts his hands, one at a time, to the overhead position, and then repeats the climbing procedure. To climb down, he lowers his legs with his feet slightly spread, in order to allow the rope to slide freely. He then clamps his feet together in the foot lock and, one hand at a time, moves his hands down the rope to a position in front of his chest.

SCISSORS CLIMB

Facing the rope, the performer stands and grasps the rope with his hands in an overhead position. The rope passes between his legs. He climbs the rope by pulling up until his hands are in front of his chest, raising his legs, and clamping or squeezing the rope with his thighs, calves, and feet. His left lower leg and foot are crossed in front of his right lower leg and foot. He repeats this process until he has climbed the desired height.

HANDS-ALONE CLIMB FROM STANDING POSITION

Grasping the rope with his hands in an overhead position, the performer stands with the rope positioned directly in front of him and passing between his legs. As he jumps upward, he pulls with both hands and flexes both arms as much as possible. He then releases his grasp with his bottom hand and quickly regrasps the rope as high as possible above the other hand. The performer may execute any of the following leg actions to benefit from the action-reaction that results:

1. Swings both legs upward simultaneously, flexing at the hips and knees, and flexing the arms as the legs swing upward. At the height of the forward leg swing, the bottom hand is raised as high as possible.
2. As the left leg is raised, lower the right leg and raise the left arm and hand as high as possible.
3. As the left leg is raised the right leg is lowered, and the right arm and hand are raised as high as possible.

HANDS-ALONE CLIMB FROM SITTING POSITION

With the rope passing between his legs, the performer sits on the mat in a position directly below the rope. His legs are spread, his arms are stretched overhead, and his body is leaning slightly backward. Without pushing off with his feet at the start, using an arm pull only, the performer climbs hand-over-hand, using his legs in any of the three ways previously described.

Peg Climber

The peg climber is a vertically mounted board that contains two rows of holes which are spaced from six to fifteen inches apart. The holes are from one to one-and-a-half inches in diameter, and are located six to twelve inches above one another. The pegs are wooden handles approximately one inch in diameter and twelve inches long, which are inserted in the holes at a slight upward angle from the horizontal. A wooden ladder, with self-locking handles that slide, may be used in the same manner as the peg climber, except that the ladder may be mounted at less than a 90-degree angle.

PEG CLIMBING (FIGURE 12-3)

With his body and arms straight, the performer grips the pegs. Grasping a peg in each hand, he does a pull-up and attempts to hold himself in this raised position with his right hand while he pulls the other peg out and inserts it in a higher hole with his left hand. He then pulls up and attempts to hold this position with his left hand while he pulls the lower peg out and puts it in the next

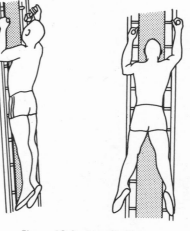

Figure 12-3. Peg climbing.

higher hole with his right hand. The performer should restrict his climbing to the first four to six holes until he is able to travel up and down this limited course several times without loss of control because of muscular fatigue. The feet may be used to grip the sides of the climber as an aid in holding the one-arm position, but in this case a spotter should *always* stand behind the climber.

Climbing Poles

Climbing poles are two vertical metal poles, usually from one-and-a-half to two inches in diameter, that are placed parallel to each other at a distance of two to three feet. Climbing poles are generally considered to be easier to climb than a climbing rope. The poles do not sway and, by pulling inward on each pole, decreased grip strength is needed to retain the grasp on the poles. Although the hands will not be burned while sliding down climbing poles, the safest method of descending is by climbing down.

HANDS-AND-LEGS CLIMB: FEET OUTSIDE POLES (FIGURE 12-4)

With his arms overhead and with his feet positioned outside of the poles, the performer stands between the poles and grasps one pole with each hand. He pulls with his arms and raises his legs. He then squeezes his feet against the outside portion of the poles and straightens his legs while sliding his hands upward. Both hands may be moved upward at the same time, or one hand may be moved upward while the other grasps the pole.

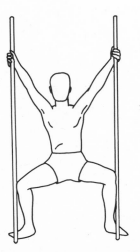

Figure 12-4. Hands-and-legs climb: feet outside poles.

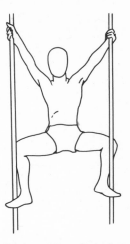

Figure 12-5. Hands-and-legs climb: feet inside poles.

HANDS-AND-LEGS CLIMB: FEET INSIDE POLES (FIGURE 12-5)

With his arms overhead, the performer stands between the poles and grasps one pole with each hand. He pulls up with his arms and raises his legs by flexing them. He spreads his legs vigorously and braces his feet against the inside of the poles before sliding his hands upward, moving one hand at a time. He then extends his legs and raises his body. He continues to climb by repeating these actions.

SCISSORS CLIMB ON ONE POLE

Facing one pole with his arms extended overhead, the performer grasps the pole with both hands. He climbs the pole by pulling up to a position in which his chest is in front of his hands. He next raises his legs and squeezes them around the pole in a scissors-like fashion. He straightens his legs and body and slides, one hand at a time or both hands simultaneously, to an overhead position on the pole. He repeats these actions as he continues to climb the pole.

SQUEEZE CLIMB ON ONE POLE

Facing the pole, the performer grasps the pole with both hands in an overhead position. He climbs the pole by pulling up to a position in which his chest is in front of his hands. He next raises his legs, spreads his thighs, and squeezes the soles of his feet against the pole. He straightens his legs and slides, one hand at a time or both hands simultaneously, to an overhead position on the pole.

HANDS-ALONE CLIMB

With one hand on each pole, the performer stands between the poles. He climps the poles by pulling with both arms and then gripping the pole with one hand while he reaches up the other pole with the other hand, grips it, and pulls himself up. As he moves his hand upward, he may swing both legs upward or swing one leg upward while the other leg scissors downward. When climbing, he may also swing his legs and body from side to side, moving the hand that is on the side toward which the legs are swinging upward.

HANDS-ALONE CLIMB ON ONE POLE

With both hands overhead and grasping the pole, the performer stands in front of the pole. He climbs the pole by pulling up with both arms and gripping the pole with one hand while he reaches up with the other hand to obtain a higher grasp, from which position he again pulls up with both arms. His legs are extended and his body is straight or slightly arched.

Horizontal or Overhead Ladder

The horizontal or overhead ladder is mounted parallel to the floor and usually one to two feet above the reach of the performers. It has two side rails or runners, and either fixed or revolvable rungs that are spaced from twelve to twenty inches apart.

TRAVEL ON ONE RAIL OF LADDER

The performer hangs at arm's length at the end of one rail of the horizontal ladder. By swinging both legs together or by spreading his legs and scissoring them with each movement, he moves from one end of the ladder to the other, using any of the following variations:

1. Moving sideward by sliding one hand at a time along the rail.
2. Moving forward hand-over-hand.
3. Moving backward hand-over-hand.

TRAVEL ON BOTH RAILS OF LADDER

Grasping both rails, the performer hangs at arm's length at one end of the horizontal ladder. By swinging both legs forward simultaneously or by swinging one leg forward at a time, the performer traverses the ladder, using one of the following methods:

1. Moving forward by sliding or moving one hand at a time.
2. Moving backward by sliding or moving one hand at a time.

TRAVEL ON RUNGS OF LADDER

The performer hangs at arm's length on one rung at the end of the ladder. By swinging the legs and body forward simultaneously or by swinging one leg forward at a time, he traverses the ladder, using one of the following methods:

1. Moving forward by bringing the rear hand forward to the same rung that is grasped with the front hand.
2. Moving forward by bringing the rear hand to one rung past that held by the front hand.
3. Moving forward by bringing the rear hand two rungs past the front hand.
4. Moving backward by bringing the front hand to the same rung that is grasped with the rear hand.
5. Moving backward by bringing the front hand one rung past the rear hand.
6. Moving backward by bringing the front hand two rungs past the rear hand.

Traveling Rings

Traveling rings are a series of single rings suspended by straps from the ceiling and spaced approximately ten to fifteen feet apart. The height of each ring from the floor is adjustable and each ring should be adjusted to a position slightly above the standing performer's reach. In performing on the rings, an overload is obtained by increasing the distance traveled (number of trips back and forth), the time spent in grasping the rings, or the height of the arc of each swing.

SWINGING BETWEEN TWO RINGS

The performer grasps one ring in each hand. Retaining his grasp on each ring, he swings from side to side by pulling on the ring toward which he is swinging.

HAND-OVER-HAND TRAVEL FORWARD (FIGURE 12-6)

Standing between the two end rings, the performer grasps the rear ring with his left hand and the front ring with his right hand. He swings backward by flexing his left arm at the elbow and by extending his right arm. As he swings forward he

Figure 12-6. Hand-over-hand travel forward.

releases the rear ring with his left hand and, retaining his grasp with his right hand, continues to swing forward to a position from which he can grasp the next ring with his left hand. He continues to swing from ring to ring, facing the direction of his travel.

HAND-OVER-HAND TRAVEL BACKWARD

Standing between the two end rings and facing somewhat in the direction of the end ring, the performer grasps the end ring with his left hand and the front ring with his right hand. He then swings forward toward the end ring by flexing his left arm at the elbow and by extending his right arm. He swings backward and releases the end ring with his left hand. Retaining his grasp with his right hand, he swings backward and grasps the next ring with his left hand. He continues to swing from ring to ring, facing backward to the direction of travel.

HAND-OVER-HAND TRAVEL WITH FULL CIRCLE

Standing between the two end rings, the performer grasps the end ring with his left hand and the front ring with his right hand. He swings backward by flexing his left arm at the elbow and by extending his right arm. He then swings forward and lets go of the back ring with his left hand. Retaining his grasp with his right hand, he turns his body 360 degrees during the forward swing and grasps the next ring with his left hand. He continues to swing from ring to ring, executing a full circle between rings. A variation is to face back-

ward to the direction of travel each time after completing the full circle.

Low Horizontal Bar

A low horizontal bar is a metal bar, six to eight feet in length and usually one inch in diameter. It is placed parallel to the floor and about waist height above the floor, but this height may range from thirty inches to six feet. Except for vaulting stunts, which are presented in the section on vaulting and tumbling activities, all the stunts that are performed on the low horizontal bar can also be performed on the high horizontal bar, which is seven to eight feet above the floor. However, certain horizontal bar stunts can be learned and performed with increased safety, ease of spotting, and confidence, if first practiced on a low horizontal bar.

Three different types of grasps, similar to those employed in weight training, are used when performing on the horizontal bar. The grasp most commonly used is the regular or overhand grasp. For this grasp, when the hands are overhead the palms of the hand face the same direction that the performer faces. The reverse or underhand grasp is sometimes used. For this grasp, when the hands are overhead the palms of the hands face backward. The mixed grasp, in which one hand is in the regular grasp position and the other hand is in the reverse grasp position, is used least of all.

For increased gripping power when performing horizontal bar stunts, the thumb is always wrapped around the bar in the direction opposite to that of the fingers. It is important to rub a liberal amount of chalk on the palms when performing stunts on the horizontal bar. For all circling stunts, the performer should maintain a tight grip on the bar. In the event that he does not successfully complete a stunt, he should flex his body and stay as close to the bar as possible, in order to inhibit his swinging motion.

SINGLE KNEE SWING-UP (FIGURE 12-7)

Facing the bar, the performer grasps it with a regular or overhand grasp, raises his right leg upward, passes it between his arms, and hooks the back of his right knee over the bar. Keeping his arms straight, he swings his free extended leg in as wide an arc as possible. As his body reaches the rearmost part of the swing and his left leg is

Figure 12-7. Single knee swing-up.

whipped downward, the performer pulls in toward the bar with his arms, flexes his head toward the bar, swings, and pulls his body to an erect sitting position on his right leg on top of the bar. Standing to one side, the spotter places his hands around one of the performer's shoulders as he starts his circle to the top of the bar. The spotter should be prepared for the possibility that the performer does not stop his motion but continues to swing forward past the bar.

AIRPLANE SPIN OR CROUCH CIRCLE (FIGURE 12-8)

With a mixed grasp on the bar a few inches in

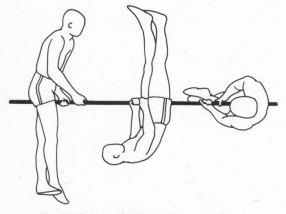

Figure 12-8. Airplane spin or crouch circle.

front of his hips, the performer sits in a straddle position on the bar. Holding his legs straight, he interlocks his legs by crossing them at the ankles. Sitting as straight as possible, he leans to one side and circles the bar, crouching slightly forward as he comes around and up to his starting position. The performer must be alert and retain his grasp if he does not complete the circle and falls back to the side, or if he overshoots the circle. One or two spotters may stand on either side and behind the performer to assist him to come to a sitting position on top of the bar.

BACK HIP PULL-OVER (FIGURE 12-9)

The performer grasps the bar in a regular grasp, flexes and raises his legs to a position between his arms, extends his legs upward, and places the backs of his legs against the near side of the bar. His back is arched, his head is back, and his arms are straight. By flexing his arms while arching his back, he pulls his body over the bar until his buttocks pass over the bar at which time he assumes a sitting position on top of the bar. To dismount, he takes a reverse grasp with his right hand, pivots around by making a half turn to the right, and regrasps with his left hand so that he is in a front-support position with his abdominal area

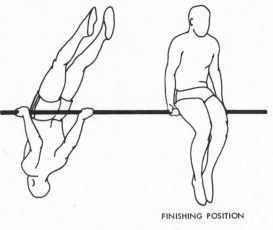

FINISHING POSITION

Figure 12-9. Back hip pull-over.

resting against the bar. He then lowers to a standing position.

The difficulty sometimes encountered in performing this stunt is to keep the center of gravity of the body on the side of the bar opposite to the body during the pull-up stage. If the performer loses his balance during the pull-up, and his body swings backward, he should retain his grasp and tuck his body. If he overbalances in coming to the

sitting position, he may either do a quick half twist to a front-support position, or he may quickly extend his body, push on the bar with his hands, and with his body slightly arched, land on his feet in front of the bar.

BACKWARD HIP CIRCLE (FIGURE 12-10)

The performer is in a front-support position on the bar, with his lower abdomen resting against the bar. His body is straight and he grasps the bar with a regular grasp. Leaning slightly forward, he flexes his hips, bringing his legs forward, and extends his legs and pushes his hips a few inches away from the bar. He pulls his hips into the bar and, as they contact the bar, vigorously pikes his legs forward and throws his head backward. By pulling with his arms, he holds his body tightly against the bar and executes a backward circle, returning to a bent-arm support with the bar located between his waist and hips.

BACKWARD SINGLE-KNEE CIRCLE (FIGURE 12-11)

Using a regular grasp, the performer sits on the bar with his right leg in front of and his extended left leg behind the bar. By extending his arms, he

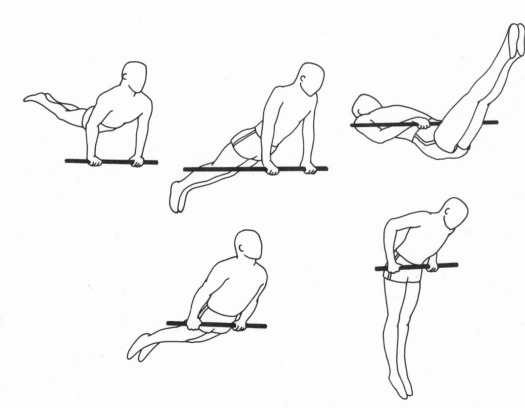

Figure 12-10. Backward hip circle.

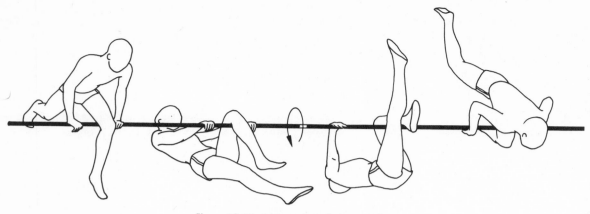

Figure 12-11. Backward single-knee circle.

raises his body and hips. He places the back of his right knee against the bar, while flexing his right lower leg as much as possible. He casts his body and head backward and, as his body swings under and starts upward in front of the bar, flexes his hips and arms slightly, swinging back up to the starting position. The spotter stands next to the bar and to one side of the performer in order to steady him as he returns to the starting position. If the performer goes past the starting position, he may either do another complete circle or he may tuck his body and remain in an upsidedown position. If the performer fails to do a complete circle, he should sharply flex his body and wrists, in order to retain his grasp as he rotates backward to an upsidedown position.

FORWARD SINGLE-KNEE CIRCLE

The starting position for this stunt is the same as that for the backward single-knee circle, except that the reverse or underhand grasp is used. The performer casts his trunk and head forward and downward and, as his body starts swinging upward, flexes his hips and arms slightly, swinging to the starting position. The spotter stands next to the bar and to one side of the performer in order to steady him as he returns to the starting position. If the performer circles past the starting position, he may either do another complete circle or he may tuck his body and flex his wrists in order to return safely to an upsidedown position.

High Horizontal Bar

All the stunts listed for the low horizontal bar may also be performed on the high horizontal bar.

HANG VARIATIONS: STRAIGHT-ARM HANG

Using either the reverse or the regular grasp, the performer hangs at arm's length below the bar. He remains in this position until fatigue causes him to release his grasp, at which time he drops to the mat.

HANG VARIATIONS: BENT-ARM HANG

Using either the reverse or the regular grasp, the performer pulls himself up so that his upper arms are parallel with the floor. When he is unable to maintain his upper arms in a position parallel to the floor, he releases his grasp and drops to the mat.

PULL-UP VARIATION (REGULAR)

Using either a regular or reverse grasp, the performer hangs at arm's length below the bar. The performer usually takes a shoulder-width grip on the bar, but he may utilize a narrow or a very wide grip. By flexing his arms, he pulls himself up until his chin rises above the level of the bar. He lowers his body to the starting position and repeats the pull-up action as many times as possible. The performer should avoid kipping or swinging his body, or kicking his legs, as he pulls up to the bar.

PULL-UP VARIATION: BACK OF NECK (FIGURE 12-12)

The regular or overhand grasp is usually employed for back-of-neck pull-ups, and a wider-than-shoulder-width grip is recommended. The performer repeats the actions that are performed for a regular pull-up, except that as he pulls up he thrusts his head forward and touches the back of his neck to the bar.

Figure 12-12. Pull-up variation: back of neck.

PULL-UP VARIATION: ONE HAND ON UPRIGHT
(FIGURE 12-13)

Using either grasp, the performer hangs at arm's length, with one hand grasping the horizontal bar about two feet from an upright. He grasps the vertical upright with his other hand. The lower the position below the horizontal bar that the hand is placed on the upright, the more strength required to perform the pull-up. By pulling with the hand grasping the horizontal bar, and first pulling and then pushing with the hand grasping the upright, he does a pull-up.

PULL-UP VARIATION: HAND AND ONE FINGER

Using a mixed, reverse, or regular grasp, the performer hangs at arm's length below the bar. He grips the bar with one hand and the middle finger of the other hand. He does as many regular pull-ups as possible. This type of pull-up can be performed with increased ease if a mixed grasp is used and if the hand grasping the bar is the dominant or stronger arm.

PULL-UP VARIATION: ONE HAND

Using a reverse grasp, the performer hangs by

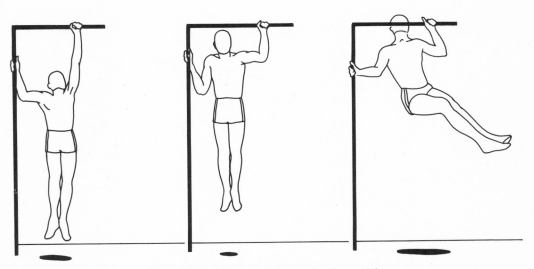

Figure 12-13. Pull-up variation: one hand on upright.

one arm at arm's length below the bar, with his body facing partially sideways. By flexing his arm, he pulls up until his chin is level with the bar. He lowers to the starting position and continues to do one-arm pull-ups as long as he is able.

SKIN THE CAT AND RETURN

Using a reverse grasp, the performer hangs at arm's length below the bar. He tucks his legs, raises them, passes them between his arms and under the bar; then he lowers them as far as possible behind his body. He returns to the starting position and repeats this movement as many times as possible.

MONKEY HANG

The performer hangs below the bar, using a regular grasp. He tucks his legs, raises them between his arms, and then slowly lowers them behind him, extending his body as far as possible. He releases his grasp with his left hand and, while gripping the bar with only his right hand, rotates his body a full turn of 360 degrees. He regrasps the bar with his left hand and dismounts by dropping to a standing position.

DOUBLE-LEG RAISE (FIGURE 12-14)

Using a regular grasp, the performer hangs below the bar with his body in an extended position. With both legs extended, he flexes his hips and raises his legs, attempting to touch his insteps to the bar. If possible, the performer should avoid kipping or swinging his body when raising his legs. He slowly lowers his legs to a straight body position and then repeats the leg raises. If the performer can not do a double-leg raise, he raises only one leg as high as possible.

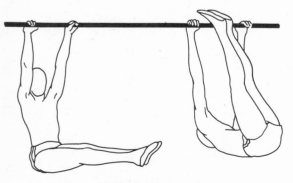

Figure 12-14. Double-leg raise.

HALF LEVER OR "L" POSITION

From a hanging position below the bar, with his legs extended, the performer flexes his hips and raises both legs until they are parallel to the floor. He holds this position as long as possible.

FRONT HIP PULL-OVER (BELLY GRINDER) (FIGURE 12-15)

Using either a regular or a reverse grasp, the performer assumes a hanging position below the bar. He pulls upward by flexing his arms and, at the same time, raises his extended legs to the bar by flexing his hips. He extends his head backward and continues to pull up, sliding his legs up and over the bar until he attains a front-support position on the bar. He returns to a hanging position by reversing these actions. He performs as many front hip pull-overs as possible.

BACK LEVER (FIGURE 12-16)

Using a reverse or underhand grasp, the performer hangs in an extended position below the bar. He tucks his body and raises his legs between his arms. He slowly extends his legs directly behind him, to a position in which his slightly arched body is parallel to the floor. In this position, his hands should be located directly above his hips or at the small of his back. He holds this position as long as possible and then tucks his body and returns to the starting position, or he may go to a skin-the-cat position and then drop to the mat.

SINGLE-ARM MUSCLE-UP (FIGURE 12-17)

The performer hangs below the bar in an extended position, using a regular grasp. As quickly as possible, he does a pull-up, flexing his legs at the beginning and quickly extending them at the completion of the pull-up movement, when he quickly shifts his right arm to a support position by raising his elbow directly over his hand. He quickly shifts his left arm to a support position, and pushes his body upward by extending his arm, so that he comes to a front-support position on the high bar. The performer should keep his body as close to the bar as possible during the muscle-up. If the performer has sufficient strength, he does not need to kip his legs during the muscle-up. He performs as many single-arm muscle-ups as possible.

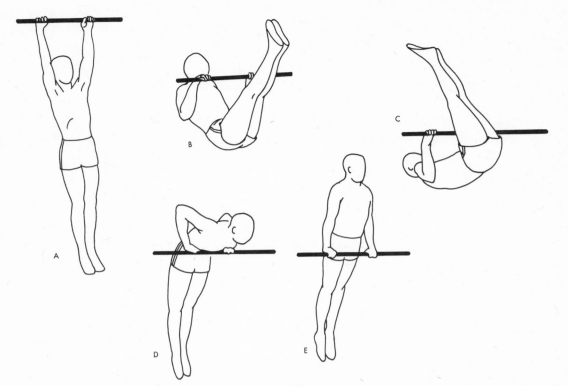

Figure 12-15. Front hip pull-over (belly grinder).

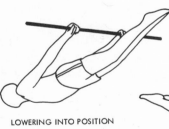

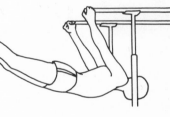

LOWERING INTO POSITION

Figure 12-16. Back lever.

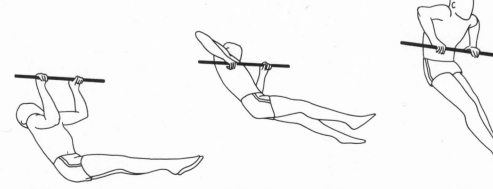

Figure 12-17. Single-arm muscle-up.

Still Rings

The performer executes stunts on the still rings by holding his body in certain positions or by moving his body in swinging-type movements. Considerable strength, timing, coordination, and practice are required before the performer can execute any but the most elementary stunts on the still rings. For most still-ring stunts the palms of the hands face each other, or the hands are held in a regular grasp position. All the stunts, except the first one, may be performed on rings that are only five or six feet high, in order to minimize the chance of an accident. A spotter may stand to one side of the performer and steady him, give assistance, or be ready to support his upper body in case he falls.

HANG AND SWING

With his body in an extended position, the performer hangs from the rings and, by flexing and extending his legs at the hips and his trunk at the shoulders, swings his body in any of the following ways:

1. Back-and-forth swinging.
2. Side-to-side swinging.
3. Circular swinging, in which the above two motions are combined.

INVERTED HANG

From a hanging position, the performer pikes or tucks his body and raises his body and legs to a vertical position between his arms. He holds this position, keeping his upper body straight or slightly arched, while he looks down at the floor.

BASKET (FIGURE 12-18)

The performer raises his body to an inverted position and then pikes his body as sharply as pos-

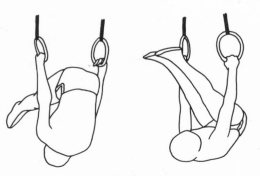

Figure 12-18. Basket.

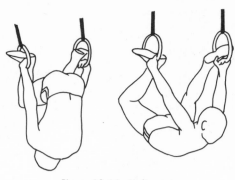

Figure 12-19. Bird's nest.

sible, keeping his legs together and his feet and toes pointed backward. His head is in line with his trunk, so that he is looking upward toward his shins.

BIRD'S NEST (FIGURE 12-19)

The performer pulls up into a basket position and then inserts each foot into a ring. He pushes his hips to the other side of the rings, until the abdominal area of his trunk faces the floor and is parallel to it.

SINGLE LEG (KNEE) ROCK-UP (FIGURE 12-20)

From a basket position, the performer rocks his body forward by extending his legs forward and downward. His left leg passes between his arms and swings downward, while the back of the knee of the right leg is hooked over the right forearm. He presses his head and body forward and lifts his body, by pulling with his right arm and pushing with his left, until it is supported in an erect sitting position on his right forearm. He then slowly rolls backward into a basket position. The performance of this stunt is facilitated by first doing a few rocking movements while in the basket position.

MUSCLE-UP (FIGURE 12-21)

The performer assumes a hanging position, with his hands in a false grasp, in which the ring passes from the butt of the thumb, along the heel of the hand, and as close as possible to the wrist. He pulls up as quickly as possible, piking his body. When his shoulders are even with his hands, he extends his body and changes his hands from a hanging to a support position by flexing his wrists and raising his elbows to a position above his hands. Then he

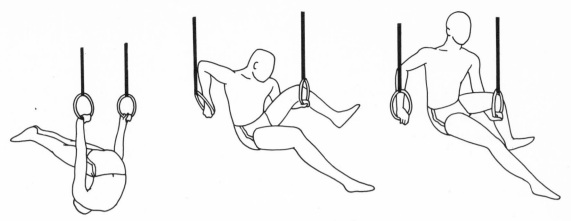

Figure 12-20. Single leg (knee) rock-up.

leans forward, extends his arms, and places his hands alongside the rear of his hips. To dismount, he slowly lowers his body to a hanging position and then drops to the mat.

OTHER STILL-RING STUNTS

Other stunts that may be performed on the still rings are leg raises, half-levers, and back levers. The same techniques should be employed as were used when performing these stunts on the horizontal bar.

SUPPORT-TYPE ACTIVITIES

Support-type activities are valuable for developing the triceps muscle of the arm as well as the muscles of the shoulders, chest, upper back, and abdominal area. Mats should be placed under the apparatus on which support-type activities are performed.

Balancing Stunts

The balancing stunts included in this section are designed to be performed by one man on a grassy area, the floor, or on a mat. A mat is preferable if it is available. During the learning stages, the performer can benefit by being steadied by another person, but this is not necessary. When performing balancing stunts, it is essential that the performer keep his center of gravity directly over and within his area of support. For example, in a head-and-hand balance, the area of support is the triangular area that lies within the lines connecting the left hand, right hand, and head.

Figure 12-21. Muscle-up.

Figure 12-22. Squat hand balance.

SQUAT HAND BALANCE (FIGURE 12-22)

The performer squats with his arms bent between his legs, and places his hands—fingers spread and pointing straight ahead—on the mat. Keeping his head up so that he continues to look forward, the performer places his right lower leg on his right upper arm, just above the elbow. He places his left leg on his left arm in a similar manner, and balances in this position as long as possible. Movement of the head controls the balance; however, if the performer starts forward, he should push hard with his fingertips.

HEAD-AND-HAND BALANCE: HEAD STAND

The performer squats, bends over, and places the top of his forehead on the mat about eighteen inches in front of his hands, which are spread about eighteen inches apart. The fingers of his hands point forward. He raises one leg, which is semi-flexed, directly over his hips and then raises the other leg alongside the first. He extends his legs and arches his body slightly. Less than half of the performer's body weight should be supported by his hands. If the performer starts to fall on his back, he should tuck-up and do a forward roll. If he starts to fall on his stomach, he should press hard with his arms; but if he continues to fall, he should tuck his body and land on his feet.

Figure 12-23. Forearm stand.

FOREARM STAND (FIGURE 12-23)

The performer squats, leans forward, and places his forearms and palms on the mat. His forearms are parallel to each other and spread about shoulder-width apart. Kicking one leg upward at a time, he raises his legs overhead and assumes a slightly arched position. His head is facing forward at all times. If he falls forward, he should arch his body and place his feet on the mat, while supporting his weight on his forearms. If he falls backward, he should flex one leg and place his foot on the mat.

TWO-ARM LEVER (FIGURE 12-24)

The performer kneels, leans forward, and places his hands, fingers pointing outward, about twelve inches in front of his knees. His hands are spread ten to twelve inches apart. He leans forward and raises his legs off the floor, supporting his weight on his hands while holding his elbows tightly against his sides. He attempts to keep his body slightly arched and approximately parallel to the floor.

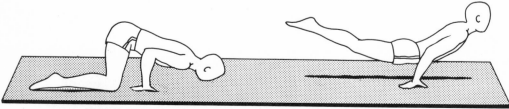

STARTING POSITION

Figure 12-24. Two-arm lever.

HANDSTAND OR HAND BALANCE

The performer places his left foot about two feet in front of his right foot, bends his left leg, leans forward and places his hands, fingers pointing straight ahead, directly below his shoulders. He kicks his right leg to an overhead position and brings his left leg alongside his right. His head faces forward so that his body is extended and slightly arched. If he starts to overbalance, he should either press hard with his fingers, take a step forward with one hand, or pivot around on one hand and land on his feet, facing the opposite direction. If he starts to underbalance, he should either bend his arms slightly in order to lower his center of gravity, or lower one flexed leg to the floor. In learning the handstand, the performer should first practice in a corner, then against a wall, and then in an open space. Having someone hold the legs when in a handstand position is a helpful learning aid. A variation of the handstand is to slightly overbalance and then walk forward with the hands, taking small steps.

PRESS FROM HEADSTAND TO HANDSTAND

From a headstand position, the performer underbalances so that his weight is mainly supported on his hands. He presses with his arms, raising his head forward as soon as possible, until he is in a handstand position. To lessen the difficulty of this stunt, the performer can tuck his legs and then kick upward, as he begins the pressing movement to a handstand.

OTHER BALANCING STUNTS

The half-lever stunt, which was described in the section on high horizontal-bar activities, may be performed from a sitting position on the floor.

Parallel Bars

Spotters are not needed when performing the stunts described in this section. For the stunts described below, except for the sloth walk and the inverted hand walk, the thumb should encircle the bars in a direction opposite to that of the fingers. As an added safety precaution, the stunts may be performed with the bars set at less than five feet high.

HAND-TRAVEL VARIATIONS (FIGURE 12-25)

When performing hand travels on the parallel bars, the performer assumes a straight-arm cross-support position (in which the body is perpendicular to the bars) between and at the end of the bars. For inverted walks, he assumes a cross-support position, with his body in an inverted-hang position. He moves from one end of the bars to the other end, by means of one of the following variations.

1. Forward hand walk.
2. Backward hand walk.
3. Forward double-hand jump, swinging both legs forward during each jump.
4. Sloth walk (the hands and legs are inside the bars, with the body in an inverted position in which the abdominal area faces the floor).

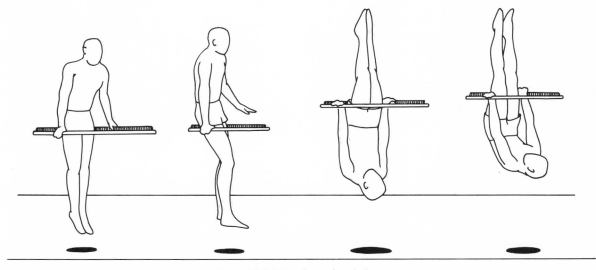

Figure 12-25. Hand-travel variations.

5. Hand walk while in an inverted position.

STATIONARY DIPS

The performer takes a straight-arm cross-support position on the end of the bars. By flexing his arms, he lowers his body as low as possible, and then raises it until his arms are extended. He repeats the dipping movement a specified number of times, or as many times as possible.

SWINGING ON PARALLEL BARS

From a straight-arm cross-support position on the end of the bars, the performer, primarily by swinging his legs back and forth, swings his body back and forth while keeping his arms straight. A more advanced type of swinging motion is to keep the body straight or slightly arched and to originate the swinging action from the shoulders.

FORWARD-SWINGING DIPS

The performer takes a straight-arm cross-support position at the end of the bars. He swings his body back and forth, and, at the end of the backward swing, he lowers his body and touches his shoulders to the bars by flexing his arms. His body continues to swing in a forward direction and, toward the end of the forward swing, he raises his body by extending his arms. He repeats the swinging dip movement a specified number of times, or as many times as possible.

BACKWARD-SWINGING DIPS

The performer takes a straight-arm cross-support position at the end of the bars and then swings his body back and forth. At the end of the forward swing, he lowers his shoulders to the bar by flexing his arms. His body continues to swing in a backward direction and, toward the end of the backward swing, he raises his body by extending his arms.

DOUBLE-SWINGING DIPS

From a cross-support position at the end of the bars, the performer swings his body back and forth. On each forward swing he does a forward-swinging dip, and on each backward swing he does a backward-swinging dip.

OTHER PARALLEL-BAR STUNTS

The following stunts, which were described in previous sections of this chapter, may also be performed on the parallel bars.

1. Leg raises.
2. Half-lever.
3. Single-arm muscle-up on end of bars.

Side Horse

The side-horse stunts listed in this section are quite safe to attempt, and no spotter is needed. When performing support stunts on the side horse, the arms should always be completely extended and the shoulders should remain directly over the point of support on the side horse.

SINGLE-LEG HALF-CIRCLE AND RETURN: LEG CUT

From a front support position with his thighs resting against the side horse, the performer swings both legs to the left; this action is termed a *feint*. On the return swing, he swings his extended right leg to the right, raises it, and brings it forward over the end and on the far side of the horse. He releases his right hand (his weight is momentarily supported on his left arm) and brings his extended right leg in front of the center of the horse. He regrasps the right pommel with his right hand, reverses his actions, and returns his right leg to the starting position. He reverses the direction of the above actions and does a leg cut with his left leg.

FULL SINGLE-LEG CIRCLE (FIGURE 12-26)

From a front-support position, the performer feints both legs to the right. On the return swing, he swings his extended right leg to the left, between his left leg and the horse; raises it over the left end of the horse; releases his left hand; and then regrasps with it, as he moves his right leg along the front center portion to his right. He releases his right hand, and regrasps with it as his right leg moves past the right pommel and on past the right end of the horse. He completes the clockwise circling movement with the right leg and returns to a front-support position. He may repeat this action by moving his left leg in a circle in the opposite direction. In a variation, he can initially move his right leg to the right, and circle the horse in a counterclockwise motion.

DOUBLE-LEG HALF-CIRCLE AND RETURN (FIGURE 12-27)

From a front-support position, the performer re-

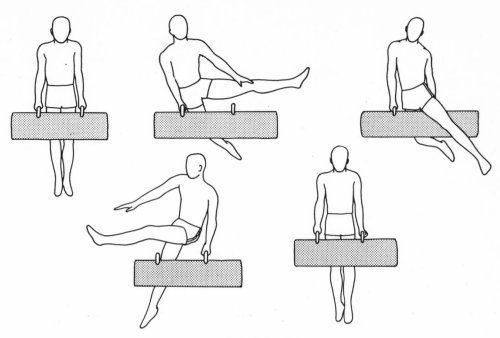

Figure 12-26. Full single-leg circle.

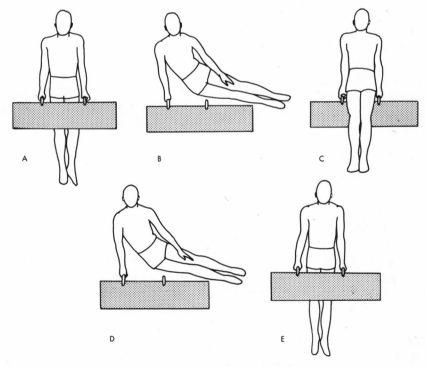

Figure 12-27. Double-leg half-circle and return.

peats the action used to perform the single-leg half-circle, except that he keeps both legs together and extended, and passes them around the horse to a rear support position. He reverses the direction of travel of both legs and returns to the starting posi-

tion. In performing this stunt, the performer may initially circle his legs to the left or to the right. A variation is to continue the circling movement of both legs until the side horse has been completely circled.

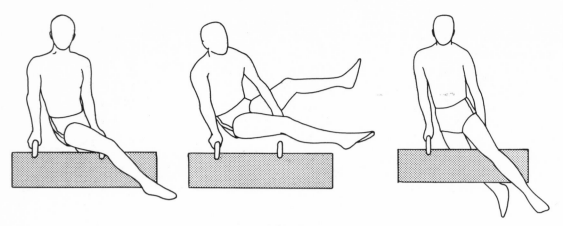

Figure 12-28. Scissors.

SCISSORS (FIGURE 12-28)

Grasping both pommels, the performer straddles the horse, placing his right leg in front of the horse and his left leg behind it. With his arms completely extended, he faces toward his left, and swings his body to his right and then to his left. As he swings his legs to his left, he raises and crosses (scissors) them, releasing his left hand. He regrasps with his left hand and returns to the starting position, except that the position of his legs is reversed. The performer may also scissor when he swings to his right, or he may scissor at each end of his swing.

ACTIVITIES FOR DEVELOPING LEGS AND CIRCULORESPIRATORY ENDURANCE

The acquisition of skill in elementary tumbling and vaulting activities serves as a natural foundation for learning how to protect one's self when falling. Many of the injuries that are caused by falls might be minimized if the proper methods of tucking, rolling, and otherwise distributing the force of the fall had been learned and applied.

Participation in tumbling and vaulting activities, including trampolining, is valuable for developing the musculature of the legs, and circulorespiratory endurance is developed as well.

Simple tumbling and vaulting activities that require a minimum amount of muscular strength have been selected for this section, to enable the performer to properly utilize the correct methods of execution and thus protect himself from possible injury. To avoid the possibility of straining the muscles of the neck, a spotter should give assistance to those performers who do not have sufficient strength to momentarily support their weight with their flexed arms while performing tumbling movements in which they are upside down. Such support is given by placing a hand or both hands on the performer's shoulder and lifting at the proper time.

Tumbling Activities

The tumbling stunts listed below should be performed on mats until considerable proficiency has been acquired. Most of the stunts in this section aid in developing the muscles of the upper arms that extend the forearm and the muscles that extend and flex the trunk.

FRONT BREAKFALL

With his trunk erect, the performer kneels on the mats, his head directly above his shoulders and his chin in. Keeping his trunk straight or slightly arched, he leans forward and falls toward the mat, keeping his fingers pointing forward and his arms extended and perpendicular to his shoulders. As soon as his hands contact the mat, he flexes his arms and "gives" with his weight, progressively resisting his falling motion until he has completely checked it by the time that his chest touches the mat. He should focus his eyes on the mat throughout the fall, to properly gauge when and how much to break his fall. This stunt should be performed from a standing position only after the performer is confident of his ability to break his fall from a kneeling position.

ROCKER

With his body arched as much as possible and with his arms extended sideward from his shoulders, the performer assumes a prone position on the mat. By raising his legs, moving his arms forward, and thrusting his head downward, he rocks forward on his chest. He then rocks backward by arching his head backwards, moving his arms backward, and lowering his legs. He continues the rocking action, attempting to rock as high as possible.

FORWARD ROLL

The performer squats with his arms outside his knees. His shoulders are next to his knees, his head is brought forward between his knees, and his hands are on the mat with the fingers facing forward. Keeping his chin tucked in, he pushes with his feet and rolls forward, maintaining his body in a tucked position. He supports his weight with his flexed arms until his body has rotated to a position where he can lower his upper back and shoulders to the mat. He places his hands on his shins, tucks tightly, and completes the roll by coming to a standing position after his feet have touched the mat.

SIDE ROLL

With his right side facing the length of the mat, the performer kneels on all fours, with his knees directly below his hips and his hands directly below his shoulders. Flexing his arms, he rolls sideways to his right, first contacting his right shoulder, hip, and side to the mat; then his back; and finally his left side, shoulder, hip, hand, and knee; finishing in the all-fours starting position.

The performer may also do side rolls to his left. After proficiency has been acquired in this type of side roll, the performer can start with a slow run in which he jumps and lands in an all-fours position on his hands and feet. He then executes a side roll and completes it by coming to a standing position.

SHOULDER ROLL

Facing the length of the mat, the performer squats and turns his body diagonally to the left. He places his right arm across his body so that the back of his right hand rests on the mat outside of and just in front of his left foot. Rolling down the center of the mat, the performer rolls on his right hand, arm, shoulder, and diagonally across his flexed back to his left hip. He completes the roll by coming to a standing position, as soon as his tucked left leg comes under him.

When the performer can do a standing shoulder roll with skill, he should start the shoulder roll with a slow run during which he whips his right arm down and across his body, when his right foot is in front and while he is bending forward. Shoulder rolls on the left shoulder may also be performed.

BACKWARD ROLL

With his back facing the length of the mat, the performer squats and tucks his body by placing his chin and knees next to his chest. He sits back and rolls backward, keeping his knees next to his chest, his head between his knees, and his hands above his shoulders. As his shoulders touch the mat, he forcefully pushes on the mat with his hands. He completes the roll by coming to a squatting or standing position on his feet.

BACKWARD EXTENSION ROLL

Starting from the same starting position as used for the backward roll, the performer initiates a backward roll. When the performer is upside down, he begins pushing with his hands, and vigorously shoots his legs above and slightly behind him. At the same time, he presses forcefully with his arms, so that he comes to a momentary handstand position. He then pikes sharply at his hips and returns to a standing position with his body and legs flexed. To begin the backward extension roll with increased momentum, the performer may initiate the stunt by falling backward from a semi-crouched position and then piking sharply before his hips contact the mat.

CARTWHEEL (FIGURE 12-29)

Standing in the center of the mat and facing the side of the mat, the performer spreads his feet about three feet apart, extends his arms overhead, and archs his body slightly. Keeping his right leg straight, he forcefully bends sharply toward his right, whips his extended right arm downward, and places it about fifteen inches to the right of and in line with his right foot. He quickly raises his extended left leg overhead, while keeping his body arched and looking between his hands at the

Figure 12-29. Cartwheel.

mat. His extended left leg is then piked to the mat, in line with the line formed by his hands, and the performer returns to the starting position. Cartwheels may also be performed to the left or in series.

ROUNDOFF (FIGURE 12-30)

Starting from the same starting position as used for the cartwheel, the performer initiates the same actions as for the cartwheel, except that he brings his legs together as quickly as possible after lifting them off the mat. When the performer is upside down and his weight is supported on both hands, he executes a one-quarter twist with his body and, as he pushes hard with his arms and shoulders and thrusts his head upward, whips his piked legs to the mat. He lands on both feet, facing the direction

from which the roundoff was started. After some proficiency is acquired, the performer can begin the roundoff by holding his arms overhead, taking a slow run, hopping on his left foot, and then stomping his right foot to the mat just in front of his left foot. He immediately flexes his body and places his hands on the mat, with his left hand directly in front of his right hand.

Trampolining Activities

In addition to developing circulorespiratory endurance and the musculature of the legs, participation in trampolining activities can aid in increasing the flexibility of the body, particularly the joints of the back and the ankles. Trampolines were widely

A   B   C

Figure 12-30. Roundoff.

used by the armed forces during World War II to develop balance, coordination, courage, and body control in aviators, and to accustom them to being in unusual body positions.

If the trampoline performer will observe common-sense safety precautions, and proceed to advance stunts only after he has thoroughly mastered the elementary stunts, bouncing on a trampoline and performing the trampoline stunts described in this section may be done with little danger of injury. The guiding principle to observe is that the trampoline performer should proceed with caution and should not attempt a new stunt or combination of stunts, until he thoroughly understands how to perform such stunts and has mastered all related lead-up stunts.

When bouncing or performing on the trampoline, the performer, especially the novice, should practice and observe the following trampoline techniques and safety precautions:

1. When bouncing on the trampoline, bounce only as high as complete control of the body position and balance will permit. During the learning stage, it is best to deliberately keep the height of the bounce low.

2. During the upward motion of the bounce, the arms, which are extended, swing forward and upward, until they are in an overhead position that is slightly in front of the head. The arms pause in this position (the length of the pause depends on the height of the bounce) and then swing sideward and downward as the body is descending. As the legs contact and push against the trampoline bed, the arms, still extended, come down alongside and slightly behind the body. The arms begin their forward and upward swing as the body starts upward from the bed. This type of arm action aids in maintaining proper body balance and, if performed vigorously, increases the height of the bounce.

3. When in the air during the bounce, the body is straight or slightly piked; it should not be arched.

4. When first landing or taking off from the trampoline bed, the head should be erect, the body straight, and the legs bent slightly at the knees. On the takeoff, the legs extend and the feet are flexed downward for a final pushoff from the trampoline bed. This causes the feet to be pointed downward during the time that the performer is in the air.

5. The feet are spread about shoulder-width apart when in contact with the trampoline bed, and are brought together as soon as the feet leave the bed.

6. For increased balance and awareness of body position, the performer should focus his eyes on the end of the trampoline frame. He should never look down directly under his body, except when landing after performing a stunt.

7. The body weight should always be located directly over the feet. A slight lean during the takeoff may cause the performer to travel several feet in the direction of the lean. The performer should strive to stay on or above the center of the trampoline bed at all times.

8. When not landing on his feet, the performer should always come straight down without any travel, so that he does not slide on the bed when he lands and get mat burns on his knees or elbows. For the novice, a sweat shirt and sweat pants will also help to avoid mat burns.

9. Safety pads should be in place on top of the sides and the ends of the trampoline frame at all times.

10. Four spotters, one on each side and one on each end, should be present at all times when hazardous stunts are performed without the benefit of a safety belt. The spotters should be alert and in a position to push the performer toward the center of the trampoline if he falls or bounces toward their area of the frame. In such an event, the spotters must move quickly and not be hesitant in contacting the performer. If the performer should bounce completely off the trampoline, the spotter should grasp and support his upper arms, shoulders, chest, back, or head in order to help him land on his feet.

11. The trampoline stunts listed in this section should be learned in the order that they appear, because they are listed in their approximate order of difficulty.

FEET BOUNCE

Starting from a standing position in the center of the trampoline bed, the performer jumps into the air and attempts to land on the center of the trampoline bed. He continues to bounce up and down on the trampoline bed, but deliberately keeps the height of his bounce low.

CHECK BOUNCE: BREAK STOP, OR KILL BOUNCE

The performer bounces and, with his legs slightly spread, lands on his feet on the trampoline bed. He immediately flexes his legs at the knees and his body at the hips, so that his body is moving downward in order to absorb the reaction of the trampoline bed, thus nullifying its upward action and stopping or killing the bounce. It is essential that the performer learns to apply the check bounce instinctively any time he is off balance during a bounce or when landing on the bed after performing a stunt.

TUCK BOUNCE

The performer rebounds upward from a feet bounce and, shortly before or at the height of his bounce, tucks his legs by bringing his knees to his chest, briefly encircling his lower legs with his hands. As he begins his descent, he unclasps his hands and extends his legs, landing in the regular position. The tucked position can be taken at the height of each bounce, when several bounces are performed in succession. By keeping the legs straight and piking at the hips, the performer can do a pike bounce in a similar manner.

ONE-HALF PIROUETTE: FEET BOUNCE AND ONE-HALF TURN (FIGURE 12-31)

The performer does one or two feet bounces in the center of the trampoline bed. As he bounces upward, he turns his body to the right (or left) by rotating his head to the right, bringing his left arm, slightly bent, across his chest and in front of his right shoulder, while the flexed right arm is directed to his rear. His body should be extended and his legs should be together while he executes the one-half turn. He lands on his feet facing the direction opposite to that which he originally faced. One-half pirouettes may be done on each succeeding bounce (swingtime). With practice, full pirouettes, in which a turn of 360 degrees is made, may be performed.

KNEE BOUNCE: KNEE DROP

The performer does one or more low feet bounces. While rising from a feet bounce, he flexes his legs at the knees and lands on both knees, shins, and feet, which are extended at the ankles. The performer's body and thighs form a straight line with little or no bend at the hips. His head is up and, except for landing on the knees and feet, the action and body position is identical to that used for a feet bounce. With practice, the performer can alternate knee bounces and feet bounces in swingtime.

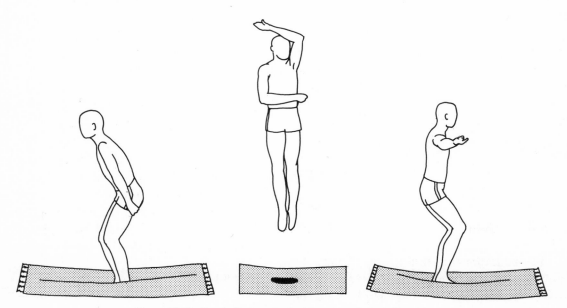

Figure 12-31. One-half pirouette: feet bounce and one-half turn.

Figure 12-32. Seat bounce: seat drop.

SEAT BOUNCE: SEAT DROP (FIGURE 12-32)

The performer does one or more feet bounces and then, while rising from the trampoline bed, he flexes his legs at the hips and lands on his buttocks and legs in a sitting position. His body is erect, his legs are straight, and his hands are placed on the trampoline bed beside his hips, with his fingers pointing in the direction that he is facing. With practice, the performer can come to a feet-bounce position after landing, by pushing with his hands, leaning forward with his body as he leaves the bed, and flexing his legs and bringing them underneath his body. When he has mastered this, he may practice alternating seat bounces and feet bounces in swingtime.

SEAT BOUNCE, ONE-HALF TURN, SEAT BOUNCE: SWIVEL HIPS (FIGURE 12-33)

The performer does one or more feet bounces

Figure 12-33. Seat bounce, one-half turn, seat bounce: swivel hips.

and then does a seat bounce. As he rises from the bed, he pushes with his hands, leans forward, and unpikes his legs so that his body is straight and he is in a standing position with his feet positioned above the trampoline bed. By raising his arms overhead and continuing to swing them until they point in the opposite direction, and rotating his head one-half turn, he turns or pivots his body a half-turn, so that he is facing the opposite direction. He pikes his body and lands in a seat-drop position. With practice, consecutive swivel hips may be performed in swingtime.

HANDS-AND-KNEES BOUNCE: ALL-FOURS BOUNCE

When learning the hands-and-knees bounce it is recommended that the performer begin the stunt from a knee-bounce position. The performer does one or more low bounces and, as he rises from the trampoline bed, gradually flexes his body forward at the hips, in order that he may land simultaneously on his knees, the tops of his insteps, and hands. His body is parallel with the trampoline bed, his knees are directly under his hips, his hands are directly under his shoulders, and his arms are straight. The performer may continue to bounce on his hands and knees or he may push with his hands, tuck his legs, and land either on his feet or in a knee-bounce position. To learn the proper all-fours landing position, it is helpful to assume the hands-knees position on the trampoline bed and then begin bouncing, gradually building up the height of the bounces.

FRONT DROP (FIGURE 12-34)

The performer does a few low feet bounces and, as he rises from the trampoline bed, he slowly flexes his trunk forward at the hips, until it is almost parallel to the trampoline bed at the height of his bounce. As he starts to drop, he unpikes his legs behind him, but always keeps his feet closer to the bed than any other part of his body. His head is up, he is facing the end of the trampoline, and his arms are in front of his shoulders. Keeping his neck muscles tense, he lands flat on the bed, making contact with his hands, forearms, chest, stomach, thighs, and the tops of his insteps. His stomach should land on the spot where he started his takeoff; he should avoid traveling forward. After landing on the bed, he may continue to bounce and land in a front-drop position after each bounce, or he may push with his hands, lift his head, arch his back, tuck his legs under him, and come to a standing position. Some beginners experience decreased difficulty in learning the front drop if they first do a hands-and-knees bounce and then extend their legs and arms while in the air. With practice the performer can alternate front drops with feet bounces.

FRONT-DROP, ONE-HALF TURN, FRONT DROP: ONE-HALF TURNTABLE

The performer does a front drop and, as he begins to rise from the bed, he pushes both hands to his left, turns his head vigorously to his right, and tucks his body. As his body revolves clockwise to his right, he continues to pull in that direction with his head, while he maintains the tucked body position. When his body has made a one-half revolution and he is facing in the opposite direction from which

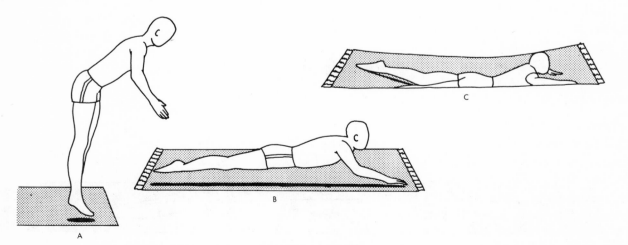

Figure 12-34. Front drop.

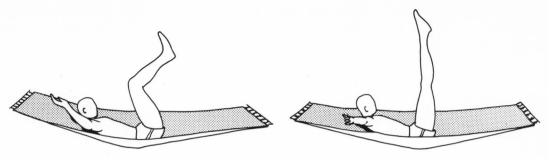

Figure 12-35. Back drop.

he started, he extends his body and lands in a front-drop position. After mastering this stunt, the performer may attempt a full turntable.

BACK DROP (FIGURE 12-35)

With his legs slightly bent and his body slightly flexed, the standing performer raises his right leg until it is parallel to the trampoline bed. With his head forward so that his chin is on his chest, he leans backward; as he falls off balance, he brings his lower leg alongside his raised leg, and flexes his legs. With his legs in a semi-tucked position, he lands on his hips, back, and shoulders. After landing, he may continue to bounce and land on his back each time, or as he starts to rise from the bed, he may forcefully extend his legs forward and then tuck them underneath his body while he curls his body forward, in order to land on his feet. Throughout the back drop, the performer should keep his hands and arms in front of him, and avoid a tendency to place his hands on the bed when falling backward or when landing.

Once the performer has become skilled in performing modified back drops, he can perform regular back drops by doing some very low feet bounces. As he rises from the bed, he raises his legs toward his chest and gradually rotates his body backward, so that he lands in a regular back-drop position. With practice, the performer may alternate back drops and feet bounces.

FRONT DROP, ONE-HALF TWIST, BACK DROP

The performer does a front drop and, at the height of the bounce, he rotates his head to his right and looks toward the ceiling. At the same time, he brings his left flexed arm across his chest to his right shoulder, while his right elbow is vigorously positioned behind his shoulder. He lands in a back-drop position with his legs extended and in

line with his body. When performing this stunt, the performer must avoid pushing with his hands as he rises from the bed, because this action will cause his body to somersault and thus prevent him from landing in a safe back-drop position. The performer should maintain a straight body position throughout the performance of the stunt.

BACK DROP, ONE-HALF TWIST, FRONT DROP

Keeping his legs extended and his body straight, the performer does a back drop and lands simultaneously on his shoulders, back, hips, calves, and heels. Immediately before the top of his rebound, the performer turns his head to the right, looks at the trampoline bed, and brings his left arm across his right shoulder and his right elbow behind his right shoulder, until he has completed a one-half twist. He lands in a front-drop position with his body extended and his legs together.

BACK DROP, ONE-HALF FORWARD TURN, FRONT DROP

With his legs held in a semi-tucked position, the performer does a back drop, landing on the upper part of his back. As he rebounds from the bed, he vigorously extends his legs forward and slightly upward, curls his body, and thrusts his head forward. He loosely tucks his body and holds this position, until he has completed a one-half forward somersault, at which time he extends his body and lands in a front-drop position.

FRONT DROP, ONE-HALF BACKWARD TURN, BACK DROP

With his lower legs flexed at the knees, the performer lands in a front-drop position. As he rebounds from the bed, he pushes forcefully with his hands, tucks his legs forward toward his chest, and momentarily thrusts his head back. He maintains a semi-tucked position, while his body rotates through a one-half backward somersault, at which time he lands in a regular back-drop position with the legs flexed. The amount and speed of a somersaulting action is controlled by the length of time the semi-tucked position is held and the compactness of the body position.

COMBINATIONS OF TRAMPOLINE STUNTS

Utilizing the trampoline stunts described in this section, many different combinations of stunts may be performed. Some possible combinations are listed below:

1. Three feet bounces, three tuck bounces, one check bounce.
2. Tuck bounce, one-half pirouette, tuck bounce, one-half pirouette, check bounce.
3. Knee drop, feet bounce, knee drop, feet bounce, seat drop, feet bounce, seat drop, check bounce.
4. Knee drop, seat drop, knee drop, seat drop, feet bounce, check bounce.
5. Hand and knee drop, front drop, hand and knee drop, knee drop, check bounce.
6. Front drop, feet bounce, back drop, feet bounce, front drop, feet bounce, back drop, feet bounce, check bounce.
7. Front drop, one-half twist to back drop, one-half twist to front drop, feet bounce.
8. Back drop, one-half turn forward to front drop, one-half turn backward to back drop, check bounce.
9. Back drop, one-half turn forward to front drop, one-half turntable, check bounce.

Vaulting Activities

Participation in vaulting activities aids in developing the muscles of the legs, arms, and shoulders, as well as the sense of balance.

Mats should always be placed on both sides of the vaulting apparatus. For vaults performed by beginners, one or two spotters should stand on the opposite side of the apparatus from which the beginner is vaulting, in order that the vaulter's chest, upper arms, or shoulders may be instantly grasped whenever he is landing incorrectly or off balance. For those vaults in which the vaulter swings his legs toward one end of the apparatus, the spotter should stand near the opposite end of the apparatus. As much as possible, the vaulter should keep his body over his base of support during the vault. The vaulter should first learn all vaults from a standing position. Later he may walk or slowly run toward the apparatus and vault over it. The vaulter should use a two-footed takeoff in beginning any of the vaults described in this section.

Side-Horse Vaulting

The starting position for learning vaults on the side horse is one in which the vaulter faces the side horse, stands at arm's length from it, and grasps a pommel with each hand.

SQUAT VAULT (FIGURE 12-36)

The vaulter squats slightly and jumps forward and upward, pushing down while pulling forward with his hands and arms. He tucks his feet as close

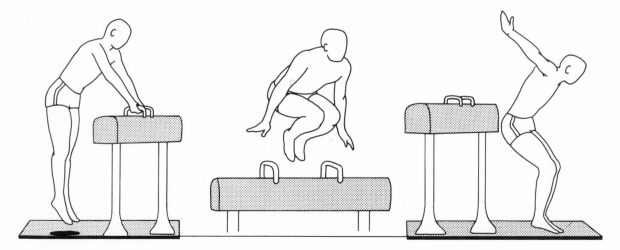

Figure 12-36. Squat vault.

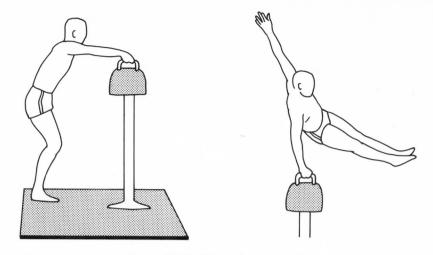

Figure 12-37. Side vault: flank vault.

to his hips as possible as he vaults over the top of the side horse. At the same time, he keeps his arms extended and supports his weight with his arms. As his body swings beyond the other side of the side horse, he pushes backward with his arms, releases his grip, extends his legs, and absorbs the force of his landing by flexing his legs slightly. As he lands, he extends his arms sideward. To learn the squat vault, it is helpful to jump as high as possible and land, with the body tucked, in a standing position on the horse.

SIDE VAULT: FLANK VAULT (FIGURE 12-37)

The vaulter jumps, pulls forward, and pushes with his hands, as he swings his extended legs over the left side of the top of the horse. As his legs start to pass over the horse, he releases his grip with his left hand. After he has vaulted over the

top of the horse, he releases the right pommel with his right hand, and lands in front of the center of the horse with his back toward the horse. As he lands, he flexes his legs slightly and extends both arms sideward. During the vault, the vaulter should always keep the right side of his body facing the horse, his legs should be together, and his legs and body should form a straight line.

FRONT VAULT (FIGURE 12-38)

The front vault resembles the flank vault, but differs in that the vaulter rotates his body as he begins the vault, so that the front of his body is facing the horse as he vaults over it. He lands with his right hand still grasping the right pommel and with his right side facing toward the side horse. His body should be extended or slightly arched as he vaults over the horse.

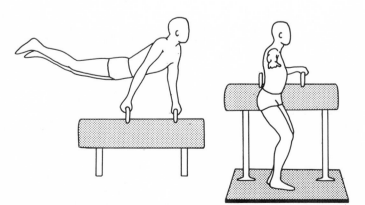

Figure 12-38. Front vault.

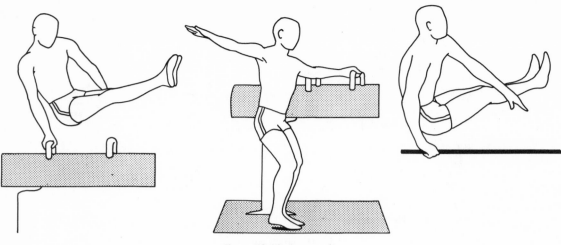

Figure 12-39. Rear vault.

REAR VAULT (FIGURE 12-39)

The rear vault is started as is the flank and front vault. However, as soon as possible, the vaulter releases his grasp on the left pommel and rotates his body, so that his back and hips are facing the horse as he vaults over it. Just after he passes over the side horse, he releases his grasp on the right pommel with his right hand and regrasps the left pommel with his left hand. He lands with his left side facing toward the horse and with his left hand grasping the left pommel.

STRADDLE VAULT (FIGURE 12-40)

One or two spotters should be present when this stunt is first attempted. Keeping his head, chest, and shoulders forward, the performer jumps upward and forward. He pushes down and backward with his hands, while spreading or straddling his

legs as wide as possible, and immediately before his feet start to pass outside of his hands, he releases his grasp with both hands. He lands with his back toward the horse, and flexes his legs and raises his arms sideward as he lands. It is imperative that the vaulter lifts his hips as high as possible and spreads his legs as wide apart as possible when performing a straddle vault. As an aid in learning the straddle vault, the vaulter should first jump to a straddle stand on the side horse several times.

Low-Horizontal-Bar Vaulting

FLANK (SIDE) VAULT FROM FLOOR

Standing in front of and facing the bar, the vaulter grasps it with a mixed grasp, with his right hand in a reverse-grasp position. He springs upward and forward, swings his body and legs to the

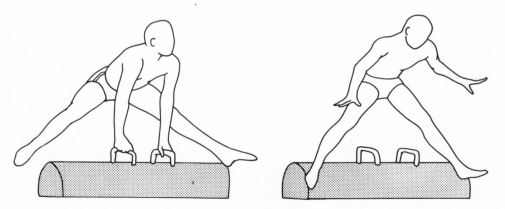

Figure 12-40. Straddle vault.

left, pulls and then releases his grasp with his left hand, and passes over the bar with the right side of his body facing the bar. He retains his grasp with his right hand and lands with his back toward the bar. His body is straight throughout the vault. To absorb the impact of the landing, he flexes his legs when he lands. The spotter stands to the right of the vaulter and grasps the vaulter's upper arm during a faulty vault.

FRONT VAULT FROM FLOOR

The vaulter faces the bar and grasps it with a mixed grasp, with his right hand in a reverse or underhand-grasp position. He springs upward, swings his body and legs to his left, releases his grasp with his left hand, and passes over the bar with his body rotated one-quarter of a turn, so that the front of his body faces the bar during the vault. He retains his grasp with his right hand and lands with his right side facing the bar. He flexes his legs slightly when he lands.

REAR VAULT FROM FLOOR

Facing the bar, the vaulter grasps it with a mixed grasp, with his right hand in a reverse or underhand grasp. He springs upward, pulls toward the bar, and pikes his body as he swings his legs to his left. He releases his grasp with his left hand just before he passes over the bar in a piked position, with his buttocks facing the bar. After his legs and hips have passed to the other side of the bar, he releases his grasp with his right hand and extends his body, bringing his feet underneath his hips. Immediately before he lands with his left side facing the bar, he regrasps the bar with his left hand. Upon landing, he flexes his legs slightly.

13. medicine-ball activities

For many, the medicine ball provides an interesting and enjoyable means for engaging in resistance exercises. Throwing and catching the heavy medicine ball helps to strengthen the muscles of the arms, the shoulder girdle, and the trunk. In addition, medicine-ball activities present a challenge to the performer each time he handles the ball: the challenge of throwing accurately or the challenge of catching successfully.

The medicine-ball activities described below are intended to serve as guides for the student. The reader is urged to exercise his ingenuity in utilizing these activities in various informal games and in inventing additional ways of propelling the ball.

Figure 13-1. Starting position.

Figure 13-2. Chest push.

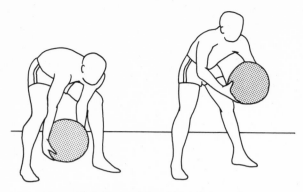

Figure 13-3. Forward throw from between legs.

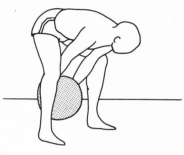

Figure 13-5. Overhead backward throw.

STARTING POSITION (FIGURE 13-1)

For each of the exercises that follow, the starting position of the performer is the same. He holds the ball next to his chest with his hands slightly behind and under the center of the ball. He stands with one foot slightly ahead of the other.

CHEST PUSH (FIGURE 13-2)

The performer assumes the starting position. Stepping in the direction of the throw, he pushes the ball from his chest by extending his arms at the elbow.

FORWARD THROW FROM BETWEEN LEGS (FIGURE 13-3)

The performer assumes the starting position. He bends forward, swinging the ball backward and between his legs. With his arms held straight at the elbows, he swings the ball forward and upward, releasing it for the throw.

ONE-ARM THROW (FIGURE 13-4)

The performer assumes the starting position and then turns to his right. With both hands he brings the ball back past his right hip, so turning the ball that his right hand is behind it. In a continuous motion he causes the ball to circle backward and upward. When the ball reaches shoulder height, he steps forward on his left foot and throws the ball with his right arm by moving the arm forward in a sweeping arc. The one-arm throw may also be executed with the left arm.

OVERHEAD BACKWARD THROW (FIGURE 13-5)

Assuming the starting position, the performer bends forward, swinging the ball backward and between his legs. With his arms held straight at the elbows, he swings the ball forward and upward and, at the same time, straightens up. He so releases the ball that it goes over his head and behind him.

OVERHEAD FORWARD THROW (FIGURE 13-6)

The performer assumes the starting position. He raises the ball overhead, dropping it down slightly

Figure 13-4. One-arm throw.

Figure 13-6. Overhead forward throw.

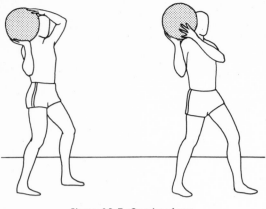

Figure 13-7. One-hand put.

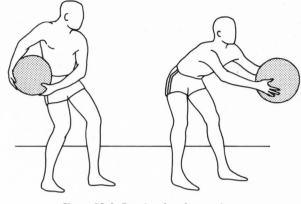

Figure 13-8. Two-hand underarm throw.

behind his head. He then steps forward and, by swinging both arms forward, throws the ball.

ONE-HAND PUT (FIGURE 13-7)

The performer assumes the starting position and then turns to his right. He raises the ball to his right shoulder, so turning the ball that his right hand is under and slightly behind it. He extends his legs and pushes the ball forward and upward with his right hand.

TWO-HAND UNDERARM THROW (FIGURE 13-8)

The performer assumes the starting position. With both hands he swings the ball back past his right hip. He then swings the ball forward and releases it for the throw.

14. rope jumping

Rope jumping is an interesting and challenging activity. The rope is an inexpensive piece of equipment and can be readily obtained. With a modest amount of work, a high degree of jumping skill can be achieved. The conditioning value of rope jumping is unquestioned. Boxers have used rope jumping as a form of conditioning exercise for many years.

SELECTING THE ROPE

Proper selection and correct fitting of the rope are essential to success in rope jumping. The rope should be heavy enough that it turns easily, but not so heavy as to cause blisters to form on the index fingers. Number-twelve sash cord makes a satisfactory rope. To fit the rope, the performer should hold one end at the top or crest of the right side of his pelvis (hip bone). He should then step on the loop of the rope and spread his feet slightly wider than his hips. If the rope fits correctly, the remaining end will come at least to the top of his left hip bone.

BASIC JUMPING FORM

THE JUMP (FIGURE 14-1)

The jumper stands with his legs and feet held together, his legs slightly flexed at the knees. By extending his legs at the knees and his feet at the ankles, he jumps from the balls and toes of both feet simultaneously. Because most of the force for the jump comes from the extension of the feet at the ankles, the legs appear to be almost completely extended throughout the jump. He jumps off the floor only high enough to allow the rope to pass between the soles of his feet and the floor (not more than two inches). He absorbs the shock at landing by bending at the ankle and the knee.

The performer may learn the basic jumping form by practicing in short sessions of five to ten jumps each, without using the rope.

THE ROPE SWING

To learn the rope swing, the jumper may hold the rope at the *loop* and swing the *ends* of the rope past his body. With his elbows close to his sides, his hands are moved in small circles so that the

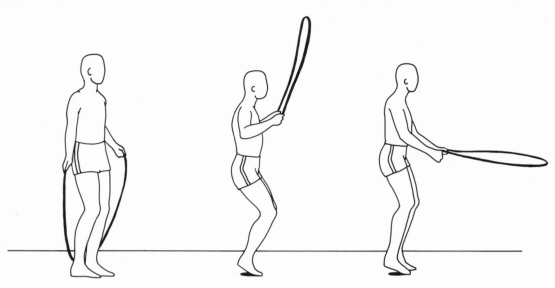

Figure 14-1. The jump.

ends of the rope hit the floor simultaneously. Most of the force for turning the rope is supplied by the wrists and forefingers, while the movement of the forearms is held at a minimum.

To learn to control the rope, the jumper may hold the rope at the ends and swing it forward over his head, so that the loop hits the floor in front of his feet. When the loop hits the floor, he swings the rope backward and over his head, so that the rope hits the floor behind his heels. Repeated forward-and-backward rope swinging will aid the jumper in learning to control the rope. If he hits his head or his ankles with the loop of the rope, he should emphasize the lowering of his hands on the downswing and the raising of his hands on the upswing.

SWINGING AND JUMPING

To learn to time the rope swing with the jump, the jumper may hold both ends of the rope in his right hand and swing the doubled rope in a circle by his right side. He flexes his knees slightly as the rope moves upward, and jumps from the floor as the rope slaps the floor.

To combine the jump with the complete swing, the jumper stands in an erect position with the ends of the rope held in his hands, the loop of the rope behind him. As he swings the rope overhead, he flexes his legs at the knees, and when the rope hits the floor in front of his feet, he jumps. He should make only one jump for each turn of the

rope—that is, he should not make a big jump when the rope passes under his feet and another small jump immediately before the next big jump (an error commonly made by beginning jumpers).

VARIATIONS IN ROPE JUMPING

A number of variations in rope jumping are possible. Such variations include both variations in style of jumping and variations in tempo. In addition to the basic forward swing, single jump described above, the student is encouraged to master the following jumps.

BACKWARD SWING, SINGLE JUMP

To start, the rope is held in front of the jumper. He swings the rope backward and over his head, and jumps the rope as it hits the floor.

CROSSED-ARMS FORWARD SWING, SINGLE JUMP
(FIGURE 14-2)

To start, the rope is held behind the jumper. He swings the rope overhead and, on the downswing, moves his hands across in front of his body, swinging the rope from the crossed-arms position. After he jumps the rope, he brings his hands back to his sides again. The crossed-arms jump is usually alternated in some fashion with the basic jump; for example, basic jump, basic jump, crossed-arms jump, basic jump, basic jump, crossed-arms jump, and so on.

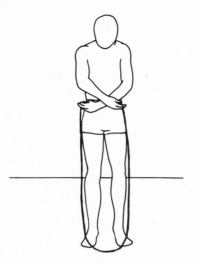

Figure 14-2. Crossed-arms forward swing, single jump.

CROSSED-ARMS BACKWARD SWING, SINGLE JUMP

To start, the rope is held in front of the jumper. With a backward swing, he crosses his arms as in the crossed-arms forward swing, jumping the rope as it passes from back to front under his feet.

DOUBLE FORWARD SWING, SINGLE JUMP

To start, the rope is held behind the jumper. He swings the rope hard and fast, twirling it twice under his feet each time he jumps. The jump must be high to enable him to twirl the rope twice before he lands on the floor. He may be required to flex his thighs at the hips and legs at the knees, in order to clear the second swing of the rope.

DOUBLE BACKWARD SWING, SINGLE JUMP

To start, the rope is held in front of the jumper. The jump is executed in the same fashion as for the double forward swing, but with a backward swing instead.

JUMPING ON ONE FOOT

The jumper stands on one foot, with the other foot held out in front of his body and above the floor. Jumping only from the one foot, he executes any of the jumps described above.

JUMPING WITH ALTERNATE FEET

With the rope held behind him, the jumper stands on his right foot, and holds his left foot out in front of his right foot and above the floor. He twirls the rope forward and reverses the position of his feet each time he jumps the rope.

SLOW JUMP

With the rope held behind him, the jumper stands on his right foot, and holds his left foot out in front of his right foot. Swinging the rope slowly and rhythmically, he executes two jumps on the right foot while swinging the left leg like a pendulum, first backward, then forward, then back to the floor. The rope passes under the feet alternately on the first of each of the two jumps.

RUNNING IN PLACE

The jumper holds the rope behind him and stands in a stride position. Swinging the rope rapidly, he jumps, alternating the feet with each jump.

15. games

Games have a proper place in any program of physical conditioning. They provide an interesting form of activity that is both vigorous and enjoyable. Many of the games presented here may be modified slightly and played by the family at home or by groups at informal social events held out-of-doors.

In those instances in which the official rules of the games are subject to change, the sources from which the rules may be readily obtained at little cost are given, rather than a listing of the current rules.

FOUR-WALL COURT GAMES

HANDBALL

Handball is a game played in a four-wall court. When it is played by two players, it is termed singles; by three players, cutthroat; and by four players, doubles. A brief description of the game follows.

The server stands in the service zone, drops the ball to the floor, and strikes the ball in such a manner that it hits the front wall and rebounds to the floor behind the short service line. The receiver attempts to return the ball in such a way that it strikes the front wall before it again touches the floor. The opposing sides continue to alternate play until an error is made. Errors made by the server cost him the serve; loss of the serve is termed a *handout*. Errors made by the receiver, however, score points for the server. Twenty-one points constitute a game.

In doubles the server's partner must stand in the service box during the serve. The pair serving for the first time in the game is allowed only one handout during the first serve. Thereafter, both partners serve. It is not necessary for doubles partners to alternate hits. Either partner may play several shots in succession.

The official rules of handball may be obtained from the United State Handball Association, 505 N. Michigan Ave., Chicago, Illinois, or from the Amateur Athletic Union, 233 Broadway, New York, New York.

PADDLEBALL

Paddleball, basically, is handball played with a paddle. Paddleball may be played as a one-wall game or a four-wall game. The paddleball ball is a skinned tennis ball. The paddle has on its handle a leather safety throng or shoelace that should be wrapped around the wrist of the user at all times. For this reason, the paddle may not be shifted from hand to hand.

In all plays and situations, the rules of handball apply.

SQUASH RACKETS

The game of squash rackets is played in a four-wall court. Each player uses a racket to hit a small hard-rubber ball. A short description of the game follows.

The server stands with one foot in one of the two service boxes. He so hits the ball that it strikes the front wall above the service line and rebounds into the opposite service court. The receiver, who stands in the service court, returns the ball to the front wall, striking the wall above the metal telltale. The server and the receiver continue to alternate hitting the ball to the front wall until an error is committed.

A point is scored on every completed play. With the exception of two situations (setting the final score of the game after a tie of 13-all or 14-all), the player who first scores fifteen points wins.

The official rules for squash rackets may be obtained from the United States Squash Racquets Association, 200 East 66th St., New York 21, New York.

CODEBALL-IN-THE-COURT

Codeball-in-the-court is a kicking game played with a soccer ball in a handball court or similar area with four walls. The rules of codeball-in-the-court are adapted from the rules of handball, and the scoring resembles the scoring in squash rackets. The game may be played by two, three, or four players. A description of the variations of the rules from handball rules follows.

The server stands in the service area between the short line and the service line. To serve, he drops the ball to the floor inside the service area. The server may kick the ball any time after it reaches the maximum height of the first rebound from the floor. Thus, the server may not drop-kick the ball

and may not kick the ball on the fly. Short serves are not allowed, but long serves are legal. The ball may be struck only with the feet.

In the returning of the ball to the front wall following the serve, the ball may be kicked on the first or the second bounce or on the fly. Also, in the returning of the ball, it may be kicked twice in succession by the same player or by his teammate, providing the ball does not, between one kick and another, hit the walls or ceiling.

A game of codeball-in-the-court consists of fifteen points. A point is scored on every play except in doubles, where only one point is scored by the defensive team when both of the servers are eliminated.

In all other plays and situations the rules of handball apply.

ONE-WALL COURT GAMES

With the exception of smash and wall tennis, most one-wall court games have been adapted from four-wall court games for use in areas where four-wall court facilities are not available. A one-wall court is less expensive to construct than are four-wall courts, and the one-wall court is more readily adaptable to multipurpose use. One-wall games can be played at home against garage or basement walls.

ONE-WALL CODEBALL

One-wall codeball is the adaptation of the four-wall game of codeball-in-the-court to an outdoor or a one-wall handball court. All the rules of codeball-in-the-court, with the exception of the rules that refer to the difference in facilities, apply to one-wall codeball.

ONE-WALL HANDBALL

One-wall handball is played against a wall with the court surface marked on the adjacent floor area. All the rules of four-wall handball, with the exception of the rules that refer to the difference in facilities, apply to one-wall handball.

ONE-WALL PADDLEBALL

One-wall paddleball is the adaption to a one-wall court of the four-wall court games of paddleball. All the rules of four-wall court paddleball, with the exception of the rules that refer to the difference in facilities, apply to one-wall paddleball.

ONE-WALL SQUASH RACKETS

One-wall squash rackets is the adaptation to a one-wall court of the four-wall court game of squash rackets. All the rules of four-wall squash rackets, with the exception of the rules that refer to the difference in facilities, apply to one-wall squash rackets.

SMASH

Smash is a game played on a small, level court that has a specially constructed backstop. To hit a small ball against the backstop, each player uses a paddle slightly larger than a table-tennis paddle. The game appears to be a combination of table tennis, paddleball, and squash rackets.

The object of the game is to score more points than the opponent by hitting the ball against the backstop in such a manner that the opponent commits errors. A short description of the game follows.

The server drops the ball on the floor in the right-hand court. He hits the ball against the backstop in such a manner that it rebounds from the backstop striking the floor in the left-hand court. The receiver returns the ball to the backstop, and play continues until a fault is committed. The server continues to serve for five consecutive points. Fifteen or twenty-one points constitute a game. The complete rules for the game of smash may be obtained from Smash, 1024 North Blvd., Oak Park, Illinois.

WALL TENNIS

Wall tennis is a game played on half of a tennis court (27-by-39 feet) that is marked adjacent to a wall. Although half of the regulation tennis area is considered to be ideal for wall tennis, the playing area may be somewhat smaller. Regular tennis equipment is used. A line called the net line is drawn at a height of three feet from the bottom of the wall. A second line, five feet above the net line, is also drawn on the wall.

The ball, which is served by being struck with the racket, is served in such a manner that it rebounds into the receiver's service box (13½-by-21 feet). Play continues until the ball is hit out of the area between the net line and the eight-foot line, touches the floor outside the court, or bounces twice on the floor. The basic rules of tennis apply throughout the game. Tennis rules may be ob-

tained from the United States Lawn Tennis Association, 120 Broadway, New York 5, New York.

TWO-WALL COURT GAMES

Two-wall games are played on a court that has two walls that join each other at a right angle. This type of facility is readily available in most homes with basements. The five games played as one-wall games (codeball, handball, squash rackets, wall tennis, and paddleball) can be easily adapted to play on a two-wall court. The one basic difference between the rules for the two-wall games and the rules for the one-wall games is: when the ball is played against two walls, the rules for the four-wall game apply; when the ball is played against only the front wall, the rules for the one-wall game apply.

CORNERBALL

Cornerball is a handball-type game played by two players on a two-wall court. The court is a six- or eight-foot square, with two adjacent walls forming two sides of the court. A diagonal line is drawn from the corner of the wall to the opposite corner of the court. This line separates two triangular courts. One player stands behind each sideline.

The server, standing behind his sideline, drops the ball and, with his hand, strikes the ball on the rebound in such a way that the ball hits, in succession, the server's side wall, the receiver's side wall, and the floor of the receiver's court. The receiver attempts to return the ball by so hitting it that it hits, in succession, the receiver's side wall, the server's side wall, and the floor of the server's court. Play continues until an error is made. The scoring is the same as in handball.

HORIZONTAL-COURT GAMES

The two horizontal-court games that are described here may be played on any 25-by-50 foot flat area. These games may be so modified that smaller areas may be used. The equipment required to play these games is relatively inexpensive.

BADMINTON

Badminton is a game in which two or more players with rackets so hit a plastic "bird" or shuttlecock that the bird flys across a net stretched across the center of a rectangular court.

The server stands in his right service box and so serves the bird with an underhand hit that the bird crosses over the net and lands in the opponent's court. The receiver attempts to return the bird back over the net and into the server's side of the court before it lands on the floor. Points are scored only by the server, and fifteen points constitutes a game. The official rules, and a description of the playing areas for badminton, may be obtained from the American Badminton Association, 77 Whittier Road, Wellesley Hills 82, Massachusetts.

PADDLE TENNIS

Paddle tennis is a game in which the players use wooden paddles and play according to rules adapted from lawn tennis. The paddle tennis court is 20-by-40 feet with a line dividing each half of the court into two service courts, each 10-by-20 feet. The net is 2 feet, 7 inches high at the sidelines and not less than 2 feet, 6 inches at the center of the court. A "dead" tennis ball may be used for the game, but the official paddle tennis ball (solid sponge rubber) is recommended for use.

One underhand serve is allowed on each play for point rather than the two overhand serves allowed in lawn tennis. The ball must hit the court before being returned to the opposite court. Otherwise, the rules of play and scoring are the same as for lawn tennis.

HAND TENNIS

Hand tennis may be played on any floor space large enough to accommodate a rectangular court about 6-by-12 feet. A line drawn midway across the court parallel to the end lines serves in place of a net.

The ball (a tennis ball) is struck with the palm of the hand instead of with a racket as in tennis. On the service and on all subsequent play, the ball must always be hit during the first bounce. A fault occurs and a point is lost when (1) the server fails to serve the ball inside his opponent's half of the court, (2) a player fails to return the ball inside his opponent's half of the court, or (3) a player fails to hit the ball during the first bounce. Scoring is the same as in paddle tennis.

MASS GAMES

The mass games described below provide fairly vigorous activity for a large group of players. Games that may be played on a basketball court or on a soccer field are presented, together with two games that are played in a swimming pool.

AMERICAN BALL

The object of the game is to score points by throwing the ball from behind a scoring line to a catcher located in the goal area and to prevent the opposing team from scoring. Either a soccer ball or a basketball may be used to play the game.

Indoors, the game is played on a basketball court; out-of-doors, on one-third of a football or soccer field. Fifteen feet from each of the end lines a scoring line is drawn across the court (parallel to the end lines). If the game is played on a basketball court, the scoring lines are made by extending the free throw lines to each sideline. Beyond each end line a distance of 4 feet or more, a line is drawn across the court that, together with the end line and the extension of the sidelines, encloses the goal area. A center jump circle 4 feet in diameter is drawn at midcourt.

A team is composed of nine players. Each team stations a catcher in the appropriate goal area and the game is started with a center jump as in basketball. For the jump, each team (except the catcher) must remain in its own half of the court until the ball is tapped. After the tap, each team attempts to advance the ball by running with it or by passing it. Dribbling the ball is not permitted.

Only one player on each team (the guard) may enter the area between the scoring line and the appropriate end line and may attempt to keep the catcher from catching the ball. The guard may not enter the goal area beyond the end line, however. The catcher's movements are restricted to the goal area.

A goal is scored when the ball is thrown in the air to the catcher, who receives it in the goal area. Each goal counts as two points.

Players attempt to guard their opponents as in basketball and, in addition, are permitted to grasp their opponents around the body between the shoulders and the waist when the opponent has possession of the ball. When a player is "tied up" in this fashion, a held ball is called as in basketball. The ball is again put into play with a jump ball at the spot where the held ball was called.

Personal fouls, for which a free throw is awarded

the player fouled, include (1) grasping a player above the shoulders or below the waist, (2) physical contact with a player who does not have the ball, or (3) unnecessary roughness. A player with four personal fouls is disqualified.

For a free throw, the player fouled is awarded an unhindered throw from any spot behind the scoring line. The guard from the opposing team may guard the catcher during the free throw but, in so doing, must remain in the area between the scoring line and the end line. A successful free throw counts as one point.

A violation is called and the ball is awarded out-of-bounds to the opposing team when (1) the catcher steps out of the goal zone, (2) a player other than the one assigned to guard the catcher steps on or beyond the scoring line, or (3) a player intentionally delays the game. Should the player assigned to guard the catcher step on or beyond the end line during a free throw attempt or a pass for goal, the free throw or goal is automatically scored; and the ball is awarded to the catcher, who puts it into play by attempting to pass it to a team-mate.

A game may consist of four five-minute quarters with a one-minute rest period between quarters.

In one popular variation of American ball, the game is played with a medicine ball. For this variation the distance between the scoring line and the end line is decreased to 8 feet.

BATTLE BALL

The object of the game is to put all players of the opposing team out of play by hitting them with a thrown ball.

The game is played by two teams of an equal number of players on a volleyball or basketball court. As many volleyballs or rubber playground balls as is feasible are placed on the center line of the court. Each team lines up behind and parallel to the end line at its end of the court. At the sound of a whistle, the players run to the center of the court, get a ball, and attempt to hit an opponent by throwing the ball at him.

Any player who is hit by a thrown ball before the ball has struck the ground is "dead" and must leave the game. However, if the player catches the thrown ball, the throw is nullified and he may remain in the game.

Players may not enter their opponent's half of the court to retrieve or throw a ball. Balls that go out of bounds may be retrieved by the team on whose half of the court the balls left the playing area, but the ball must be returned to the playing area before it may be thrown at an opponent.

The game is ended when all players on one team are "dead." As a variation, the game may be ended when all but five players on one team are "dead."

CABINET BALL

The object of the game is to score points by throwing the ball over the net so that the ball touches the floor in-bounds on the opponents' side. The necessary equipment includes a medicine ball, volleyball standards, and a volleyball net. Although a team is usually composed of twelve players, by enlarging the area of the playing court, larger groups can be accommodated. A volleyball court is used for the playing area. A service line is marked fifteen feet behind the net. The volleyball court should also have the spiking line 7½ feet from the net.

The ball is thrown from the service line; one assist on the serve is permissible. When caught, the ball should be put in play within three seconds. The ball may, before it is thrown over the net, be passed twice on the side on which it is caught. The ball should be thrown in a rising direction to the area in front of one's own spiking line. The ball may be thrown in a downward direction to the area behind the opponents' spiking line. Only one step is allowed to the player in possession of the ball. Volleyball rules apply in all other situations.

CAGE BALL

The object of the game is to score points by keeping the ball in the air until it lands on the ground inside the goal. The equipment necessary for this game includes a cage ball and two 40-foot ropes for the outline of the goal. An unlimited number of players can play cage ball. A soccer field, a football field, or a basketball court may be used for the playing area. Goals used out of doors are five feet wide and fifteen feet long and are centered out-of-bounds on the ground, five feet behind the end line. Goals used indoors are the area of the wall outlined by two volleyball standards placed ten feet apart. Penalty spots are marked in the center of the field, twenty feet from the end lines.

The game is started by two players on opposing teams who face each other and together hold the ball above their heads. All the other players must stand at least five yards from the ball but may line up at any place on the field. At the signal to start, the players attempt to keep the ball in the air by throwing, batting, or punching the ball. A ball that touches the ground is put into play by an opponent of the last player who contacted the ball. The game progresses until a foul is committed or a goal is made. Kicking the ball, leaving the playing field to make a play or to prevent a goal from being scored, and unnecessary roughness are fouls. The penalty for a foul is a free throw from the penalty spot. No defense is allowed on a free throw; but, in order for the team to score, the ball must reach the goal without contacting the ground. On a goal attempt during play, no score is allowed unless the ball goes directly from an offensive player to the goal; the ball must not bounce on the ground before entering the goal. On an attempt for a goal, the ball, before going over the end line, becomes dead when touched by a defensive player. After each shot at the goal, the ball is put in play by the team defending that goal.

CAGE CIRCLE DODGE BALL

The object of the game is to eliminate opponents from the game by hitting them with the cage ball. A cage ball is the only equipment necessary for this game. The number of possible players is unlimited.

Two teams are selected. The offensive team forms a circle around the defensive team. The ball is put in play by the offensive team, and may be kept in play by kicking, punching, or batting the ball. Any member of the defensive team touched by the ball is "dead" and leaves the game. When all but two of the defensive players have been eliminated, the teams change positions. The two contests are timed, and the team remaining the longer time in the circle wins.

CAGE CRAB SOCCER

The object of the game is to score goals by kicking the ball through the opponents' goal area and to prevent the opposing team from scoring. The number of players for the game is unlimited. The game is played with a cage ball on a basketball court on which the free-throw lines are extended to the sidelines. The goals are marked by two volleyball standards, placed twelve feet apart at the intersection of the lines for the foul lanes and the end lines. Two teams are designated. Each team has a goal keeper who is stationed in the goal keeper's area bounded by the free-throw line, the end line, and the two restraining lines at the sides of the free-throw lane. Only the goal keeper is allowed in the goal keeper's area. One half of the members of each team are designated as forwards and, upon beginning play, must cross the center line and remain on the other side of the line until a goal is scored. The remaining members of the team are designated as guards, and must remain on the half of the court adjacent to the goal they are defending. Throughout the play, all players except the goal keeper must remain in a "crab" position, and may advance the ball only by kicking it, kneeing it, or heading it. The goal keeper must remain in the "duck-walk" position, and may bat the ball with his hands or catch and throw the ball.

To start the game, each team lines up on the extended free-throw line in its half of the court. The ball is placed in the center circle, and, on the sound of a whistle, the players (in a crab position) move forward to attempt to gain control of the ball and to advance it. After each goal is scored, the forwards and guards on each team exchange positions. The ball is put in play after each goal is scored by awarding it at the center line to the team scored upon.

Fouls are called when a player other than the goal keeper (1) assumes a position other than the crab position, (2) touches the ball with his hands, or (3) is guilty of unnecessary roughness. If the foul occurs between the two extended free-throw lines, the offended player is awarded a free kick from the spot of the foul. All players must remain at least 6 feet away from him during the free kick; and the offending player must crab walk to the nearest sideline, where his services are not available to his team during the free kick. If the foul occurs in the area between the extended free-throw line and the end line, the offended player is awarded a free kick from the free-throw line, with only the opposing goal keeper defending the goal. All out-of-bounds balls are thrown in by the referee.

A goal counts two points; a successful free kick, one point. After a goal is scored, the players return to their starting positions by crab walking.

CAGE VOLLEYBALL

The object of the game is to score fifteen points before the opponents do by committing fewer errors. The equipment necessary for this game is two volleyball standards, a net, and a cage ball. An unlimited number of players may participate in the game. Depending upon the size of the group, the game is played on either a volleyball or a basketball court.

Two teams are chosen. The game starts with a serve, which may receive one assist over the net. Volleyball rules apply in all other situations.

GERMAN FIELD HANDBALL

The object of the game is to score goals by passing the ball down the field and throwing it through the goal, and to prevent the other team from scoring. The equipment necessary for this game is a soccer ball and two goals. Twenty-two players, eleven on each side, make up the teams. The game is played outdoors on a soccer field with soccer goals, or inside on a basketbal court, with four volleyball standards used as goals. The indoor goals are marked by two volleyball standards placed twelve feet apart at the intersections of the lines for the foul lane and the end lines.

The game starts as in soccer, but here the similarity ends. The ball is advanced by throwing, heading, or hitting with the leg above the knee. The ball may be caught, but not held for more than three seconds. The ball may be carried for three steps, and the runner may be blocked, but not held or roughed unnecessarily. The ball may be taken away from an offensive player only by an opponent who, with an open hand, knocks the ball out of the offensive player's hands. The goal keeper is the only player allowed in the goal area, and only the goal keeper may stop the ball with any part of his body. Penalties and out-of-bounds rules are as in soccer, except that a throw-in is used instead of a kick-in. Two ten-minute halves are played. Each goal, whether by kicking or by throwing, is scored as one point.

INDIAN DODGE BALL

The object of the game is to knock down the opposing team's indian clubs or to eliminate the opposing team's members from play. The equipment necessary for this game includes four volleyballs or playground balls and four indian clubs. The game is played on a basketball court, with indian clubs placed on the corners of the foul lines.

Two teams are chosen. They line up on the end lines behind their indian clubs. At the signal they rush to the half-court line and try to pick up one of the several balls at the line and throw it across at one of the opposing team members or at the opposing team's indian clubs. Players eliminated must retire to the sidelines. A player is eliminated (1) if he is hit by a ball which then hits the floor, (2) if he throws a ball and an opponent catches it, (3) if he dodges out-of-bounds to avoid being hit by a ball, and (4) if he steps across the midline. The entire team is eliminated when both indian clubs are knocked over.

WATER POM-POM PULL-AWAY

The object of this water game is to cross the swimming pool without being caught. An unlimited number of players may participate.

All swimmers except the swimmer who is "it" line up on the sides of the pool. At a signal from the center swimmer, who is 'it," swimmers on both sides attempt to swim to the other side of the pool without being touched. Those touched by the center swimmer join him until all swimmers have been touched.

WATER PUSHBALL

The object of the game is to score points by pushing a cage ball across the opponents' goal line and to prevent the opponents from scoring goals. The equipment necessary to play this game is a cage ball or water-polo ball. An unlimited number of players can participate in this game. The game is played in a swimming pool.

The players are divided into two groups, and the ball is placed in the middle of the pool. At a signal both teams swim toward the ball and attempt to push it across the pool and up on the deck. Unnecessary roughness is not allowed. Water-polo rules apply in most situations in water pushball.

part 3

General Methods for Utilizing Physical-Fitness Activities

16. morning exercises[1]

For many persons, one of the most convenient times to exercise is early in the morning, immediately after getting out of bed. At that time, he is wearing a minimum of clothing, and it is convenient for him to bathe when the exercise is finished. Unfortunately, however, few persons can force themselves to spring out of bed and start exercising at once. Most persons are apt to say, "Oh, gosh! I just haven't any pep this morning; I'll wait until tomorrow."

This lack of pep experienced immediately after rising from bed is a natural phenomenon. While a person is sleeping, the blood tends to collect in the abdominal viscera—the so-called "splanchnic circulation"—and immediately upon awakening, he has much less blood in his brain, and his arterial pressure is lower, than when he has been up and moving about for a time. When he arises suddenly, gravity reduces the amount of blood in his brain

still further, and he temporarily has a relative brain anemia. As a result, he feels listless and without energy. He may also suffer from dizziness for a short time.

If, *while still in bed,* the person will do about eight or ten exercises—requiring a total of three or four minutes—the blood will be distributed promptly throughout his body. He can then arise, feeling full of energy, and do his morning exercise routine.

For those who prefer to exercise early in the morning, the ten exercises described below should be done in bed before rising. After rising, these exercises may be followed by any appropriate exercise routine described elsewhere in the book. If it is inconvenient to follow the exercises in bed with an orthodox exercise routine, they should be repeated three times—that is, all ten exercises should be done once, then all ten the second time, and so on. When repeated in this fashion, the exercises in bed are a fairly satisfactory substitute for a general workout.

The starting position for all of the following exercises is lying on the back in bed. The number

[1] The material in this chapter is adapted from the unpublished paper, "For Those Who Desire to Exercise the First Thing in the Morning," by the late C. H. McCloy, Research Professor, State University of Iowa, Iowa City.

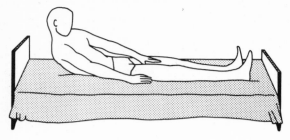

Figure 16-1. Abdominal curl.

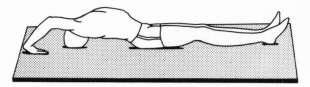

Figure 16-3. Half-arch.

of times each exercise is repeated depends upon the physical-fitness status of the performer, and the purpose for which the exercises are taken.

ABDOMINAL COMPRESSION

With his arms at his sides, the performer exhales, pulls his abdominal muscles toward his backbone as hard as he can, and holds for three counts. He then relaxes and inhales.

ABDOMINAL CURL (FIGURE 16-1)

With his arms at his sides, the performer curls his head and trunk upward and forward, keeping his lower back in contact with the bed. He then returns to the starting position.

ARM PUSH-DOWN

The performer places his upper arms at his sides, with his hands and forearms pointing up in the air. He presses his arms down on the bed and holds for three counts. He then relaxes his arms and assumes the starting position.

FULL BRIDGE (FIGURE 16-2)

The performer places his hands at the sides of his head. He arches his back, keeping only his head, hands, and heels on the bed. He then relaxes slowly and returns to the starting position.

When beginning this exercise, it may be neces-

sary to keep the shoulders, in addition to the head and hands, on the bed.

HALF-ARCH (FIGURE 16-3)

The performer points his elbows up in the air and presses downward on his pillow with doubled-up fists placed on the sides of his head. At the same time he arches his back.

LEGS APART AND TOGETHER

The performer crosses his legs (straight) at the ankles and pulls each leg against the other leg. He then places his legs together (side-by-side) and forces each leg toward the other.

LEGS FIXED, PUSH-AND-PULL

With his knees raised to a position above his hips and his lower legs parallel to the bed and crossed at the ankles, the performer forces his ankles against each other by pulling down with the ankle on top and pushing up with the ankle on the bottom. He then repeats the exercise with the ankles crossed in the opposite direction.

PUMPING

The performer raises his chest and at the same time pulls in his abdomen. He then reverses this action, raising his stomach while pulling in his chest. He repeats the exercise rapidly in a "pumping" action.

PUSH-PULL

The performer clasps his hands together and tries to push them through each other. He then tries to pull them apart.

STRETCH

The performer stretches by moving his arms slowly over his head and then clasping his hands together. He then brings his hands in an arc to his thighs.

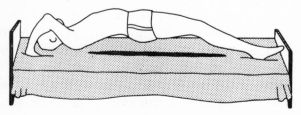

Figure 16-2. Full bridge.

17. spot exercises

Spot exercises are designed to help overcome a physical problem in one spot—that is, in one area of the body. The spot-exercise concept arose in answer to questions asked by many people as to how they might change the dimensions of a specific part of their body and, thus, improve their personal appearance. Typical questions include some of the following: How can I lose the "pot" (abdominal bulge)? What can one do about flabby thighs? Can I do something for my back? It should be noted that spot exercises do not reduce the body in the prescribed spots, but merely improve the tonus of the musculature. In some cases, spot exercises may increase the size of the musculature around these areas.

The spot exercises listed here cover the following regions of the body: abdomen, back, chest, neck, shoulder, and thigh. The exercises are listed in progression from mild to vigorous. Note that most of the exercises described here appear in other places in the book; they are assembled in this chapter to emphasize the specific part of the body most likely to be affected by the exercise in question.

ABDOMEN

Abdominal Compression

Starting position. With his arms at his sides, the performer lies on his back on the floor.

Exercise. He exhales and then pulls his abdomen toward his backbone as hard as he can and holds for three counts. He then relaxes and inhales.

Abdominal Curl

Starting position. With his arms at his sides, the performer lies on his back on the floor.

Exercise. He curls forward, raising his head and shoulders while keeping his lower back on the floor.

Rowing Curl (Figure 17-1)

Starting position. The performer lies on his back with his arms extended overhead.

Exercise. He sits up, curling his head, arms, and upper trunk toward his legs. At the same time, he raises his knees toward his shoulders. At the end of this movement he is sitting up with his knees next to his shoulders and his arms extended past

143

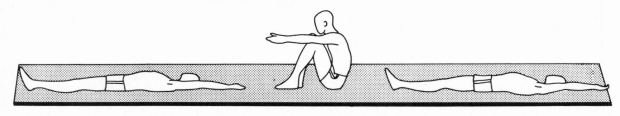

Figure 17-1. Rowing curl.

the outside of his knees. He returns to the starting position.

Lean Back (Figure 17-2)

Starting position. With his fingers interlaced and held behind his head, and with his legs extended in front of him, the performer sits on the floor.

Exercise. Keeping his upper body in the curved position, he leans back until his legs raise slightly off the floor and he is balanced on his buttocks. He holds this position for three counts, and then returns to the starting position.

Sit-Up, Bent Leg

Starting position. With his fingers interlaced and held behind his head, the performer lies on his back. His heels are next to his buttocks and his knees are raised in the air. His feet are held to the floor by a partner.

Exercise. The performer sits up, attempts to touch his right shoulder to his left knee, and then returns to the starting position. He repeats the exercise to the other side.

BACK

Back Arch on Bench, Hands Down (Figure 17-3)

Starting position. The performer so lies in a prone position on a bench that the edge of the end of the bench is slightly below his waistline. His arms are at his sides, and the hairline of his forehead rests on a pad on the floor. His partner holds his feet.

Exercise. The performer arches his head and back, raising them from the floor as high as possible, and then returns to the starting position.

Back Arch on Bench, Hands Up

Starting position. The performer so lies in a prone position on a bench that the edge of the bench is slightly below his waistline. His fingers are interlaced and clasped behind his head, and the hair line of his forehead rests on a pad on the floor. His partner holds his feet.

Exercise. The performer arches his head and back, raising them from the floor as high as possible, and then returns to the starting position.

Rolling on Back

Starting position. The performer lies curled up on his back with his knees touching his shoulders. He holds his lower legs with his hands.

Exercise. Keeping his back curved, he rocks back and forth, pushing with his head and feet.

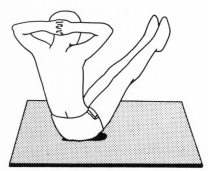

Figure 17-2. Lean back.

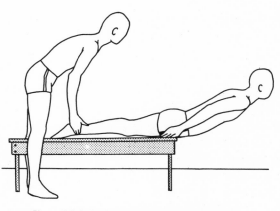

Figure 17-3. Back-arch-on-bench, hands down.

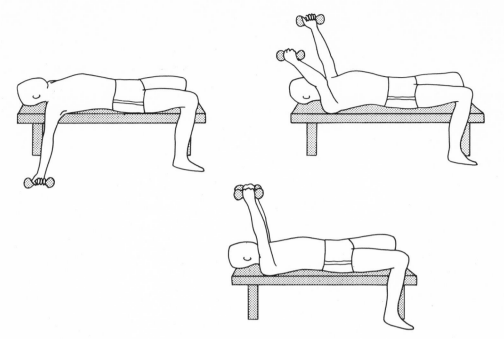

Figure 17-4. Supine lateral raise.

CHEST

Bent-Arm Pull-Over

Starting position. The performer lies in a supine position on a bench, with his head on the edge of the bench. A barbell is placed on the floor at the head of the bench. With bent arms, the performer reaches above his head and toward the floor, and, with both hands, grasps the barbell.

Exercise. The performer raises the bar in an arc, keeping his arms in the same bent position all through the movement. When the bar reaches his chest, he reverses the movement, returning the bar through the original arc to the floor.

Supine Lateral Raise (Figure 17-4)

Starting position. The performer lies on his back on a bench and places his arms out to the side and at ninety-degree angles with his body. He grasps a dumbbell in each hand (a heavy book may be used in place of the dumbbell).

Exercise. The performer raises the dumbbells over his chest and then returns them to the starting position.

Supine Press on Bench

Starting position. Holding the barbell above his shoulders with his extended arms, the performer lies in a supine position on the bench.

Exercise. The performer lowers the barbell to his chest and then pushes it back up to the starting position.

NECK

Backward Neck Push

Starting position. The performer, sitting in a chair, holds the palms of his hands on his forehead.

Exercise. He pushes with his hands and resists the movement with his head and neck.

Forward Neck Pull

Starting position. Sitting in a chair, the performer has his hands, fingers interlaced, on the back of his neck.

Exercise. He pulls forward with his hands and resists the movement with his head and neck.

Neck Twister (Figure 17-5)

Starting position. The performer sits in a chair, holds with his right hand the right side of his face along the jaw, and, with his left hand, holds the left rear side of his head.

Figure 17-5. Neck twister.

Exercise. He pushes sideways with his hands and resists the movement with his head and neck. He repeats the exercise in the opposite direction.

Sideward Neck Push

Starting position. The performer, sitting in a chair, has his right hand on the right side of his head.

Exercise. He pushes sideward with his right hand and resists the movement with his head and neck. With the left hand on the left side of the head, he repeats the exercise.

SHOULDERS

Arm Push-Back

Starting position. With his hands clasped together and held behind his buttocks, the performer stands in an erect position.

Exercise. Keeping his arms straight, he forces his hands away from his body and up in the air.

Forward Raise

Starting position. Standing with his hands spread shoulder-width apart, the performer grasps a barbell, holding it at his thighs.

Exercise. Keeping his arms straight throughout the movement, he raises the barbell forward and through an arc until it is overhead. He then lowers the barbell through the same arc, returning it to the starting position.

Lateral Raise

Starting position. The performer graps a dumbbell in each hand and stands, holding the dumbbells next to his thighs.

Exercise. He raises his extended arms sideward until the dumbbells touch overhead. He then lowers the dumbbells through the same arc to the starting position.

Military Press

Starting position. With his hands spread shoulder-width apart, the performer stands and holds the barbell in front of his shoulders near his chest.

Exercise. He presses the barbell up overhead until his arms are extended. He then lowers the barbell to the starting position.

Straight-Arm Pull-Over (Figure 17-6)

Starting position. With the barbell above his head and on the floor, the performer lies on the floor. With his hands spread shoulder-width apart he grasps the barbell.

Exercise. Keeping his arms extended, he so raises the barbell in an arc that the bar is pulled over to his thighs. He reverses his movement, returning the bar through the original arc to the starting position.

Upright Rowing

Starting position. With his hands spread shoulder-width apart and palms facing downward, the performer stands and grasps the barbell.

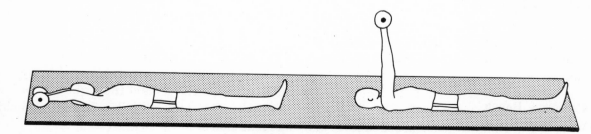

Figure 17-6. Straight-arm pull-over.

Exercise. He raises the barbell up to his chin. He then lowers the barbell to the starting position.

THIGHS

Single-Leg Raise

Starting position. With his arms at his sides and his legs extended, the performer lies on his back.

Exercise. He raises his right leg from the floor, swinging it in an arc up toward his head, and then lowers it to the floor. He repeats the exercise with the left leg.

Sit-Up, Straight Legs, Hands at Sides

Starting position. The performer lies on his back with his arms at his sides and his legs extended and slightly spread. His feet are held to the floor by a partner.

Exercise. The performer sits up, curling forward with his head and trunk, until he can move his head no closer to his legs; he then returns to the starting position.

Sit-Up, Straight Legs, Hands Behind Head

Starting position. With his fingers interlaced and held behind his head, the performer lies on his back. His legs are extended and slightly spread. His feet are held to the floor by a partner.

Exercise. The performer sits up, curls forward, and attempts to touch his right elbow to his left knee. He returns to the starting position and repeats the exercise to the opposite side.

Double-Leg Raise

Starting position. With his hands by the small of his back and his legs extended and together, the performer lies on his back.

Exercise. He moves his legs from the floor, slowly raising them until they are perpendicular to the floor. (Note: If he cannot slide his hands under the small of his back when his legs are on the floor, but can when his legs are off the floor, he should omit this exercise until his abdominal muscles are strong enough to prevent his pelvis from tipping when he raises his legs. He returns his legs to the starting position.

Sit-Up, Leg Raise (Figure 17-7)

Starting position. The performer lies on his back with his hands by his side and his legs extended.

Exercise. He sits up and, at the same time, raises his legs, touching his feet with his hands, while balancing on his buttocks. He returns to the starting position.

Legs Flexed, Push and Pull

Starting position. With his knees raised to a position above his hips, the performer lies on his back. His lower legs are parallel to the floor and are crossed at the ankles.

Exercise. He forces his ankles against each other, pulling down with the top ankle and pushing up with the bottom ankle. He repeats the exercise with his ankles crossed in the opposite direction.

Squat-Jump Variation: Full

Starting position. With his arms by his sides, his feet apart, and one foot slightly ahead of the other, the performer stands in an erect position.

Exercise. He squats, flexing his legs at the knees until his fingertips touch the floor. He jumps off the floor, throwing his arms overhead and so changing his feet in the air that he lands on the floor with the opposite foot in advance.

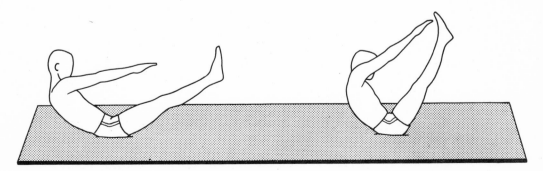

Figure 17-7. Sit-up, leg raise.

Squat-Jump Variation: Half

Starting position. The performer stands in an erect position with his arms at his sides, his feet apart, and one foot slightly ahead of the other.

Exercise. He squats, flexing his legs at the knees until the heels of his hands touch his knees. He jumps off the floor, throwing his arms overhead and so changing his feet in the air that he lands on the floor with the opposite foot in advance.

Squat-Jump Variation: Three-Quarters

Starting position. With his arms by his sides, his feet apart, and one foot slightly ahead of the other foot, the performer stands in an erect position.

Exercise. He squats, flexing his legs at the knees until his hands touch the middle of his shins. He jumps off the floor, throwing his arms overhead and so changing his feet in the air that he lands on the floor with the opposite foot in advance.

Thigh Squeezer

Starting position. The performer sits in a chair with his fists held side-by-side between his knees.

Exercise. He presses his knees together forcibly against his fists.

18. grass drills

Grass drills, which commonly include agility activities, calisthenics, and various types of running, are usually performed on a soft, grassy area. However, if care is taken to avoid falling too forcefully to the floor, they may be performed on a gymnasium floor. Although grass drills can be performed by one person alone, ordinarily they are performed by a group, in unison. Probably the most common use made of grass drills is to condition athletic teams, especially football teams.

ADVANTAGES AND DISADVANTAGES OF GRASS DRILLS

Grass drills are a concentrated form of activity which require only a few minutes of time for a vigorous workout, no equipment, and very little space. A large number and variety of activities may be included in grass drills; hence, they need not become repetitious or boring. New combinations of grass drills can easily be devised. Grass drills involve little danger to the performer, and little training is needed for an effective performance.

However, when a group first learns grass drills and begins to perform them together, the members of the group must be alert to the possibility of colliding with one another. The performer of grass drills can become fatigued quickly; consequently considerable motivation is needed if he is to perform grass drills alone for a period of several weeks. Grass drills are effective in developing only certain components of physical fitness, and are of little value for developing strength or muscular endurance. They are only of intermediate value for developing circulorespiratory endurance.

USE OF GRASS DRILLS

In order to utilize his time and efforts most efficiently, the performer should attempt to observe the following suggestions when engaging in grass drills:

1. The performer should warm up with stretching movements, running, or calisthenics before engaging in grass drills.

2. When performing grass drills that involve a change of position, the performer should move from one position to another as rapidly as possible without endangering himself. The conditioning value of grass drills depends upon the rapidity and continuity of the movements imposed by them. The performer should pause only briefly in one position before moving into next position.

3. If a leader is present, he should give a verbal command before the performers change activities or body positions.

4. The performer should participate in the various activities that constitute the grass drills one after another, with little or no pause for recovery between activities. During the first few performances, the beginner may wish to divide the period into two or more bouts of one to two minutes duration, resting between bouts, or he may wish to perform a specified number of activities and then rest before continuing the grass drills.

5. A suggested guide for the length of the period for the grass drills is to begin with one minute of activity and to increase this time by thirty seconds for each succeeding period, increasing to a maximum of five minutes of continuous activity.

6. When a group of performers engage in grass drills they may form a circle or square or rectangular-shaped formation.

7. When performing grass drills for several weeks, an overload may be obtained by (a) increasing the speed of movements, (b) increasing the number of activities performed or the length of time during which the grass drills are performed, (c) resting for shorter intervals of time between bouts, or (d) a combination of the above.

8. The performer who has a chronically weak joint or a joint that is prone to injury—such as a knee or shoulder joint—should avoid those activities in the grass drills that endanger or impose a strain on that joint.

9. Activities that specifically develop strength (such as isometric exercises), activities that specifically develop local muscular endurance (such as weight training), and activities that specifically develop circulorespiratory endur-

ance (such as running or swimming), should be included in each exercise session in which grass drills are performed.

Although one of the primary purposes of grass drills is to condition the performer to knocks and bumps, the general conditioning value to be derived from the activities comprising the grass drills can not be ignored. The qualities of physical fitness that are enhanced by regularly performing grass drills are agility, neuromuscular skills, speed of movement, and general conditioning. To a lesser degree, balance, flexibility, and circulorespiratory endurance are also improved.

ACTIVITIES FOR GRASS DRILLS

BASIC POSITION: UP

The basic position assumed by the performer in readiness for grass drills is a standing position in which his legs are slightly flexed and spaced apart, his weight is on the balls of his feet, his trunk is slightly flexed, his head is erect, and his arms are slightly flexed alongside of his body. In executing grass drills, the performer may, if he wishes, move from one position to another without returning to the basic standing position. For example, he may immediately move from a position in which he lies on his back, to one in which he lies on his stomach.

BACK

Starting from the basic position, the performer squats, sits on the floor, and stretches out in a supine position.

BICYCLING (FIGURE 18-1)

The performer assumes a supine position on the floor, flexes his legs, and rolls back until his weight rests on his upper back, shoulders, and neck. He places his hands on his hips and his elbows on the floor, so that his forearms act as braces to help him maintain the neck-and-shoulder stand position. With his feet in an overhead position, he pedals as if he were riding a bicycle.

CROSS-OVER STEP (FIGURE 18-2)

Starting from a slightly crouched position, the performer runs forward and during each step moves his legs diagonally across in front of his body. With each step, his body rotates toward the leg on which his weight is resting.

Figure 18-1. Bicycling.

FRONT

From the basic position, the performer squats on the floor, moves to a front leaning-rest position, and then stretches out in a prone position.

GO

While in the basic position, the performer sprints forward as fast as possible. If desired, he may take short steps and raise his knees as high as possible in a manner similar to running in place.

LEFT-RIGHT

Starting from the basic position, the performer runs first to his left and then to his right, frequently changing his direction. If a leader directs the activity, the performer runs in the opposite direction to which he is running each time a whistle is blown or a command is given.

LEGS OVERHEAD (FIGURE 18-3)

The performer assumes the back position and flexes his legs overhead until his feet touch the floor near his head.

LEGS UP

The performer assumes the back position, extends his arms sideward from his shoulders, and flexes his extended legs at the hips, raising them to a position in which they are perpendicular to the floor.

LEGS RIGHT AND LEFT

From a legs up position, the performer moves his legs from side to side. On each movement he touches his toes to the hand that is on the floor on that side of his body.

REAR

From a standing position, the performer runs to the rear.

ROLL RIGHT OR LEFT

The performer kneels on the floor, flexes his body, and positions his buttocks next to his heels and his shoulders near his knees. He places his head between his knees and grasps his knees with his arms and hands. Then he rolls to his right or to his left or changes the direction in which he rolls. If desired, the performer may roll right or left while maintaining his body in an extended position with his arms overhead.

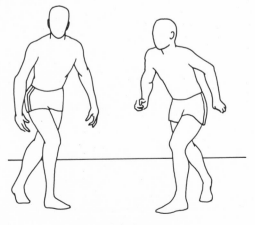

Figure 18-2. Cross-over step.

Figure 18-3. Legs overhead.

STATIONARY RUNNING

From the basic position, the performer runs in place, raising his knee as high as possible on each step.

SIT-UP

The performer lies on his back with his arms at his sides and his legs extended and slightly spread. His feet are held to the floor by a partner, or are placed under a non-movable support. He sits up, curling forward with his head and trunk until he can bring his head no closer to his legs. He then returns to the starting position. If the performer desires, he may perform this exercise while in a bent-leg position. In another variation, he lies on his back with his arms extended overhead. Bringing his knees toward his shoulders, he sits up, curling his head, arms, and upper trunk toward his knees. At the completion of this movement, he is in a sitting position with his knees next to his shoulders and his arms extended outside of his knees. He then returns to the starting position.

SPREAD-STEP RUNNING

Starting from the basic position, the performer sprints forward with his feet spread far apart.

SQUAT

Starting from the basic position, the performer squats on the floor, flexes his trunk forward, and places both hands on the floor slightly ahead of his feet.

SQUAT JUMPS

With his arms by his sides, his feet apart, and one foot slightly ahead of the other, the performer stands in an erect position. He squats, flexing his legs at the knees, until his finger tips touch the floor. Then he jumps off the floor, extends his arms overhead and changes the position of his feet while in the air so that he lands on the floor with the opposite foot in advance. This exercise may also be performed with the hands resting on top of the head throughout the exercise. Variations of the squat jump include the half and the three-quarters squat jump.

SQUAT THRUSTS

The performer stands erect in a position of attention. Then he executes the following four movements: (1) squats and places his hands on the floor outside of his feet, (2) supports himself on his extended arms, raises his feet off the floor, and thrusts his legs backward, coming to a front leaning-rest position, (3) returns to the squat position, and (4) returns to the erect standing position.

STOP

The performer may be in any of a variety of positions when the command to stop is given, but, regardless of his position, he retains it until another command is given. If desired, the performer returns to the squat position or the basic position whenever the signal to stop is sounded.

TREADMILL (FIGURE 18-4)

The performer takes a front leaning-rest position and then moves his right foot forward until it is positioned between his hands. Supporting himself on his extended arms, he changes the position of his feet so that his left foot is between his hands and his right foot is in a front leaning-rest position. He then returns to the starting position and continues to alternate the position of his feet. Other variations of the treadmill include (1) performing the exercise with the foot of the flexed leg outside the hands, and (2) moving both feet forward simultaneously and placing them either inside or outside of the hands.

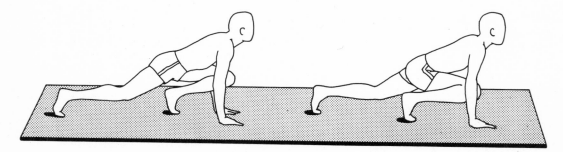

Figure 18-4. Treadmill.

UP

Regardless of his position, the performer assumes the basic position as rapidly as possible.

OTHER ACTIVITIES SUITABLE FOR GRASS DRILLS

Many of the activities described in other chapters of this book may be included in the grass drills. Some of these, however, can not be performed in the same manner as traditional grass drills, but must be modified by performing each selected activity for a short period of time:

1. Chapter 7—Calisthenics.
2. Chapter 9—Isometric Exercises.
3. Chapter 12—Apparatus and Tumbling Activities (tumbling activities only).
4. Chapter 14—Rope Jumping.
5. Chapter 17—Spot Exercises.

A TYPICAL PERIOD OF GRASS DRILLS

The activities listed below, together with the order of the activities and the time devoted to each, where applicable, exemplify a typical period of grass drills.

1. Basic Position.
2. Front.
3. Back.
4. Front.
5. Up.
6. Stationary Running (10 seconds).
7. Cross-Over Step (2 seconds).
8. Rear (2 seconds).
9. Left-Right (10 seconds).
10. Go (2 seconds).
11. Rear (3 seconds).
12. Go (2 seconds).
13. Rear (2 seconds).
14. Left-Right (10 seconds).
15. Front.
16. Back.
17. Legs Overhead.
18. Bicycling (10 seconds).
19. Front.
20. Treadmill (15 seconds).
21. Back.
22. Front.
23. Roll Right and Left (10 seconds).
24. Front.
25. Push-Up (15 seconds).
26. Stop.
27. Up.
28. Back.
29. Sit-up (30 seconds).
30. Stop.

19. guerrilla drills

The guerrilla drill was developed for the conditioning of soldiers during World War I. This activity consists of individual and dual exercises usually performed by a group that, as its members perform the activities, moves either clockwise or counterclockwise in a circle. In a short period of time and without special equipment or previous training, the guerrilla drill affords a rapid workout that enables the performer to emphasize the development of agility, balance, flexibility, and neuromuscular skill.

SUGGESTIONS FOR PARTICIPATING IN GUERRILLA DRILL

Whether a person is participating in the guerrilla drill by himself or with a group, by observing the rules listed below, he will insure the most effective utilization of his time and efforts toward an efficient workout that best contributes to the development or maintenance of physical fitness.

1. When a group performs a guerrilla drill, a leader should demonstrate the next activity while the group runs in place. Following the demonstration, the group starts the next activity and continues it until the leader signals for them to halt that activity, at which time they run in place while observing the demonstration of the succeeding activity.

2. If two or more persons perform the guerrilla drill, several activities should be selected from the category of individual exercises and a few activities from the category of dual exercises.

3. The following list illustrates how the exercise load may be progressively increased when performing the guerrilla drill.

   First day: three single exercises and one dual exercise

   Second day: five single exercises and one dual exercise

   Third day: six single exercises and one dual exercise

   Fourth day: six single exercises and two dual exercises

4. When performing the guerrilla drill, an overload may be obtained by (a) progressively in-

creasing the number of activities performed, (b) progressively increasing the speed of movements, (c) performing dual exercises with progressively heavier partners, and (d) combining (a), (b), and (c) above.

5. The performer who has a weak joint or one that is prone to injury should avoid those activities in the guerrilla drill that impose a strain or danger to that joint.

For the convenience of the reader the activities included in this chapter have been classified as individual or dual exercises and have been arranged in alphabetical order under each category.

ACTIVITIES FOR GUERRILLA DRILL

Individual Exercises

ALL-FOURS RUN

The performer assumes the all-fours position by flexing his legs slightly, bending forward, and placing his hands on the floor. The performer maintains this position while running forward with his head leading in the direction of his movement. The performer must run on all four "feet".

BEAR WALK

The performer assumes the all-fours position. He walks by first moving both limbs on one side of his body at the same time, and then simultaneously moving both limbs on the other side of his body.

BROAD JUMPING

With his arms extended and pointing downward and backward, the performer assumes a crouched position. Leaning forward, swinging both arms forward in a rapid, vigorous movement, and forcefully extending his legs, the performer jumps forward as far as possible. He continues to do a standing broad jump after each landing.

CRAB WALK

The performer sits and, with his fingers pointing forward, places his hands behind him on the floor. He assumes a crab position by raising his buttocks from the floor. Facing either forward or backward as instructed, he moves one hand and foot at a time and "walks" in the direction in which the group is moving.

CROSS-OVER STEP

The performer crouches slightly and then runs forward moving each leg diagonally across the front of his body. His body rotates slightly in the direction of each step.

CROUCH RUN

By flexing his legs and hips, the performer bends forward until his chest is parallel to the ground. Maintaining a crouched position, the performer runs forward.

FAST WALK

Maintaining an erect position, the performer walks forward as fast as he can. One foot should always be in contact with the ground; he should definitely walk, not jog.

FROG JUMP (FIGURE 19-1)

The performer squats, positioning his buttocks near his heels. He puts his arms in front of his trunk and between his knees and places his hands on the floor; this places him in the frog position. The performer then moves forward in a series of leaping movements. The spring is made as the performer reaches forward with his hands and at the same time extends his legs. He lands on his hands and quickly returns his legs to the frog position.

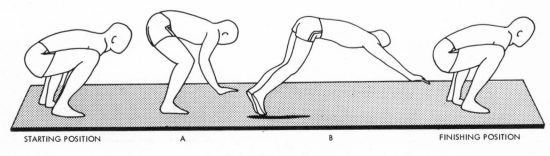

STARTING POSITION   A   B   FINISHING POSITION

Figure 19-1. Frog jump.

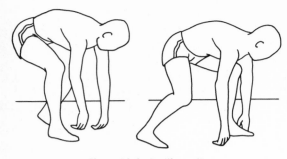

Figure 19-2. Gorilla walk.

GIANT-STEP WALK

The erect performer walks forward, taking elongated steps.

GORILLA WALK (FIGURE 19-2)

The performer flexes his legs slightly and bends forward from his hips until his fingertips touch the floor. Keeping his fingertips in contact with the floor, the performer walks or runs in the direction that he is facing.

HAND-KICK WALK

With his arms extended in front of his shoulders parallel to the ground, the performer walks forward, kicking an outstretched hand each time that he takes a step.

HOP ON ONE FOOT

The performer hops forward on one foot.

JUMPING, FORWARD HAND KICK

The performer crouches and then springs off the floor and attempts, by flexing his legs at the hips, to touch his hands with his toes. Landing in a semi-crouched position, the performer again immediately jumps and attempts to kick his hands.

JUMPING, HEEL CLICK

The performer crouches and springs upward, attempting to click his heels together twice before landing on his feet.

KNEE-RAISE RUN

The performer runs forward and with each running step raises his flexed thigh until his knee is waist high.

LAME-DOG RUN (FIGURE 19-3)

The performer assumes the all-fours position and raises his left leg behind him. He then runs on "three legs" with his head facing the direction in which he is running. The "sore" leg should not touch the ground.

STEAM-ENGINE RUN

The performer stands with his hands on his shoulders and his elbows pointing toward the floor. He runs forward and, with each step, raises his knee until it touches the elbow on the same side of the body as the upraised knee.

STIFF-KNEE JUMPING

Standing with his legs together and keeping them straight at all times, the performer moves forward in a series of hops executed by vigorously extending his ankles.

TOE-GRASP WALK

The performer bends forward and with his right hand grasps the big toe of his left foot. Facing the direction in which the group is moving and retaining his grasp on his toe, he walks forward.

WALK ON TOES

Standing on a line and facing the direction in which the line runs, the performer rises on his toes and attempts to walk on the line without losing his balance or touching his heels to the floor.

Dual Exercises

In dual guerrilla activities either a pair of performers grasp each other or the one performer holds or is carried by his partner. In the descriptions of the dual exercises, in order to distinguish between partners, the partner that holds or carries the other partner will be called the holder; the partner that is held or carried will be called the partner. When first beginning dual guerrilla activity, the

Figure 19-3. Lame-dog run.

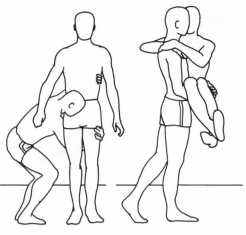

Figure 19-4. Arm carry.

performer should select a partner who does not exceed the performer's body weight.

ARM CARRY (FIGURE 19-4)

Facing his partner's side, the standing holder bends forward and places one arm around his partner's back and the other arm behind and under his partner's thighs. The partner clasps his hands together after placing an arm behind and around the holder's neck. The holder steps next to his partner's feet and then straightens up, supporting his partner's weight. Carrying his partner, the holder walks in a forward direction.

FIREMAN'S CARRY (FIGURE 19-5)

Facing his partner's right side, the standing holder bends forward and places his right shoulder in contact with his partner's abdominal area. The holder puts his right arm underneath his partner's crotch and around his right leg and grasps, with his right hand, his partner's right arm. Supporting his partner on his right shoulder the holder comes to an erect position. With his left hand the holder grasps the wrist of his partner's left arm. The holder walks forward carrying his partner.

HORSE-AND-RIDER WALK

The holder crouches slightly and stands with his back toward his partner. Mounting the holder, the partner places his upper arms on the holder's shoulders and squeezes his thighs against the holder's sides. The partner's arms may be extended and pressing downward, or they may lightly encircle the holder's chest. The holder places his arms around his partner's thighs. The holder then walks forward while carrying his partner.

LEAPFROG

With his head flexed foward, the partner assumes a semi-croched position and places his elbow on his knees. The holder takes a step forward, places his hands on the upper back of his partner, and quickly vaults over him, pushing back with his hands and straddling his legs as he executes the vault. The holder may continue to vault over other members of the group who are in a semi-crouched position; or he may assume a semi-crouched position, and his partner may vault over him. They continue to leapfrog over each other as they move forward.

Figure 19-5. Fireman's carry.

TYPICAL GUERRILLA DRILL PERIOD

A typical guerrilla drill for use by a person who is accustomed to physical activity is presented below:

1. Crouch Run (15 seconds)
2. Hand-Kick Walk (20 seconds)
3. Jumping, Heel Click (10 seconds)
4. Walk on Toes (20 seconds)
5. Horse-and-Rider Walk (25 seconds each partner)
6. Broad Jump (15 seconds)
7. Crab Walk (20 seconds)
8. Frog Jump (10 seconds)
9. Hop on One Foot (15 seconds hopping on each foot)
10. Fireman's Carry (20 seconds each partner)

20. races

Racing activities, in which a person competes against one or more others, seem to provide a challenge to participants of all age levels. Regular participation in racing activities is useful in developing circulorespiratory endurance, agility, flexibility, and neuromuscular skill. Examples of how running may be used as a conditioning activity are cited in Chapter 5—"The Overload Principle," under the heading Interval Training.

Racing takes many forms, but in the final analysis all forms of racing involve movement from a starting point to or past a finishing point. The usual practices in racing contests are to run straight ahead from the starting line to the finish line; to run from a starting line to a point, run across or around it, and then return to the original starting line; or to run a circular or an oval-shaped path, finishing at the starting point.

Proper Running Form

Running is the basic constituent of most races. Because running is performed by only one person and because it is an excellent conditioning activity,

it is important that proper running form be utilized when engaging in running activities. When running short distances at sprinting speed, or when running longer distances at paced speeds, the performer should strive to emulate the following running form:

1. Keep the head facing forward and in line with the back, maintain a slight forward body lean and focus the eyes straight ahead.
2. Keep the arms flexed but relaxed; swing them in back-and-forth movements, in a somewhat parallel arm action in which the hands cross toward the midline of the body during the forward swing.
3. For increased relaxation, keep the hands cupped but not closed tightly.
4. Move the right arm forward as the left foot is moved forward, and vice versa; observe the principle of opposition of limb movements at all times when running.
5. Keep the rotation of the trunk, from side to side, to a minimum.
6. The faster one runs, the more he should flex

his lower leg at the knee during the recovery phase of the stride; this permits a stride of increased length.

7. During the lower leg extension, the foot and knee should always point forward in the direction in which the performer is running.

8. When running at paced speeds, use a heel-ball "rock-over" foot action; when running at middle speeds, use a ball-heel foot action, making only light heel contact with the running surface; when running at sprinting speed, place only the ball of the foot in contact with the running surface.

9. Breathe naturally. When running for any distance, nose and mouth breathing is recommended.

10. Relax as much as possible while running; rhythmic running—that is, running in a regular cadence—will enhance relaxation.

Recovery

After running or participating in racing activities, the exerciser should engage in recovery activity. *Recovery activity* is the term given to activity carried on immediately following a running event for the purpose of permitting the body processes that are affected by the activity to return to a point near their pre-race level. The proper utilization of recovery activity requires that the runner should avoid such sudden cessation of activity as sitting or lying down following the end of the race. Instead, the running activity should be continued at a decreased rate of speed following the race.

The rates of many of the physiological processes of the body increase during strenuous running events. At the finish of the event, a sudden cessation of the demands of running causes an equally sudden readjustment of many of the physiological mechanisms—an adjustment that in some runners may be followed by nausea and vomiting, particularly if the runners are inexperienced. Consequently, the runner should taper the activity following the race so that the demands placed on the body will also be gradually decreased, rather than abruptly stopped. The tapering effect seems to eliminate the undesirable after-effects of the run, and is accomplished by continuing to jog and walk at decreasing speeds after the race.

After running 440 yards at full speed, recovery may be effected by running a recovery lap of 220 yards in which twenty slow running steps, ten jogging steps, and five walking steps are repeated in sequence until approximately 220 yards have been traversed. The greater the distance of the race, or the faster the speed of the race, the longer the time nedeed for complete recovery.

Types of Races

In addition to running, races can involve almost any type of prescribed propulsive action that the racer may perform which will enable him to move forward (or backward) in his race to the finish line. In this chapter the races that are described are divided into four categories: single, dual, team, and relays. The single race involves all the contestants moving at the same time in a mass race in which each contestant races against the entire group. The dual race involves two contestants holding to each other and moving together, with each pair of partners competing against all other pairs of partners. The team race involves teams of more than two members each, and all the members of a team move at the same time and race against all other teams. The relay race is a type of team race in which each member, or pair of members of a team, races one at a time against the contestant, or pair of contestants, from each of the other teams. As each team member completes his race, he starts (by tagging) the next member of his team. The relay race is completed when all members of the team have finished their lap. Relay races are subdivided into single and dual relay races, according to the way in which they are organized.

SUGGESTIONS FOR ENGAGING IN RACES

1. Be aware of safety hazards. Accidents are most apt to occur near the turning line and the finish line. Avoid the use of a wall for the turning line, and have sufficient area behind the finish line in which to slow down and stop. The teams or contestants should have sufficient room from side to side to eliminate any danger of collisions.

2. The racing contestant should not engage in racing activities that impose a hazard to him because of a joint weakness or a previous injury.

3. Start with a racing activity that provides a warm-up.

4. When racing competition is held, a leader may start the contestants with a signal of "ready go," or the contestants may count aloud to three, starting the race as soon as the count of three is sounded.

5. Progress from the less complicated to the more complicated races.

6. Select races that provide for variations in the degree and type of exertion required.

7. To avoid monotony, select a variety of races.

SINGLE RACES

The activities that comprise single races may be engaged in by a single participant for their developmental value; however, added enjoyment may be derived by competing against other contestants.

ALL-FOURS RUN

The performer flexes his legs and trunk and bends forward, places his hands on the floor directly below his shoulders, and assumes the all-fours position. At the starting signal, he runs forward in the direction that he is facing, using both hands and both feet.

BACKWARD ALL-FOURS RUN

Facing backwards to the direction of travel, the performer assumes the all-fours position. Using both hands and both feet, he runs backward.

BACKWARD RUN

Facing backwards, the performer runs backward when the starting signal is given. He should lift his knees rather high to avoid tripping himself by "stubbing" his heels on the floor.

BEAR RUN

The performer assumes the all-fours position and then walks or runs forward by moving both limbs on one side of his body simultaneously and then moving both limbs on the other side of his body in the same manner.

CRAB WALK

Sitting on the floor, the performer places his hands, fingers pointing forward or outward, beside and slightly behind his hips. He raises his buttocks from the floor to assume the crab position. At the starting signal, he runs forward on his hands and feet, keeping his buttocks as high as possible.

CROUCH RUN

The performer flexes his knees, hips, and trunk until his trunk is parallel to the floor. Maintaining the crouched position, he runs forward when the starting signal is sounded. This race may also be performed by running backwards.

CRISSCROSS TOE-HOLD RACE

The performer bends forward, crosses his arms, and grasps the big toe of each foot with the opposite hand. At the starting signal, he runs forward and, with each step, moves his leg diagonally across the front of his body. With each step his trunk rotates slightly in the direction of the leg movement of the foot crossing in front of his body.

ELEPHANT WALK

The performer assumes the all-fours position. Moving his limbs only at the shoulder and hips, he runs forward when the starting signal is given. During the race he keeps his limbs straight in order to prevent movement at the knees and elbows.

FROG-JUMP RACE

The performer squats, positions his buttocks near his heels, places his arms between his knees, and places the palms of his hands on the floor. Keeping his head up, he moves in the direction that he is facing by performing a series of springing movements. The spring is made at the instant that his body is parallel to the floor, after the performer has reached forward with his hands and as he is extending his legs. He lands on his hands and quickly returns his legs to the frog position, from which he again springs.

GALLOP-RUN RACE

The performer stands in a stride position with one leg ahead of the other. When the starting signal is given, he runs forward by stepping forward with the front foot and bringing the back foot to a position immediately behind the heel of the front foot. His legs never cross during the gallop run.

GORILLA WALK

The performer flexes his legs slightly and bends forward until his finger tips touch the floor. At the starting signal, he walks or runs forward, keeping his finger tips in contact with the floor.

HAND-KICK WALK

With his arms extended in front of his shoulders and positioned parallel to the floor, the performer walks or runs in the direction that he is facing, kicking an outstretched hand each time he takes a step.

HEAD-BALANCE RACE

The performer stands at attention in front of a mat. At the starting signal, he kneels, places his head and hands in a triangular position on the mat, raises his hips over his head and hands, and extends his legs. The first contestant to hold a head stand with his legs extended and held together is the winner.

HEEL-RUN RACE

Standing on his heels, the performer runs forward on his heels at the starting signal, keeping his toes raised off the floor throughout the race.

HEEL-TO-TOE RACE

The performer stands with one foot ahead of and touching the other foot. When the starting signal is given, he walks forward as rapidly as possible, taking extremely short steps in which he places the heel of the foot that was to the rear in contact with the toe of the foot that was forward.

HEEL-HOLD RACE

The performer bends forward and grasps the heel of his left foot with his right hand. When the starting signal is given, he runs forward as rapidly as possible without releasing his grasp on his heel.

HOP-RACE VARIATIONS

The performer stands on one or both feet and hops forward toward the finishing line when the starting signal is given. He may hop on both feet, by holding his ankles together at all times. He may hop on one foot and either grasp the ankle of the raised leg or allow the raised leg to move freely, in which case he should swing it vigorously forward during each hop.

KANGAROO JUMP

The standing performer holds a five-by-eight-inch card in place between his ankles, by squeezing his legs together. Upon the starting signal, he hops forward on both feet while holding the card between his ankles. If he loses the card, he must stop and reposition it before resuming his forward progress.

LAME-DOG RUN

The performer assumes the all-fours position and raises his left leg off the floor. When the starting signal is given he runs forward on both hands and his right foot. His left foot must remain off the floor at all times.

LEAP RACE

When the starting signal is sounded, the performer swings his right leg forward, springs from his left foot, and lands on his right foot. He next repeats this movement by swinging the left leg forward and springing from his right foot.

POTATO RACE

A number of wooden blocks are placed on the floor at varying distances from the starting line. With one foot a few inches in front of the other foot, the performer squats and places his hands on the floor about eighteen inches in front of his forward foot and immediately behind the starting line. He then raises his hips, supporting part of his weight on his hands, in order to assume the racing start position. When the starting signal is sounded he runs to the first block, picks it up, and returns it to a spot behind the starting line. He quickly turns around and repeats this procedure with the remainder of the blocks. The performer is not permitted to throw the blocks, and he should avoid stepping on any of them.

REVERSE CRAB WALK

With his back facing the starting line, the performer assumes the crab position on the floor. When the starting signal is sounded, he moves backward until he crosses the finish line.

ROPE-SKIP RACE

The standing performer holds a jumping rope in his hands and places the loop of the rope behind him. Upon a signal, he moves forward, swinging the jumping rope one complete circle for every two steps taken.

RUNNING RACE

Starting from the racing start position, the performer runs forward until he crosses the finish line.

SIDE-STEP RACE

The performer stands with his right side facing toward the finish line. When the starting signal is given, he steps sideward toward the finish line with his right foot. He quickly brings his left foot to his right and places it next to his right foot. He continues stepping sideways, but he may not cross his legs.

SKIP RACE

Starting from a stride position, the performer hops forward with his rear foot and then slides it forward until it is in line with his front foot. He steps forward with his front foot and continues to repeat the skipping movement with his rear foot. If desired, he may double skip by alternating the position of his front and back foot after each hop.

SORE-TOE RACE

The performer bends forward and with his right hand grasps the big toe of his left foot. Retaining his grasp on his toe, he moves forward toward the finish line.

STEAM-ENGINE RUN

Placing his hands on his shoulders and pointing his elbows toward the floor, the performer runs forward. As he steps, he raises each knee until it touches the elbow in front of it. An elbow must be touched each time a step is taken.

STIFF-KNEE JUMPING

Keeping his legs together and straight, the performer moves forward in a series of double-footed hops. He flexes his feet only at the ankles in order to hop—he must keep his legs stiff.

WATER BALL PUSH

Starting at one side or one end of a swimming pool the performer pushes a ball in front of him as he swims across the pool.

WATER NEWSPAPER RACE

Holding a folded newspaper in both hands, the performer stands in the water at one side of a swimming pool. When the starting signal is sounded, he moves across the pool by kicking his feet while reading the newspaper. He must hold the paper with both hands, and he should not let it get wet.

DUAL RACES

In some dual races, the partners must assist each other—that is, one partner is held or carried by the other partner. To distinguish between the partners in this type of dual race, the partner that holds or carries the other partner is called the holder and the partner that is held or carried is called the partner.

ARM CARRY

The holder faces his partner's side, bends forward, and places one arm around his partner's back and the other arm between his partner's thighs and underneath his crotch. The partner clasps his hands together after placing the other arm around the back of the holder's neck. The holder then extends his legs and back and supports his partner in his arms. At the starting signal, the holder runs forward, carrying his partner.

BACK-TO-BACK RUN

The partners stand back-to-back and hook elbows. The partner who is facing the direction of movement runs forward. The partner who is facing away from the direction of movement runs backward. The partner who is facing forward should run with his legs spread slightly, in order to avoid tripping his partner.

DEAD-MAN CARRY (FIGURE 20-1)

The partners stand face-to-face. The holder squats and places his right shoulder in the pit of his partner's stomach. The partner leans forward until his weight is supported on the holder's right shoulder. The holder clasps one or both arms around his partner's legs and then, while holding his partner, comes to an erect standing position. When the starting signal sounds, the holder runs forward to the finish line, carrying his partner.

FIREMAN'S CARRY

Facing his partner's right side, the holder bends forward and places his right shoulder in his partner's abdominal area. The holder places his right arm around the partner's right thigh and grasps the partner's right arm with his right hand. The holder comes to an erect standing position and with his left hand grasps the wrist of his partner's left arm. Supporting his partner, the holder walks or

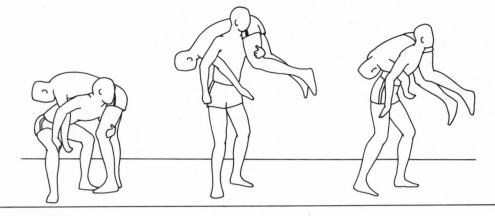

Figure 20-1. Dead-man carry.

runs toward the finish line, when the starting signal is given.

HUMAN WHEELBARROW (FIGURE 20-2)

The partner spreads his legs and assumes a front leaning-rest or push-up position on the floor. Standing between his partner's legs, the holder grasps his partner's ankles and comes to an erect position. When the starting signal is sounded, the partner walks forward on his hands as rapidly as possible. The holder follows his partner and supports his ankles.

REVERSE HUMAN WHEELBARROW

With his legs spread, the partner assumes a rear leaning-rest position on the floor, facing away from the finish line. The holder, facing the finish line, stands between his partner's legs, grasps his ankles, and stands erect. When the starting signal is

given, the partner walks backward on his hands and is preceded by the holder.

SIAMESE TWINS

Facing the finish line, the partners stand side by side, extend their inside arms toward each other, and tightly clasp each other's inside upper arm. Their inside arms may also be tied together with a rope. At the signal, they run toward the finish line.

TANDEM HOP

The partners stand side by side and grasp each other's inside hand. In a variation they may place their inside arm around each other's waist. They stand on their outside legs and raise their inside legs off the floor. Staying side by side, they hop toward the finish line.

RELAY RACES

All single and dual races can be adapted for relay races. Relay races can also involve such activities as carrying, passing, or kicking a basketball, soccer ball, softball, medicine ball, stuffed punching bag, football dummy, a long stick, a bat, or similar objects. In most relay races, each team member usually runs to a line or point located some distance from the starting line, returns to the starting point, and tags or starts the next team member in line. An alternate method is the shuttle system, in which the team is divided into two groups and each group stands facing each other behind lines that are 30 to 150 feet apart. In the shuttle system, when a teammate crosses his finish line,

Figure 20-2. Human wheelbarrow.

the next teammate starts from what is his starting line. Often each team member runs twice during the relay race and, thus, finishes the race at the line behind which he was located before the race started. The relay races described in this section are only a few of the many types that can be utilized.

CALISTHENICS

Each member of the team in turn performs a different calisthenic exercise, doing a set number of repetitions. While no specific form is required during the performance of each calisthenic exercise, each team member is expected to use correct form during his performance. When the starting signal is given, the first team member runs to the front of his group and does his prescribed exercise. When he finishes, he tags the second team members, who leaves the line and performs his exercise. Each team continues this pattern until all the members have completed the calisthenic exercise assigned to them.

CRAB KICK

For each team, the first team member in line assumes the crab position behind the starting line. A ball rests on each team's starting line (a medicine ball may be used). Kicking or pushing with his feet, the first team member attempts to move the ball to a turning line and back to the finish line, at which time he kicks the ball to the second team member in line. When dribbling the ball with his feet, a team member must remain in the crab position throughout his turn, and he may not touch the ball with his hands.

IN-AND-OUT

With the members spaced five feet apart, each team lines up in a single file. At the starting signal, the first member on each team turns around and runs through the column in a zigzag fashion, by alternately going to the right of one teammate and to the left of the next teammate. Upon completing his run, he lines up five feet behind the teammate who was last in line. As soon as the first member has passed the second teammate in the line, the latter turns around and begins running a zigzag pattern to the rear of the line. This continues until all the players have returned to their original positions. If desired, this relay may be continued

until all the members of a team have run through their team two or three times.

LEAPFROG

Each team lines up in a column with the members spaced six feet apart. Each team member bends forward at the waist and places his hands on his knees. At the starting signal, the last member in the column leapfrogs over each of his teammates in turn. When he gets to the front of the column, he stands six feet in front of the teammate that was first in line and assumes a bent-over position. As soon as a teammate becomes the rear man in the column, he begins jumping over his teammates. The relay ends when the teammate who was originally at the head of the column is again at the head of the line. If desired, the relay may be continued until all the teammates have had two or three turns.

MEDICINE-BALL VARIATIONS: BETWEEN THE LEGS PASS

Any type of ball may be used in these races. The team members form a column and place the hands of their outstretched arms on the shoulders of the teammate immediately in front of them. The team member at the front of the line holds the medicine ball at waist height. When the starting signal is given, the first man in the column bends forward and passes the ball between his legs to the second man. Each team member, except the last man in line, repeats this performance. When the last man in line receives the ball, he carries it to the head of the line and initiates the passing of the ball between the legs. The race is finished when the team members return to their original positions in the column, and the team member at the front of the line has touched the medicine ball to the floor.

MEDICINE-BALL VARIATIONS: CIRCLE OVERTAKE

With the opposing team members taking every other position in the circle, two teams form one circle with all members facing the center of the circle. A designated member (or team captain) of each team stands on opposite sides of the circle, and holds a medicine ball in front of him at waist height. Upon the signal, each ball is rapidly passed to members of the same team in an attempt to overtake and pass the other team's ball. Both balls are passed in the same direction. A team scores one point each time that their ball passes the other team's ball.

MEDICINE-BALL VARIATIONS: MOVING OVERHEAD PASS

The team forms a circle with the left shoulders of the members facing to the inside of the circle. One member of the group holds a medicine ball. As the team slowly jogs counterclockwise around the circle, the team member holding the ball throws it over his head and to the man behind him. Each team members repeats this performance. One point is scored each time that the ball completes a trip around the circle without being dropped. If the ball is dropped, it should be picked up and the passing is resumed at that spot.

MEDICINE-BALL VARIATIONS: SINGLE CIRCLE PASS

Each team forms a circle with the members of the team facing the center of the circle. One of the team members holds a medicine ball. When the starting signal is given, the ball is passed around the circle from team member to team member. One point is scored for each time the ball is passed around the circle and past the starting point without being dropped on the floor.

MEDICINE-BALL VARIATIONS: TADPOLE

Two teams, composed of equal numbers of team members, form the head and tail of a tadpole. The head is outlined by one team, which forms a circle, and the tail is outlined by the opposing team, which forms a single line in which the first man in line stands directly behind one of the opposing team members. The team forming the head passes the ball around the circle as many times as there are members on the team. One at a time, each of the team members forming the tail run around the outside of the circle, running in the same direction that the ball is being passed. The team that finishes first wins the contest.

MEDICINE-BALL VARIATION: UNDER-AND-OVER PASS

The team members form a column by placing the hands of their outstretched arms on the shoulders of the teammate immediately in front of them. The man at the front of the column holds the medicine ball at waist height. When the starting signal is given the man at the front of the column bends forward and passes the ball between his legs to the second man. The second man then makes an overhead pass behind him to the third man, who repeats the between-the-legs pass. The type of pass is

alternated until the team member at the end of the line receives the ball and carries it to the head of the line. The passing procedure is repeated until the original head man is again at the head of the column, at which time the relay is completed.

TUNNEL RELAY

The members of each team stand in a single column with their legs spread in a straddle position. When the starting signal is given, the member at the rear of the column assumes an all-four position and crawls between the legs of his teammates, until he reaches the front of the column, at which time he assumes a straddle position. Each team member, as soon as he is the rear man, crawls to the front of the column. The relay ends when the team member originally at the front of the column is again in this position.

TEAM RACES

All members of the team move together at the same time during a team race.

CENTIPEDE

Standing in a single column, each team member places his arms around the waist of the teammate in front of him. When the starting signal is given, the team runs as a unit toward the finish line. If the team comes apart—that is, if a member loses his grasp around the waist of a teammate—then the members must stop, regroup, and start again.

CATERPILLAR (FIGURE 20-3)

Forming a column, the team members assume the all-fours position. Each team member grasps the ankles of the team member in front of him. Upon the signal, the team runs toward the finish line, retaining their grasp on their teammates ankles. If a team member loses his grasp on the

Figure 20-3. Caterpillar.

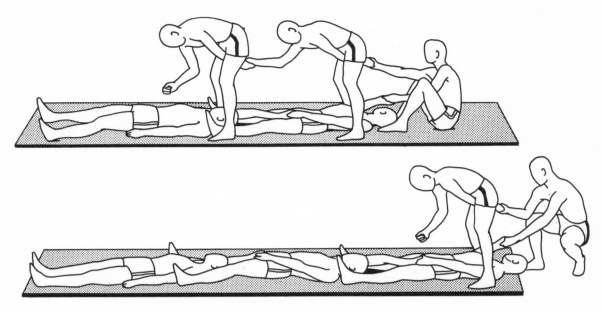

Figure 20-4. Skin the snake.

ankles of the man in front of him the team must stop, regroup, and start again.

CHAIN CRAB

Forming a column, the team assumes the crab position. Each team member grasps the ankles of the person behind him. Retaining their grasp on their teammates' ankles, they move feet first toward the finish line. If any of the team members become separated, the team must stop, regrasp ankles, and resume their movement toward the finish line.

CIRCLE RACE

The team members hold hands and form a circle in which all but one of them face the outside of the circle. The person facing the inside of the circle is the "driver," who gives directions to his teammates during the race. When the starting signal is given, the team runs to a line located fifty feet in front of the starting line. All the team members cross this line and the team returns to the starting line, keeping the circle intact at all times. If the circle is broken, it must be re-formed before the team can continue the race. If desired, the team may run only past the line that is located fifty feet (or any other set distance) from the starting line.

INDIAN FILE

Standing in a compact column, each team member places his arms around the person in front of him. At the starting signal the team runs forward past the finish line, maintaining an unbroken column throughout the race. If desired the team may face backward and run backwards to the finish line.

SKIN THE SNAKE (FIGURE 20-4)

Forming a column, each team member reaches his right arm through his legs and behind him, and grasps the left hand of the person behind him. With his left hand, he grasps the right hand of the person in front of him. When the starting signal is given, the team member at the rear of the line lies down on his back and, continuing to hold hands, the other team members walk backward, straddling the reclining team member. As each team member becomes the last one standing at the rear of the line, he lies down on his back. When all the team members are lying on their backs, the last person to lie down gets up and, walking forward, pulls the next person up. Without releasing hands, this action continues until all team members are standing erect.

21. activities for circuit training

As mentioned in Chapter 5, circuit training is a type of conditioning that involves participation in rapid succession in a group of activities that comprise a circuit. *Circuit* is the term given to the group of activities. The activities in the circuit are conducted at various locations, called *stations*. The performer completes a given number of repetitions of the activity at one station and then proceeds, in turn, through the remaining stations, performing the number of repetitions required for each activity at each station. He continues until he has passed through all of the stations one or more times, as required.

The activities for the circuit should be so selected and arranged that the efforts required of any one portion of the body are changed alternately from an active to a passive phase as the performer works his way around the circuit. For example, if the muscles of the arms and shoulder girdle are exercised vigorously in performing the activity at one station, the activity at the next station in the circuit might be one in which the legs are exercised vigorously. Also, the primary components of physi-

cal fitness that are developed should vary from station to station: for example, the activity at one station might be selected to develop strength primarily; the activity at the next station, to develop cardiorespiratory endurance; at the next, flexibility; and so forth, until the development of all components of physical fitness are provided for in the circuit.

An overload can be produced by (1) increasing the number of stations in the circuit, (2) increasing the number of repetitions at each station in the circuit, (3) increasing the number of times the circuit is completed, or (4) so increasing the speed of performance at each station that the total time required to complete the circuit is decreased.

In this chapter the activities are organized according to specific components of physical fitness. The components included here in the order of their appearance are: agility, balance, circulorespiratory endurance, flexibility, and local muscular endurance. In reality, the organization of activities according to specific components of physical fitness is a theoretical procedure because participation in almost any activity brings into play more than one of the qualities of physical fitness. Balance activities, for example, involve strength and local muscular endurance as well as balance. Circulorespiratory activities involve strength, local muscular endurance, flexibility, and balance as well as circulorespiratory endurance. Thus, all the activities included here for circuit training call into play a combination of several of the components of physical fitness. The only logical explanation for grouping activities under specific components of physical fitness is that certain activities are useful for developing primarily one component of physical fitness. In many cases, the same activity is included in two or more categories because the component of physical fitness that is predominantly developed changes as the use of the activity is changed. For example, jumping a few times is considered to be an agility activity, but jumping many times is considered to be a circulorespiratory activity.

AGILITY ACTIVITIES

BOARDING-HOUSE REACH (FIGURE 21-1)

The performer takes a front leaning-rest position on the floor. He moves his arms toward his feet until his left elbow is close to his hip. Keeping his toes on a line and supporting himself with his left arm, he attempts to draw a chalk line as far from the toe line as possible.

DODGING

The performer bends his legs at the knees, taking a slightly crouched position. His feet are spread about hip-distance apart. Pushing on the floor with either foot, he moves sideways and attempts to avoid another person or object.

FLANK VAULT ON THE FLOOR (FIGURE 21-2)

From a front leaning-rest position on the floor, the performer attempts to do a flank vault, finishing in a rear leaning-rest position.

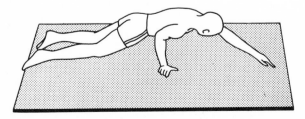

Figure 21-1. Boarding-house reach.

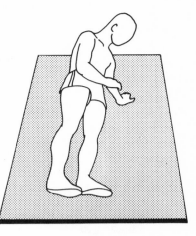

Figure 21-2. Flank vault on the floor.

FORWARD HAND KICK

From a crouch position the performer springs off the floor and attempts to touch his toes with his hands by flexing his legs at the hips. He tries to land in a standing position.

FULL TURN

From a crouch position the performer springs off the floor and attempts to make one complete turn before landing on his feet.

HEEL CLICK

From a crouch position the performer springs off the floor and attempts to click his heels together twice before landing on his feet.

HEEL SLAP

From a crouch position the performer springs off the floor, flexes his legs at the knees, and attempts to slap his heels before landing on his feet.

HOP-STEP-JUMP

From a crouch position, the performer takes one hop, then a long step, and then broad jumps.

HUMAN BALL (FIGURE 21-3)

The performer sits on the floor in Turk fashion. With his hands he grasps the ankles of the opposite legs. He attempts to roll to his left and return to the Turk position, facing in the opposite direction. He starts the roll by leaning forward and to his left. First his left leg and knee touch the floor. Then his left arm and shoulder touch the floor. He next rolls across his back, then to his right shoulder and arm, and, finally, to his right leg and knee.

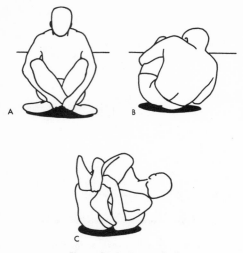

Figure 21-3. Human ball.

Figure 21-4. Jump-over-leg.

JUMP-OVER-LEG (FIGURE 21-4)

The performer runs slowly toward a wall. He jumps off the floor and places his left foot against the wall, keeping his left leg parallel with the floor. As he springs from the floor, he attempts to swing his right leg over his left leg while making a half turn with his body, keeping his left foot in contact with the wall until his right foot again touches the floor.

JUMP THROUGH CIRCLE (FIGURE 21-5)

The performer bends over and with his right hand grasps the big toe of his left foot. This movement forms a circle. He tries to jump through the circle with his right foot and land on his right foot with-out breaking the circle. After the performer can jump through the circle, he should try to jump back out again.

KNEEL, JUMP TO FEET

The performer kneels on the floor and extends his feet at the ankles. He attempts to swing his arms forcefully upward, spring off the floor, and land in a crouch position with his feet on the floor.

LEG CIRCLING

The performer squats on his left leg, places his hands on the floor, and extends his right leg out to the side. He attempts to move his right leg in a circular motion, lifting any supporting limb that obstructs the circling movement.

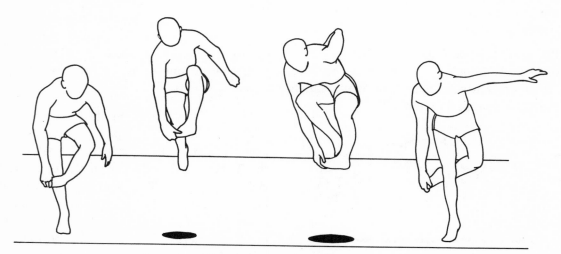

Figure 21-5. Jump through circle.

LEG EXTENSION

With his legs extended and his hands placed on his hips, the performer sits on the floor. He flexes his legs at the knees and his thighs at the hips, drawing his upper legs toward his chest and his heels toward his buttocks. He extends his legs to the starting position.

SEAL SLAP

The performer takes a front leaning-rest position on the floor. He lowers his body slightly and then pushes upward forcefully. When the arms are extended completely, he attempts to remove his hands from the floor and clap them together before using them again for support.

SIDE KICK (FIGURE 21-6)

The performer crouches. He springs off the floor and swings his right leg to the side. While in the air, he attempts to swing his left leg up to the right leg and to land standing on both feet.

SPRING TO HEELS

The performer assumes a squat position. He springs upward, throws his arms out to the side, and lands on his heels. He attempts to balance himself in this position with his toes off the floor.

SQUAT THRUST

The performer stands at attention. He bends forward and places his hands on the floor outside his feet. As soon as his hands touch the floor, he

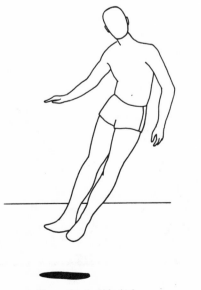

Figure 21-6. Side kick.

thrusts his legs back to a front leaning-rest position. When he reaches the front leaning-rest position, he returns to the half-squat position and then stands up.

SQUAT VAULT ON FLOOR

The performer takes a front leaning-rest position. He attempts to slide his legs between his arms and move to a rear leaning-rest position.

STANDING BROAD JUMP

The performer takes a crouch position with his arms extended backwards. Flinging his arms forcefully, he jumps forward and upward and lands on his feet.

STRIDE JUMP

The performer crouches. He springs upward, spreads his legs apart with one leg in front of and one behind his body. He attempts to land on the floor with both feet together again.

TUCK JUMP

The performer crouches. He springs upward, flexing his thighs at the hips and his legs at the knees so that he may clasp his shins with his hands. This position is termed the *tuck position*. He attempts to land on the floor on his feet with both legs extended.

VERTICAL JUMP

The performer stands with his side next to a wall. He crouches, then jumps upward, throwing both arms upward. Near the top of the jump, he throws the arm that is away from the wall downward. At the peak of the jump, he attempts to slap the wall with the hand that is next to it.

BALANCE ACTIVITIES

BALANCE ON TOES

The performer stands with his arms at his sides. He rises on his toes and extends his arms to the side. He extends his left leg to the side, balancing on the toes of his right foot.

CRANE DIVE

The performer stands with his arms at his sides. He raises his right leg behind him and bends forward, placing his hands on the floor. He attempts

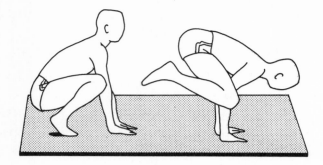

Figure 21-7. Frog stand or tip-up balance.

to touch his forehead to the floor and to return to the starting position without touching his right leg to the floor.

FROG STAND OR TIP-UP BALANCE (FIGURE 21-7)

Placing his hands between his legs and his thighs on his elbows, the performer squats on the floor. He tips forward, placing his weight on his hands, and continues forward until he finds the point of balance.

HANDSTAND WITH SUPPORT (FIGURE 21-8)

The performer bends forward and places his hands on the floor near a wall or in front of a partner. He places his shoulders over his hands and locks his arms at the elbows. He places his right foot under his hip and extends his left leg back. He then swings the left leg up over his head and, at the same time, pushes off with the right foot. As the legs swing upward, he extends his right leg and

places both feet on the wall or in his partner's hands. His body should have a slight arch, and his head should be parallel with the floor.

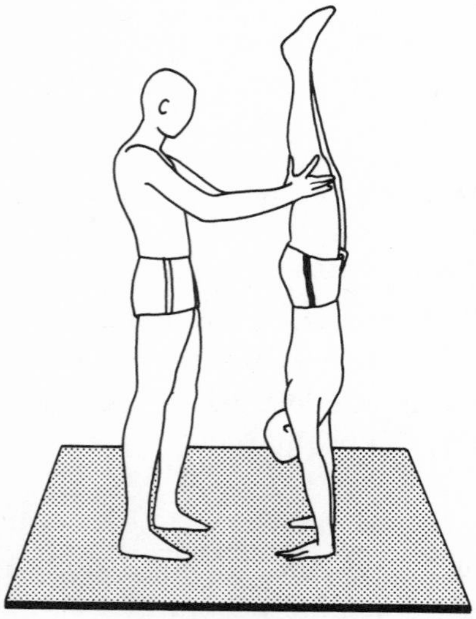

HEADSTAND

The performer kneels on the mat and forms a triangle with both hands and the hairline of his forehead. An alternate starting position is to assume the frog stand and overbalance forward, placing the forehead on the mat. He moves his hips over his head and raises his legs off the ground. He attempts to balance in a low tucked position. When successful with the low tucked balance, he extends his legs overhead, moving his hips slightly toward the hands and arching his body slightly.

KNEE TOUCH (FIGURE 21-9)

The performer stands on his right foot and, with his left hand, holds his left leg at the ankle. He does a deep knee bend on his right leg until his left knee touches the ground and then extends his right leg again.

ONE-FOOT BALANCE

With his arms extended to the side, the performer stands on his right foot. He bends forward at his waist until his body, his arms, and his left leg are parallel with the ground.

ONE-KNEE BALANCE, HEAD TOUCH

The performer kneels on the floor. He extends his left leg to the rear and extends his arms to the side. Thus balanced, he attempts to bend forward, touch his forehead on the floor, and, without losing balance, return to the starting position.

SINGLE SQUAT BALANCE

The performer squats on the floor. He extends

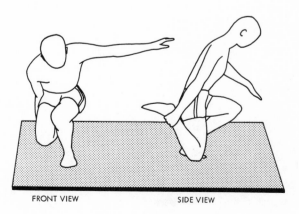

FRONT VIEW   SIDE VIEW

Figure 21-9. Knee touch.

Figure 21-8. Handstand with support.

his right leg forward and attempts to balance on the toes of his left foot.

SIT BALANCE

The performer sits on the floor, leans slightly backward, and keeps his legs extended as he raises them from the floor. He balances himself on his buttocks.

STORK STAND

The performer stands with both feet together, raises his right foot, and places it behind his left knee. He balances himself on his left foot.

WALKING A LINE ON TOES

The performer stands on a line with his right foot in front of his left foot. He rises to his toes and attempts to walk down the line without losing his balance or without touching his heels to the floor.

CIRCULORESPIRATORY ACTIVITIES

JUMPING, FORWARD HAND KICK

From a crouch position the performer springs off the floor and, at the height of his jump, attempts by flexing his upper legs at the hips, to touch his toes with his hands. He tries to land in an erect standing position with the legs slightly bent.

JUMPING, HEEL CLICK

From a crouch position the performer springs off the floor and attempts to click his heels together twice before landing on his feet.

JUMPING, HEEL SLAP

From a crouch position the performer springs off the floor, flexes his legs at the knees, and, at the height of his jump, attempts to slap his heels before landing on his feet.

JUMPING, SIDE KICK

The performer crouches, springs off the floor, and swings his right leg to the side. While in the air, he attempts to swing his left leg up to the right leg and to land standing on both feet.

JUMPING, STRIDE JUMP

The performer assumes a crouched postion. He springs upward and spreads his legs apart with one leg in front and one behind his body. He attempts to land on the floor with both feet together again.

JUMPING, TUCK JUMP

The performer assumes a crouched position. He springs upward, so flexing his thighs at the hips and legs at the knees that he may clasp his shins with his hands. (This position is termed the *tuck position*.) He attempts to land on the floor on his feet with both legs extended.

JUMPING, VERTICAL WALL SLAP

The performer stands with his side next to a wall. He crouches, jumps upward, and vigorously extends both arms upward. Near the top of the jump he quickly brings the arm that is away from the wall downward. At the peak of the jump he attempts to slap the wall with the hand that is next to it.

ROPE JUMPING

See Chapter 14 for information regarding rope jumping.

RUNNING DRILL, LAST MAN PASS

A group of four to eight runners form a column and jog in the column formation. The last man in line sprints past the group to become the leader of the column. As soon as he is in place, the new last man sprints past the group and goes to the head of the line. The runners should pass on the outside and to the right of the column.

RUNNING FOR FORM

Four to eight runners form a column. The group runs in a column formation and imitates the form of the group leader. They should stay in line and concentrate on any of the following problems: correct use of the arms, correct position of the feet, proper push-off, and correct stride. The runners should not attempt to concentrate on more than two problems at any one time.

RUNNING IN PLACE, HIGH

The performer starts in an erect position, his forearms flexed at the elbows. He runs in place, raising his knees as high as they can be raised. At the same time, he pumps his arms, swinging them through arcs at his sides.

RUNNING IN PLACE, LOW

The performer stands in a bent-over position with his feet spread apart about the width of his hips. When he runs in place, his feet are just barely raised from the floor. When properly executed, this form of running in place sounds much like a pneumatic drill in action.

RUNNING IN PLACE, MEDIUM

The performer stands in an erect position, his forearms flexed at the elbows. He runs in place, raising his knees up as high as his waistline. At the same time, he pumps his arms, swinging them through arcs at his sides.

STAIR CLIMB

The performer stands at the foot of the stairs. He climbs the stairs one step at a time, keeping to the right side. He returns to the foot of the stairs, keeping to the left side of the steps.

STEP UP, STEP DOWN

The performer stands in front of a small stool that is twelve to eighteen inches in height. He places his right foot on top of the stool, steps up, and places his left foot on top of the stool. Shifting his weight to his left foot, he steps down again on his right foot. At the end of one minute of stepping, he may change the starting leg to the left leg by shifting his weight to his right foot and stepping up with his left foot.

FLEXIBILITY ACTIVITIES

ARM CIRCLING

The performer stands in an erect position with his arms so raised sideward that they are parallel to the floor. He then moves his arms in a circular motion with his hands moving in circles that become larger and larger until finally they reach the limiting ranges of motion. He then reverses the direction of the circular motion and repeats the process.

BOTTOMS UP OR SQUAT BENDER

From an erect standing position the performer squats in a deep knee bend until his fingertips touch the floor by his toes. Keeping his fingertips touching the floor, he straightens his legs, then squats again, and finally returns to the starting position. This is a four-count exercise.

HAMSTRING STRETCHER

With his legs spread as wide apart as possible, the performer sits on the floor. He flexes forward and attempts to touch his elbows to the floor, first

in the middle, then by the right knee, and then by the left knee. Next, he grasps his legs at the calves and pulls himself forward, first between his legs, then toward the right knee, and then toward the left knee.

HIGH KICK

The performer stands in a position of attention. He transfers his weight to his left foot and swings his right arm out in front until it is parallel with the floor. At the same time, he swings his right leg forward, attempting to touch the palm of the hand with his toe. He returns the kicking foot to the floor and steps in place—right, left, right. Then, on the third step in place, when his weight is transferred to the right foot, he kicks with his left foot and attempts to touch the toe to the palm of the left hand.

LAY-OUT ON BACK (FIGURE 21-10)

With his body in an erect position, the performer kneels. He leans backward until he can support himself on his hands and then moves his hands back until he can move them no more.

LEG CIRCLING

The performer lies on his back and raises his legs to a position perpendicular to the floor. His arms are on the floor and are extended at right angles from his body. Keeping his legs straight and his arms braced against the floor, he moves his feet in ever-widening circles. When the maximum circumference is reached, the size of the circles is decreased until the feet are back in the starting position.

LEG ROLL-BACK

The performer lies on his back with his arms at his sides. He raises his legs up in the air, moving

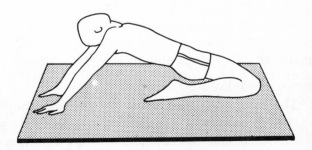

Figure 21-10. Lay-out on back.

them on over his head until his toes touch the floor. He then returns to the starting position.

MAD CAT

The performer places his hands, knees, and toes on the floor. The back should be straight or arched downward toward the floor. He humps his back, trying to raise his back as high as possible in the air. He returns to the starting position.

ONE-ARM DIP

The performer takes a front leaning-rest position on the floor. He removes one hand from the floor and centers his weight over his other hand. In an easier variation, he takes a side leaning-rest position. He flexes his forearm at the elbow until his chin touches the floor; then he pushes up, extending his arm again.

FULL PULL-UP

The performer hangs at arm's length below the bar, using a reverse grip. He so pulls up (without kicking) that his chin is higher than, but not over, the bar. He then returns to the starting position.

LOWER-HALF PULL-UP

The performer hangs at arm's length below the bar. He uses a reverse grasp. He pulls up (without kicking) until his upper arms are parallel with the floor. He then returns to the starting position.

UPPER-HALF PULL-UP

The performer hangs below the bar with his upper arms parallel to the floor. He uses a reverse grasp. He so pulls up (without kicking) that his chin is higher than, but not over, the bar. He then returns to the starting position.

WALL PUSH-AWAY

With his arms extended and his hands touching the wall at about chest height, the performer stands facing a wall. He moves his feet backward a distance of about twice the length of his foot and lowers his hands on the wall about six inches. With his arms at an angle to his body, he is now leaning against the wall. He flexes his arms until his face is from one to two inches away from the wall. Then he extends his arms and pushes vigorously with his hands and fingers until the hands leave the wall and his body approaches an erect position. He leans forward until his hands again touch the wall, and returns to the starting position.

SIDEWARD LEG RAISE

The performer stands at a position of attention. He shifts his weight to his left foot and raises his right leg sideways to his right. He returns to the starting position and repeats the exercise to the left.

SIDEWARD LEG STRETCH

With his arms at his sides and his legs spread as wide apart as they will go, the performer stands in an erect position. He bends his right leg, moves his body to the right, and, at the same time, presses down on his right knee with his right hand. He returns to the starting position and repeats the exercise to his left.

STOMACH ROLLER

With his legs flexed and his hands clasping his ankles, the performer lies in a face-down position. He pulls on his ankles and rocks back and forth on his thighs, stomach, and chest.

TOE TOUCH TO FOREHEAD

The performer stands in a position of attention. He moves his weight to his left foot. Grasping his right foot in his hands, he attempts to bend forward and touch his right toe to his forehead.

TRUNK STRETCHER

With hands on hips and legs slightly apart, the performer stands in an erect position. He moves his upper trunk as far forward as possible and returns to the starting position. He repeats these movements to his left, to his rear, and to his right.

WINDSHIELD WIPER

With his legs raised in a position perpendicular to the floor, the performer lies on his back. His arms are on the floor and are extended at right angles from his body. Keeping his legs straight and his arms braced against the floor, he moves his legs as far to his right as possible and attempts to lightly touch the floor with his right foot. He returns his legs to the starting position and repeats the exercise to his left.

WRESTLER'S BRIDGE (FIGURE 21-11)

The performer lies on his back with his heels drawn up next to his buttocks and his hands placed on the floor next to his head. He raises his body off the floor and supports his weight on his feet, his head, and his hands.

Figure 21-11. Wrestler's bridge.

Figure 21-12. Half-lever.

MUSCLE-ENDURANCE ACTIVITIES

ANKLE BOUNCING

The performer places his hands on his hips and, keeping his trunk erect, squats on his heels. He extends his feet at the ankles as forcefully as possible.

BACK ARCH ON BENCH, HANDS DOWN

The performer so lies face-down on a bench that the edge of the bench is slightly below his waistline. He rests his forehead on a pad on the floor and his hands by his thighs; his legs are held on the bench by a partner. The performer arches his back, raises his head and trunk as high in the air as possible, and then returns to the starting position.

BACK ARCH ON BENCH, HANDS UP

The performer so lies in a prone position on a bench that the edge of the bench is slightly below his waistline. His fingers are interlaced and clasped behind his head, and the hair line of his forehead rests on a pad on the floor. His partner holds his feet. The performer arches his head and back, raising them from the floor as high as possible, and then returns to the starting position.

HALF-LEVER (FIGURE 21-12)

The performer flexes his thighs at the hip and makes an *L* with his body. He may assume this position while hanging from a high bar, supporting himself on the parallel bars, or pushing himself up from the floor. He holds this position as long as possible.

BENT-ARM HANG

The performer so pulls himself up that his chin is above the level of but not over, the top of the horizontal bar. He uses a reverse grip (palms fac-

ing body). He remains in this position until his chin falls below the level of the bar, at which time he lets go and drops off the bar.

PARALLEL-ARM HANG (FIGURE 21-13)

The performer so pulls himself up that his upper arms are parallel with the floor. He uses a reverse grip. He remains in this position until the musculature of the arms fatigues and causes him to fall from the starting position, at which time he lets go and drops off the bar.

STRAIGHT-ARM HANG

The performer hangs at arm's length below the bar. He uses the reverse grip. He remains in this position until the muscles fatigue and cause him to let go and drop off the bar.

KNEE TOUCH

The performer stands on his right foot and holds

REAR VIEW   FRONT VIEW

Figure 21-13. Parallel-arm hang.

his left leg at the ankle with his left hand. He does a deep knee bend on his right leg until his left knee touches the ground, and then he extends his right leg again.

BACK-ARCH PUSH-UP

With his feet together and his hands underneath his shoulders, the performer lies in a prone position on the floor. He pushes his upper body up by extending his arms, keeping his legs and his abdomen on the floor. He lowers his body to the starting position.

KNEE OR HALF PUSH-UP

With his feet together, his knees and feet resting on the floor, and his hands underneath his shoulders, the performer lies in a prone position on the floor. He pushes up, keeping his body, from head to knees, in a straight line, until his arms are fully extended. He lowers his body to the starting position.

TOE OR FULL PUSH-UP

With his feet together, his toes resting on the floor, and his hands underneath his shoulders, the performer lies in a prone position on the floor. He pushes up, keeping his body, from head to toe, in a straight line, until his arms are fully extended. He lowers his body to the starting position.

ONE-LEG PUSH-UP

With his hands underneath his shoulders and one leg raised off the floor, the performer lies in a prone position on the floor. He pushes up until his arms are fully extended, keeping his body, from head to toe, in a rigid line and keeping the raised leg off the floor. He lowers his body to the starting position.

HANDS-ON-BENCHES-OR-CHAIRS PUSH-UP

The performer bends forward and places his hands on top of two benches or chairs, which are placed slightly more than shoulder-distance apart. Supporting his weight on his extended arms, he extends his legs and lower trunk until his body is in a straight line. His body weight is now supported in a front leaning-rest position. He lowers his body, keeping it in a straight line from head to toes until he can lower it no farther. He then returns to the starting position.

FEET-ON-BENCH-OR-CHAIR PUSH-UP

With his feet on a chair and his hands on the floor underneath his shoulders, the performer takes a front leaning-rest position. He lowers his body, keeping it in a straight line from head to toe until his chest touches the floor. He then returns to the starting position.

FEET-ON-WALL PUSH-UP

Standing with his back to a wall and with his feet next to the wall, the performer assumes a front leaning-rest position. He then walks his feet up the wall, while moving his hands toward the wall until they are from four to two feet from the wall (the more vertical the body position, the more difficult is the push-up movement). It is wise to place a small pillow or cushion under the head of the performer. The performer lowers his body, keeping it in a straight line from head to toe until his head touches the floor. He then returns to the starting position. This is an extremely difficult push-up movement to perform and requires considerable arm and shoulder strength relative to body weight.

SIDE LEANING-REST

The performer takes a front leaning-rest position and so turns his body to the right that he is supported by his right foot and right hand. He raises his left arm sidewards until it is perpendicular to his body, at the same time, raises his left leg until it will go no higher. He returns to the right side leaning-rest position and then repeats the movement, using the other arm to support his weight.

ONE-ARM PUSH-UP: SIDE-FACING

The performer takes a side leaning-rest position. He lowers his body sideways until his shoulder touches his hand. He then returns to the starting position.

ONE-ARM PUSH-UP: FLOOR-FACING

The performer takes a front leaning-rest position. He removes one hand from the floor, places it on the small of his back, and centers his weight over the other hand. He lowers his body, keeping it in a straight line from head to toe, until his chest touches the floor. He then returns to the starting position.

REAR LEANING-REST HIP-RAISING

The performer takes a rear leaning-rest position on the floor. He sits on the floor, and then raises his hips as high as they will go. He then returns to the starting position.

SIT-UP AND LEG RAISE

With his hands by his sides and his legs extended, the performer lies on his back. He sits up and, at the same time, raises his legs, touching his feet with his hands while balancing on his buttocks. He then returns to the starting position.

SIT-UPS: BENT-LEG

With his fingers interlaced and held behind his head, the performer lies on his back. His heels are next to his buttocks and his knees are raised in the air. His feet are held to the floor by a partner. The performer sits up, attempts to touch his right shoulder to his left knee, and then returns to the starting position. He repeats the exercise to the other side.

SIT-UP WITH STRAIGHT LEGS, HANDS AT SIDES

With his arms at his sides and his legs extended and slightly spread, the performer lies on his back. His feet are held to the floor by a partner or are placed under a heavy object. The performer sits up, curling forward with his head and trunk, until he can bring his head no closer to his legs; he then returns to the starting position.

SIT-UP WITH STRAIGHT LEGS, HANDS BEHIND HEAD

With his fingers interlaced and held behind his head, the performer lies on his back. His legs are extended and slightly spread. His feet are held to the floor by a partner or are placed under a non-movable support. The performer sits up, curls for-ward, and attempts to touch his right elbow to his left knee. He returns to the starting position and repeats the exercise to the opposite side.

FULL SQUAT JUMP

With his arms by his sides, his feet apart, and one foot slightly ahead of the other, the performer stands in an erect position. He squats, flexing his legs at the knees until his fingertips touch the floor. He then jumps off the floor, extending his arms overhead and so changing his feet in the air that he lands on the floor with the opposite foot in advance. This exercise may also be performed with the hands clasped on top of the head throughout the exercise.

HALF SQUAT JUMP

The performer stands in an erect position with his arms at his sides, his feet apart, and one foot slightly ahead of the other foot. He squats, flexing his legs at the knees until the heel of his hand touches his knee. He then jumps off the floor, throwing his arms overhead and so changing his feet in the air that he lands on the floor with the opposite foot in advance. This exercise may also be performed with the hands placed on top of the head throughout the exercise.

THREE-QUARTERS SQUAT JUMP

With his arms by his sides, his feet apart, and one foot slightly ahead of the other foot, the performer stands in an erect position. He squats, flexing his legs at the knees until his hands touch the middle of his shins. He then jumps off the floor, throwing his arms overhead and so changing his feet in the air that he lands on the floor with the opposite foot in advance.

part 4

The Evaluation of Physical Fitness

22. evaluation of physical fitness

A multitude of physical-fitness tests have been devised with which to evaluate various components of physical fitness and/or overall physical fitness. This section attempts to answer the following question: If physical fitness should be regularly measured, what test or tests should be employed for this purpose?

PURPOSES OF PHYSICAL-FITNESS EVALUATION

Most medical doctors, physiologists, and physical educators agree that a periodical evaluation of one's physical fitness can serve a number of worthwhile purposes.

Testing for What?

Medical doctors, physiologists, and physical educators often have different purposes in mind when testing for physical fitness. The medical doctor usually checks the increases in pulse rate and blood pressure brought about by a short bout of mild activity, and determines the time required for these measures to return to the resting rate. He is chiefly interested in the responses of the cardiovascular system, when one is subjected to such simple exercises as stool stepping in place, for example. The physiologist is generally most concerned with the efficiency of the body during the performance of a fixed amount of work. For example, he is trained to measure the amount of oxygen consumed per minute, and to compute the cost of performing such work as treadmill running or stationary bicycle riding (ergometer). The physical educator usually confines his own efforts to measuring the various components of physical fitness by making use of such motor tests as sit-ups, pull-ups, shuttle run, and vertical jumping.

Physical-Fitness Tests in Physical Education

At the present time, physical-fitness tests are administered in physical-education programs to enable the instructor and the student to determine the following:

1. The student's overall level of physical fitness.
2. The progress that the student has made toward

achieving a satisfactory level of physical fitness.

3. The components of physical fitness in which the student is deficient and needs additional training.

4. The effectiveness of the physical-fitness program in which the student is participating, the instruction that is given, and/or the motivation afforded the student.

5. The manner in which students should be grouped, to insure groups of similar levels of fitness.

Contents of Older Physical-Fitness Tests

Physical-fitness testing has been conducted on a somewhat extensive scale for several decades, especially during times of war. The tests and batteries of tests used in the past to evaluate components of physical fitness or overall physical fitness in the United States have included the following:

1. *Tests of accuracy* such as throwing or kicking at a target.

2. *Tests of agility* such as short shuttle runs, side-step-touch test, speed-agility run, dodge run, zig-zag run, and direction-change test.

3. *Tests of balance* such as dynamic balance test, stick balance test, squat balance, and balance beam test.

4. *Body measurements* such as chest-girth measurements, body fat measurements, body weight, and ratings of body type.

5. *Tests of cardiorespiratory endurance* such as the Harvard Step Test, the Carlson Fatigue Curve Test, mile run, three-hundred-yard run, and shuttle runs.

6. *Tests of cardiovascular efficiency* such as step tests, pulse-ratio test, changes in pulse rate before and after exercise, changes in blood pressure after shifting to a standing position from a reclining position, and stool stepping.

7. *Tests of flexibility* such as trunk flexion forward, trunk flexion backward, shoulder flexibility, and ankle flexibility.

8. *Tests of muscular endurance* such as rope climbing, sit-ups, push-ups, squat jumps, and bent-arm hang.

9. *Tests of muscular power* such as the medicine ball put, the shot put, three continuous broad jumps, standing vertical jump, basketball throw, fence vault, and softball throw.

10. *Tests of speed* such as swimming tests, running thirty to one hundred yards, reaction time tests, and speed of movement tests.

11. *Tests of strength* such as grip strength tests, dips on parallel bars, leg-strength tests, push-and-pull tests, back lift test, and ten-executions maximum capacity with barbell.

12. *Tests of vital capacity* including breath-holding for time, maximum breathing capacity, and test of force exerted by blowing.

Characteristics of an Ideal Physical-Fitness Test

Ideally, a physical-fitness test battery should have a number of specific characteristics, some of which are difficult to attain:

1. The physical-fitness test battery should be valid —that is, it should measure physical fitness.

2. The physical-fitness test battery should be reliable—that is, it should yield the same results from test session to test session.

3. The physical-fitness test battery should be objective—that is, it should yield the same results or scores, regardless of who administers the test.

4. The test battery score should be capable of yielding scores for each component of physical fitness.

5. Nationwide and local norms should be available, by which the overall test score and the scores on each component of physical fitness can be compared for various classifications of persons.

6. The tests should be easy to administer—that is, the person administering the tests should, with little or no training, be able to obtain accurate results. The tests should be conducive to self administration.

7. The persons being tested should be able to complete the test battery during one testing session and without undue fatigue.

8. The tests should require a minimum of space and be suitable for both indoor and out-of-doors administration.

9. The tests should require little or no special equipment.

WEAKNESSES OF PRESENT PHYSICAL-FITNESS TESTS

Because it is impossible to obtain a complete appraisal of physical fitness with one or two motor tests, an ideal physical-fitness test battery will probably never be developed. Although the physical-fitness test batteries used have steadily been improved in quality, certain weaknesses are evident in many of these test batteries:

1. Nationwide norms have not been developed for many of the physical-fitness test batteries. Most of the norms have been based on samples obtained from a single college or university, a town, a state, or a branch of the Armed Forces.
2. National standards or norms have not been developed for different stages of training for various types of physiques, for adults, or for children below the fifth grade level.
3. The samples from which some of the norms have been derived were not stratified and randomized and, hence, can not be assumed to be truly representative of the nationwide population.
4. Many physical-fitness test batteries do not directly measure all components of physical fitness. However, because some of the components of physical fitness are often substantially related to one another (e.g., agility and speed of movement) and because high school and college students are primarily interested in motor-type tests involving vigorous physical work, this is not a serious weakness.

TESTING PHYSICAL FITNESS

Before one tests his physical fitness, he should:

1. Have recently passed a physical examination to insure that he is medically fit.
2. Determine the components of physical fitness that he would like to measure and then select a physical-fitness test battery that will measure the desired components of physical fitness.
3. Make certain that he understands the directions for the physical-fitness tests.

TESTS OF PHYSICAL FITNESS

Appraising physical fitness and interpreting physical-fitness test scores are difficult tasks. Each person should be appraised as an individual, rather than being compared to a large group, because one set of criteria is not applicable to everyone.

AAHPER Youth Fitness Test[1]

In 1957–1958, the American Association for Health, Physical Education, and Recreation developed a physical-fitness test to which some of the objections to earlier test batteries do not apply. National norms, based on a sample of over ten thousand boys and girls, were developed for the first time. The norms are presented according to sex, age level, classification (based on age, height, and weight) and for college students.

For high school and college boys, the AAHPER Youth Fitness Test consists of seven test items (plus three aquatic tests that may also be included).

PULL-UP TEST

Using a regular grasp, the performer hangs at arm's length from a high horizontal bar with his body extended. He flexes his arms and—without swinging his body, or raising or kicking his legs—raises his body until his chin is above the level of the bar. He lowers his body until his arms are extended. He does as many pull-ups as possible. His score is the number of complete pull-ups performed.

SIT-UP TEST

The performer assumes a supine position on the floor or a mat with his legs extended and his feet spread approximately twenty-four inches apart. With his fingers interlocked, he places his hands behind the back of his head. A partner assists the performer by grasping his ankles and holding his heels to the floor throughout the test. The performer curls his trunk and performs a sit-up, rotating his trunk and touching his left knee with his right elbow. He returns to the starting position and repeats the sit-up movement, rotating his trunk to the right and touching his right knee with his left elbow. He continues to perform the sit-up movements in this manner until he can perform no more or until he has completed one hundred sit-ups. Throughout the sit-up test, the performer must

[1] American Association for Health, Physical Education, and Recreation (Paul A. Hunsicker, director), *AAHPER Youth Fitness Test Manual* (Washington, D.C.: AAHPER, 1958).

keep his interlocked fingers touching the back of his head. He may bend his knees slightly when touching them with his elbow; otherwise, the knees must rest on the floor. Each time that the performer returns to the supine position, he must touch both elbows to the floor.

SHUTTLE-RUN TEST

The performer stands behind a line and, when the signal "ready, go" is sounded, runs to a line thirty feet away, picks up a 2-by-2-by-4-inch wooden block that is sitting behind and parallel to the line, and then runs back and places the block behind the starting line. He immediately turns around, runs back, grasps a second block, and returns back past the starting line. The time (to the nearest tenth second) required to run the course is obtained. The performer receives the best time of two trials.

STANDING BROAD JUMP TEST

With his feet spread several inches apart, the performer stands in a semi-crouched position just behind a take-off line. He swings his arms backward, flexes his legs, swings his arms forward, extends his legs and feet vigorously, jumps as far as possible, and lands in a squat position. The longest jump of three jumps, recorded in feet and inches, is measured from the take-off line to that part of the performer's body that touches the floor nearest the take-off line.

FIFTY-YARD DASH

Upon the signal of "Are you ready? Go," the performer starts from a position behind the starting line. His time for running 50 yards is recorded to the nearest tenth of a second.

SOFTBALL THROW FOR DISTANCE

Remaining between two lines that are six feet apart and which run perpendicular to the direction of the throw, the performer throws a twelve-inch softball three times, using an overhead throw. The distance from the landing point of the best throw to the nearest point on the restraining line is recorded to the nearest foot.

SIX-HUNDRED-YARD RUN-WALK

When the starting signal of "Ready, go" is given, the performer traverses 600 yards by running as much as possible and walking a minimum distance. His time is recorded in minutes and seconds.

PERCENTILE SCORES (TABLE 22-I)

The special table that follows is used to convert the raw scores for each of the seven tests into percentile scores. If desired, a Profile Record of the seven percentile scores may be charted on a special form that the AAHPER provides for this purpose. A composite percentile score may be computed by summing the seven test percentile scores and dividing the total by seven. The composite percentile score is an indication of overall physical fitness as compared to scores achieved by male college students.

Iowa Physical Fitness Test Battery

The Iowa Physical Fitness Test Battery consists of three tests (sit-ups for two minutes, pull-ups, and the 300-yard shuttle run) which can be taken in one period without undue physical stress. The norms for the scores on these tests were established in 1960–1961 from the scores of about two thousand male college students, over 90 per cent of whom were freshmen.

SIT-UPS FOR TWO MINUTES

The starting position is one in which the performer lies on his back with his legs extended and his fingers interlaced and held behind his head. His heels are held on the floor by a partner. Unless he wears a shirt, the performer may use a shirt as a pad for his lower back, but it may not be used as a pad for his shoulder blades. The performer's partner kneels on the floor and places both knees between the performer's ankles. The partner holds the performer's ankles with sufficient pressure to keep his heels in contact with the floor but yet allow them to slide on the floor. Upon the signal to begin, the performer curls his head and trunk forward and touches one elbow to his knee on the opposite side of his body. His knees may be flexed slightly, if necessary, to allow his elbow to touch his knee during the sit-up. He lies back and touches both shoulder blades to the floor. He continues to sit-up and lie back, alternating the knee touch each time, until the signal to stop is given at the end of two minutes. For each sit-up correctly performed, one sit-up is counted by the partner each time that

table 22-1 PHYSICAL FITNESS TEST NORMS

*Percentile Scores for College Men**

PERCENTILE	PULL-UPS	SIT-UPS	SHUTTLE RUN	ST. BROAD JUMP	50-YD DASH	SOFTBALL THROW	600-YD RUN-WALK
100	20	100	8.3	9'6"	5.5	315	1:12
95	12	99	9.0	8'5"	6.1	239	1:35
90	10	97	9.1	8'2"	6.2	226	1:38
85	10	79	9.1	7'11"	6.3	217	1:40
80	9	68	9.2	7'10"	6.4	211	1:42
75	8	61	9.4	7'8"	6.5	206	1:44
70	8	58	9.5	7'7"	6.5	200	1:45
65	7	52	9.5	7'6"	6.6	196	1:47
60	7	51	9.6	7'5"	6.6	192	1:49
55	6	50	9.6	7'4"	6.7	188	1:50
50	6	47	9.7	7'3"	6.8	184	1:52
45	5	44	9.8	7'1"	6.8	180	1:53
40	5	41	9.9	7'0"	6.9	176	1:55
35	4	38	10.0	6'11"	7.0	171	1:57
30	4	36	10.0	6'10"	7.0	166	1:59
25	3	34	10.1	6'9"	7.1	161	2:01
20	3	31	10.2	6'7"	7.1	156	2:05
15	2	29	10.4	6'5"	7.2	150	2:09
10	1	26	10.6	6'2"	7.5	140	2:15
5	0	22	11.1	5'10"	7.7	125	2:25
0	0	0	13.9	4'2"	9.1	55	3:43

* American Association for Health, Physical Education, and Recreation, *AAHPER Youth Fitness Test Manual for the National Physical Fitness Test Program*, unnumbered page. Copyright, by the American Association for Health, Physical Education, and Recreation. Courtesy of the American Association for Health, Physical Education, and Recreation.

the performer touches his shoulder blades to the floor. A sit-up is not counted if any of the following errors are committed during the sit-up movement:

1. Unlacing the fingers and removing the hands from behind the head.
2. Failing to touch both shoulder blades to the floor.
3. Flinging one or both hands from their position behind the head.
4. Assisting the sit-up motion by pushing on the floor with one arm or elbow.

PULL-UP TEST

The starting position for the pull-up test is assumed by jumping and grasping the horizontal bar with the arms extended and with a reverse grasp (palms toward the face). At the signal to begin, the performer raises his body by flexing his arms. He pulls the upper arms down toward his sides until the bottom of his chin is above the bar. The chin should *not* rest on the bar. He lowers to the starting position and continues to do pull-ups until completely fatigued. One-half pull-up is deducted whenever any of the following errors are committed during the performance of the test:

1. Failure to pull up to the top of the bar.
2. Failure to straighten the arms between pull-ups.
3. Kicking or kipping with the legs.
4. Resting more than one second following each pull-up.

After two errors have been committed, the performer may not continue performing pull-ups.

THREE-HUNDRED-YARD SHUTTLE-RUN TEST

At the signal, "Runners, take your marks," the performer should move to the starting line and take a crouched position behind the center of the starting line. The feet of the next runner may be used as starting blocks if he is willing. The starting commands are, "Runners take your marks . . ., get set . . ., go." When the starting signal is sounded, the performer runs 60 yards to the end line, steps across it, turns around, runs back to the starting line, crosses it, turns around, and runs back. He repeats this procedure until he has run five laps of 60 yards each. The performer's time is recorded to the nearest one-tenth second.

PERCENTILE SCORE

The percentile score for each of the raw scores of the three tests may be determined from Table 22-2. A composite percentile score may be derived by summing the three percentile scores and dividing the total by three. A percentile score indicates the rank of a score in terms of a scale that ranges

from zero to 100 per cent. If fifteen pull-ups are performed, the percentile score equivalent is 70, which indicates that a score of fifteen pull-ups exceeds the pull-up score of 70 per cent of the entire two thousand students on whom the norms were derived. It should be pointed out that the normative group had participated in a strenuous physical-conditioning program for several weeks before being tested; hence, the test scores achieved by the group were higher than would probably be obtained from a general sample of male college students enrolled in a required program of physical education.

Mile Run

Reproduced below are the times and percentile scores achieved in 1962–1963 by approximately 1,300 male college students enrolled in the required program of physical education at the State University of Iowa. These students had completed a few periods of training and pacing prior to the mile-run test, but most of them had never before run a mile for time.

Time	Percentile Score
Under 5:11	99
5:20	95
5:26	90
5:30	85
5:35	80
5:41	75
5:44	70
5:45	65
5:49	60
5:51	55
5:54	50
6:01	45
6:05	40
6:08	35
6:12	30
6:16	25
6:21	20
6:27	15
6:35	10
6:49	5
7:45	1

It should be pointed out that the mile run is primarily a test of cardiovascular endurance, and somewhat a test of the muscular endurance of the

table 22-2 IOWA PHYSICAL FITNESS TEST PROFILE

GRADE	PERCENTILE SCORE	SIT-UPS (2 MIN.)	PULL-UPS	300 YD. SHUTTLE (5 LAPS)
A	100	88	25	44.9
A	95	72	23	47.1
A	90	69	21	47.8
B	85	66	19	48.3
B	80	64	17	48.8
B	75	62	16	49.1
B	70	60	15	49.4
B	65	59	14	49.7
C	60	57	13	50.0
C	55	56	12	50.3
C	50	55	11	50.6
C	45	54	10	51.0
C	40	53	9	51.4
C	35	51	8	51.7
C	30	50	7	52.0
D	27	49	6	52.3
D	25	48	5	52.5
D	20	46	4	53.1
D	15	44	3	53.7
D	10	41	2	54.5
F	5	37	1	56.0
F	0	25	0	60.0

table 22-3 DESIRABLE WEIGHTS FOR MEN OF AGES 25 AND OVER*

Weight in Pounds (in Indoor Clothing)
According to Frame

HEIGHT (WITH 1-INCH-HEEL SHOES)		SMALL FRAME	MEDIUM FRAME	LARGE FRAME
FEET	INCHES			
5	2	112–120	118–129	126–141
5	3	115–123	121–133	129–144
5	4	118–126	124–136	132–148
5	5	121–129	127–139	135–152
5	6	124–133	130–143	138–156
5	7	128–137	134–147	142–161
5	8	132–141	138–152	147–166
5	9	136–145	142–156	151–170
5	10	140–150	146–160	155–174
5	11	144–154	150–165	159–179
6	0	148–158	154–170	164–184
6	1	152–162	158–175	168–189
6	2	156–167	162–180	173–194
6	3	160–171	167–185	178–199
6	4	164–175	172–190	182–204

* Metropolitan Life Insurance Company, *How To Control Your Weight*, p. 4. Copyright, 1958, by Metropolitan Life Insurance Company. Courtesy of the Metropolitan Life Insurance Company.

legs. The mile run should not be construed as a complete test of physical fitness.

Height-Weight Chart

In Table 23-3 are listed desirable body weights based on the standing height of males 25 years of age and over. These standards should also apply to high school and college youths with a high degree of validity. Persons who are heavily muscled are often depicted as being overweight in such charts, when, actually, for their amount of muscular tissue, their body weight falls within a normal range. It should also be noted that the use of this table for estimating physical fitness is an extremely crude measure, because a person could be quite average in body weight for his height and still possess an exceedingly low degree of physical fitness. On the other hand, a person who is markedly underweight or overweight generally has a low degree of physical fitness. The use of this table can be a valuable reference in future years when the maintenance of normal body weight becomes a difficult problem for many middle-aged adults.